STATISTICAL ANALYSIS

OF

STATIONARY TIME SERIES

A WILEY PUBLICATION
IN
MATHEMATICAL STATISTICS

STATISTICAL ANALYSIS

OF

STATIONARY TIME SERIES

BY

ULF GRENANDER

DOCENT, UNIVERSITY OF STOCKHOLM

and

MURRAY ROSENBLATT

ASSOCIATE PROFESSOR OF MATHEMATICS

INDIANA UNIVERSITY

JOHN WILEY & SONS, NEW YORK

ALMQVIST & WIKSELL, STOCKHOLM

To

HARALD CRAMÉR

FOREWORD

The new results contained in this monograph were obtained by the authors in the joint work they carried out in Chicago, Illinois, and Stockholm, Sweden, during the years 1952–1953. Our thanks are due to the Office of Naval Research and the University of Chicago for their generous support of our collaboration. The efforts of H. Cramér, H. Robbins, and W. A. Wallis were most helpful in carrying on the work on the book and its completion. We have had the benefit of the advice of many of our colleagues. We feel especially indebted to J. L. Doob, F. Mosteller, W. J. Pierson, Jr., and L. J. Tick for their helpful comments.

PREFACE

The purpose of this book is two-fold. It is written in the terminology of the theoretical statistician because one of our objectives is to direct his attention to an approach to time series analysis that is essentially different from most of the techniques used by time series analysts in the past. The second objective is to present a unified treatment of methods that are being used increasingly in the physical sciences and technology. We hope that the book will be of considerable interest to research workers in these fields. Keeping the first objective in mind, we have given a rigorous mathematical discussion of these new topics in time series analysis. The existing literature in time series analysis is characterized with few exceptions by a lack of precision both in conception and in the mathematical treatment of the problems dealt with. To avoid this vagueness we have devoted more space to rigorous proofs than may appear necessary to some readers, but we believe that a study of the proofs will furnish valuable clues to the practical validity of the results and be an important guide to intuition. We have tried to balance the formal proofs with intuitive remarks and comments on practical applications. While the regularity assumptions we have required in many cases may seem restrictive, appropriately interpreted they give an indication of the range in which the methods are practically valid. We have made such interpretations in the comments accompanying the formal proofs.

The reader is assumed to have a knowledge of statistics and basic probability theory equivalent to that contained in H. Cramér, *Mathematical Methods of Statistics*. The statistical techniques suggested in this monograph use concepts and relations from the theory of stochastic processes. However, we shall develop the results we need in the two first chapters. The reader who is not familiar with the mathematical techniques used in this book may find it easier to skip some of the more difficult proofs during a first reading. This is especially true with respect to Chapters 2, 4, 6 and 7. A deeper understanding of the results (and their limitations) will be obtained by returning to these proofs later.

The early attempts to formulate a theory for the statistical analysis of time series made use of a rather simple model. The observed series y_t was considered as the sum of a component m with no stochastic element in it,

9

and a disturbance x_t, where the x's are supposed to be independent and identically distributed. As an example consider the case

$$m_t = \sum_{\nu=1}^{p} A_\nu \cos\left(t\,\lambda_\nu + \varphi_\nu\right)$$

and let x_t be normally distributed with mean m and variance σ^2, where the constants are not specified. A typical problem would then be to estimate one or several of these parameters. A more general and flexible approach to this subject was based upon the assumption, made explicitly or not, that the underlying stochastic process was one of the so-called *finite parameter schemes*. These include the *moving average*

$$x_t = a_0\,\xi_t + a_1\xi_{t-1} + \cdots + a_p\,\xi_{t-p}$$

and the *autoregressive scheme*, defined as a solution of the difference equation

$$b_0\,x_{t+p} + b_1 x_{t+p-1} + \cdots + b_p\,x_t = \xi_t.$$

Here $\{\xi_t\}$ is a sequence of identically and independently distributed stochastic variables and $\{a_\nu\}$, $\{b_\nu\}$ are constants. Modified processes with a nonrandom trigonometric or polynomial regression m_t superimposed, $y_t = x_t + m_t$, were also considered. The nonnegative integer p is called the order of the scheme.

These schemes have been important in the development of methods for the statistical analysis of time series. They have been used with a varying degree of success to describe many types of phenomena encountered in applications. From the discussion in Chapter 1 it will be apparent that by using these schemes, it is possible to approximate a large and important class of stationary processes, viz. the so-called *linear processes* (see 1.6). For this to be possible p must take large rather than small values and parameters involved in the scheme must be adjusted adequately.

During the last ten years a good deal of work has been devoted to the construction of tests, estimates and confidence intervals appropriate for these schemes. We have described a few of the more important of these results in Chapter 3. In spite of the ingenuity and great theoretical interest of some of these methods, their practical applicability seems to be limited severely by the assumption that the process is a low (usually zero, first or second) order finite parameter scheme. After surveying a good deal of the applied literature devoted to statistical analysis of time series met with in practice, we have come to the following conclusion,

10

Only in a few special cases (some of which will be discussed later on in this book) does it seem reasonable to assume on *a priori* grounds that the process is a low order finite parameter scheme. Referring to what has been said above, we can still approximate the process by a scheme of sufficiently high order and we can then use one of the methods developed to test the fit. This procedure is legitimate, however, only if we take into consideration the power of the test; usually this power will be rather small for moderate sample sizes. Hence, when we lack information concerning the structure of the process, we will have to develop methods more generally valid. If this is not possible, we should hesitate to make quantitative statistical statements, which would be based on seemingly objective methods, hiding perhaps the weak points in the argument and giving the research worker an illusory feeling of security.

At first it may seem impossible to construct methods of inference valid for the large classes of stationary processes we have in mind. Indeed, leaving the finite parameter schemes, we now deal with classes of probability distributions characterized by an infinite number of parameters. From the finite sample we obtain information concerning these parameters. This is the same problem that is encountered in the study of *nonparametric hypotheses*, although in the present context we will have to be prepared to tackle even more complex analytical difficulties.

It may be of interest to mention the two sources of ideas that we have found most useful. The first is the applied literature, especially papers dealing with statistical questions in the natural sciences and engineering. The statistician intending to do research work in this field will benefit by getting in touch with the wealth of statistical research presented in the main journals in these fields. Some of these journals are listed in our bibliography. Second, some knowledge of the modern theory of probability is indispensable, particularly the theory of stochastic processes. A complete and rigorous exposition of this subject is Doob: *Stochastic Processes*. This can be supplemented with Blanc-Lapierre and Fortet: *Théorie des Fonctions Aléatoires*, where some of the emphasis is on applications to physics.

Results have only occasionally been put in the form of theorems. This is to emphasize that they should not be considered as parts of a rigid system that can be used immediately. In the practical applications, modifications and extensions will usually be needed.

The nonparametric approach we have spoken of has been used quite recently in various fields of the physical sciences and technology although in a somewhat disguised form. On closer scrutiny, one can see that some of the basic problems dealt with in these fields are concerned with estima-

11

tion of the spectrum of time series, detection of signals, and other statistical problems of the type discussed in this book. The success of these methods in these concrete contexts seems to be due to the fact that in these fields people know a good deal about the structure of the random phenomena studied and so have been able to devise appropriate and relevant techniques. This can be contrasted with the rather mechanical methods of time series analysis used by theoretical statisticians in the past. The power of these new techniques is to be attributed to their nonparametric character. We have especially profited from reading the many stimulating papers in the current engineering literature. Many such papers can be found in the bibliography and we strongly advise the interested reader to examine some of these. They are especially valuable because of the problems they pose.

The basic probability model considered in this monograph is that of a stochastic process (or sequence of random variables)

$$y_t = x_t + m_t, \quad E\, y_t = m_t, \quad t = \cdots, -1, 0, 1, \ldots$$

with mean value $m_t = \sum\limits_{\nu=0}^{p} c_\nu \, \varphi_t^{(\nu)}$ and known regression vectors $\varphi_t = (\ldots, \varphi_t^{(\nu)}, \ldots)$. The residuals x_t are assumed to be a stationary stochastic process, that is, a process whose probability distribution is invariant under time shifts. This means that x_t is a stable random mechanism. In particular, it then follows that the covariance sequence

$$\operatorname{cov}(y_t, y_\tau) = E\, x_t\, x_\tau = r_{t,\tau} = r_{t-\tau}$$

depends only on the time difference $t - \tau$. Such a model fits data arising over moderate lengths of time in studies of random noise, problems in turbulence and oceanography. The model is also used in small scale investigations in meteorology. The covariances r_n are Fourier–Stieltjes coefficients

$$r_n = \int\limits_{-\pi}^{\pi} e^{in\lambda}\, d\, F(\lambda)$$

of a bounded nondecreasing function $F(\lambda)$. The function $F(\lambda)$ is called the spectral distribution function of the process and knowledge of the spectrum is equivalent to knowledge of the covariance sequence. It turns out to be much more convenient statistically to deal with the spectrum rather than the covariance sequence.

The framework of the problems considered is as follows. A time series $y_1, \ldots, y_N$, a partial realization of the process $\{y_t\}$, is observed and we wish to draw inferences from the observations about the structure of the

12

process $\{y_t\}$. Problems of estimation and testing with respect to the regression coefficients are considered. A typical example would be that of a linear regression. Then there would be two regression vectors

$$\varphi^{(1)} = (\ldots, 1, 1, \ldots)$$
$$\varphi^{(2)} = (\ldots, 1, 2, \ldots, t, \ldots)$$

corresponding to the regression coefficients c_1, c_2 of the regression $m_t = c_1 + c_2\, t$. Problems of estimation and testing with respect to the spectral distribution function and spectral density (derivative of the spectral distribution function) are discussed. Confidence bands for the spectral distribution function and spectral density are set up. It turns out that many of the results have an asymptotic nonparametric character, that is, many of the limit theorems (asymptotic distribution theory, etc.) obtained do not depend on the spectrum. The approach is quite different from most of the earlier work in time series analysis and is much more general in scope.

In Chapter 1 the basic probability theory required is introduced. The concepts of stationarity and spectrum are discussed and illustrated by examples drawn for the most part from physical fields.

In the second chapter the linear problems of prediction, interpolation and filtering are discussed under the assumption that the spectrum is known. Usually the spectrum is not known unless there is a good deal of prior experience in dealing with problems arising in the same experimental context. Much of the remainder of the book is concerned with the statistical estimation of the spectrum when it is not known.

In Chapter 3, the earlier work on statistical analysis of time series is surveyed. The earlier work is especially concerned with very special finite parameter models. The new techniques proposed differ in that they deal with infinite dimensional models that cover all the special models considered before and thus provide a uniform approach. The power of the new techniques lies in their great generality. The first three chapters serve as an introduction. The remaining chapters deal with the new techniques and their application.

Estimation of the spectral density is considered in Chapter 4. Two types of estimates are discussed in some detail. The first family of estimates, called spectrograph estimates in the book, are well suited for computation on a digital computer while the second class of estimates are the natural ones to build into analogue computers. The bias and asymptotic variance of these estimates are considered. It turns out that any good estimate of the spectral density is biased. The mean square error of an estimate is a convenient measure of how good the estimate is and it is discussed in detail in the case of some special estimates.

The chapter on applications, Chapter 5, considers the model of a stationary process as it arises in several applied fields where it has been found useful. Aspects of the study of random noise, turbulence and storm-generated ocean waves are developed with this in mind.

The asymptotic distribution of a class of estimates of the spectral distribution function is developed in Chapter 6. Confidence bands are set up for the spectral distribution function and one- and two-sample tests are discussed. These results have an asymptotic nonparametric character. Remarks are made about the distribution theory of estimates of the spectral density. Examples of spectral analysis of artificially generated time series are included in this chapter.

Chapter 7 deals with regression analysis. Linear unbiased estimates of the regression coefficients are discussed. The least squares (computed under the assumption the residuals are independent) and Markov (minimum variance unbiased estimate) estimates are compared. Conditions under which the least squares estimate is as good as the Markov estimate asymptotically are given. These conditions are satisfied, for example, for polynomial or trigonometric regression. It looks as if these asymptotic results on estimation of regression coefficients are approximately valid for moderate and perhaps even small samples.

The last chapter discusses assorted problems on the maxima and zeros of time series as well as prediction when the spectrum is not known but is estimated from the time series.

The reader will notice that almost all the examples discussed in the text are chosen from the physical sciences. This is so simply for the reason that some of the most natural and successful applications of stationary stochastic processes have been in these fields.

Something should be said about the limitations of the methods presented in this monograph. As is apparent, we have studied only processes with stationary residuals. It is well known that equilibrium conditions are simpler to analyze than evolution, and the methods presented probably cannot be extended to the nonstationary case without essential changes. Futhermore, we have dealt only with discrete time, although in many of the problems we discuss, this is highly unnatural. In some cases the results can be extended to the case of a continuous time parameter (see Grenander [1] for a general outline of how this can be done) but in other cases (e.g., the problems studied in Chapter 7) unsolved problems arise, some of them of considerable analytical interest. These questions should be studied further. Very little attention is paid to vector processes although they arise in a number of important applications. Here, too, an extension seems possible and desirable (see Grenander and Rosenblatt [6] and Rosenblatt [1], [2]).

Finally, only large sample methods are considered. Because time series analysis deals with dependent observations (this reduces the amount of information obtained) and with probability distributions belonging to very wide classes, the sample size at which the asymptotic results start giving useful approximations may be fairly large. It is, of course, important to find out at what sample size such results give realistic approximations. This question deserves closer attention, perhaps via numerical methods.

If the reader is disturbed enough by these limitations to extend the methods of analysis, then this monograph will have served one of its main purposes: to stimulate research in time series analysis which will lead to practically useful and theoretically sound methods.

Each chapter of the book is divided into numbered sections. Section 6.2 refers to section 2 of Chapter 6. The numbered formulas are started *ad initium* at the beginning of each section. Formula (2) mentioned in the text of section 6.2 refers to formula (2) of that same section. Formula (6.1.2) mentioned in the text of section 6.2 refers to formula (2) of section 6.1.

Some problems have been given in the book, partly with the object of providing the reader with exercise and partly with the object of leading the reader on to derive results that supplement and extend the theory given in the text.

CONTENTS

18

19

CHAPTER 1

STATIONARY STOCHASTIC PROCESSES
AND THEIR REPRESENTATIONS

1.0. Introduction

The basic results on stationary stochastic processes are derived in this chapter.

1.1. What Is a Stochastic Process ?

We first give the general and rather abstract definition of a stochastic process. The concrete meaning and importance of this definition will be understood by considering the simple examples in this and the following sections. A *stochastic process* $x_t(w)$ is an indexed set of stochastic variables. We do not necessarily restrict ourselves to real-valued stochastic variables, but consider also complex and vector-valued stochastic variables. Here t is an element of the index set T which is not yet specified. The set T can be the real line or the set of natural numbers or a collection of points in a higher dimensional Euclidean space. It could also be the collection of all Borel sets on such a space or on the real line in which case $x_t(w)$ is a *stochastic setfunction*. These are just a few possible choices but they will be adequate for our purpose.

For every value of t, $x_t(w)$ is a function on a measure space Ω. A probability measure P is defined on a σ-algebra of subsets in Ω. The process $x_t(w)$ should be measurable with respect to P for each $t \in T$. (See Halmos [1].)

If w is fixed, $x_t(w)$ is a function of t, a *sample function* or *realization* of the process, and by letting w take all values in Ω we get a collection or ensemble of such functions.

In a given situation one can choose Ω and define P in many different ways but the following one is adequate in many cases. Choose Ω as the set of all functions on T. The set of values of the process is denoted by A and this will always be a finite dimensional complex or real vector space in this book. For any finite set of t-values $t_1, t_2, \cdots, t_n$ we consider the event

$$\{x_{t_j}(w) \in A_j; j = 1, 2, ..., n\} \in \Omega, \tag{1}$$

where A_j are Borel sets in A. The probabilities of all such events are given This defines a finitely additive measure on these events. If the probabilities

21

of all such events are defined in a consistent manner, it has been shown that this measure can be extended to a completely additive probability measure P defined on the Borel field generated by these events. One can then attribute a probability to sets determined by values of $x_t(w)$ at a denumerable number of t-values. For a detailed statement and proof see Kolmogoroff [1].

In many cases one is interested in the behavior of the process at more than a denumerable number of t-points. There are difficulties that arise in considering such a problem. However, they can be overcome in most of the usual contexts. Before proceeding with the main development, we shall discuss a few specific processes and see how these difficulties are overcome. Imagine that we could observe a particle in linear Brownian movement. It has been observed that such a motion has a very erratic and irregular character and it has seemed appropriate to use a stochastic model. Denoting the position of the particle at time t by $x_t(w)$, assume that the particle starts out at position zero at $t = 0$, $x_0(w) \equiv 0$. The changes in position of the particle over nonoverlapping time intervals are assumed to be independent. This means that the change of position is not influenced by the past. Furthermore the distribution of the displacement during a time interval (a, b) is supposed to be normal with mean zero and variance $\sigma^2(b - a)$. It is clear that these properties determine completely the probabilities of sets of the type (1) so that the procedure of Kolmogoroff can be carried out.

However we might be interested in the probability that the particle does not reach an absorbing barrier placed at the point $x = 1$ during a time interval $(0, \tau)$, i.e., the probability of

$$\{x_t(w) < 1 \quad \text{for all } t \text{ in } (0, \tau)\} \subset \Omega, \tag{2}$$

This set does not belong to the Borel field considered.

What probability should one attribute to such an event? If we instead consider the set

$$\{x_t(w) < 1 \quad \text{for all rational } t \text{ in } (o, \tau)\} \subset \Omega \tag{3}$$

it belongs to the Borel field and hence it has a well-defined probability. If the "absorbing barrier" probability has any intuitive meaning it should be equal to the probability of the last set. Now, if we had been able to assume from some *a priori* grounds that the only possible paths are fully determined by their values at any denumerable dense set of points, the sets (2) and (3) would be the same and hence there would be no difficulty in defining probabilities of sets such as (2). One possibility would be to consider continuous paths only, which can be shown to be the natural set of sample functions in the case of Brownian motion (see Doob [2]).

Another model of the linear Brownian motion is the following. Take

$$x_t(w) = z_0(w)\, t + \sum_{\nu=1}^{\infty} z_\nu(w)\, \frac{\sin \nu t \pi \sqrt{2}}{\nu \pi}, \quad 0 < t < 1, \tag{4}$$

where the z_ν's are independent stochastic variables normally distributed with mean zero and standard deviation σ. A theorem of Paley–Wiener (see Paley–Wiener [1]) shows that this series converges uniformly in t with probability 1. Because of the uniform convergence of (4) the sample functions are almost certainly continuous. As a linear combination of normal stochastic variables, $x_t(w)$ is a *normal process* in the sense that all the finite dimensional distribution functions are multivariate normal. It is easily verified that $E\, x_t(w) \equiv 0$ and

$$E\, x_s(w)\, x_t(w) = \sigma^2 t^2 + \frac{2\,\sigma^2}{\pi^2} \sum_{\nu=1}^{\infty} \frac{\sin \nu \pi s \,\sin \nu \pi t}{\nu^2} = \sigma^2 \min(s, t).$$

This implies that all the finite dimensional distributions are the same as in the previous representation. Note that in spite of this it is not the same model as that originally considered. The space of sample functions has again been restricted to the subset of continuous sample functions. The probability measure induced by this model is essentially the same as the probability measure induced by the modification of the original model considered above.

As another example let us consider a very simplified model of a single line in a telephone network. We are interested in the number of calls made on this line from time a to time $b > a$. The calls are assumed to be so short that they can be considered of zero duration. Let $n(b) - n(a)$ be the number of calls made in the time interval (a, b). For convenience let $n(0) = 0$. Then the variation of $n(t)$ over nonoverlapping time intervals is independent and $n(b) - n(a)$ is Poisson distributed with mean $\lambda(b - a)$, so that all finite dimensional distributions are determined. This process is commonly called the *Poisson process*. One will be interested in the probability of sets like

$$\{n(t) - n(a) < 1; \quad a < t < b\}.$$

Again, the intuitively plausible procedure would be to set the probability of this set equal to that of

$$\{n(t) - n(a) < 1; \quad a < t < b, \, t \text{ rational}\}$$

which is well-defined. The natural set of sample functions determined by their values on a denumerable everywhere dense set would now turn out

23

to be the set of nondecreasing jump functions rather than the set of continuous functions.

A formal difficulty of the same sort as the one just discussed is the definition of the integral of a stochastic process. This difficulty does not arise if the sample space Ω can be chosen so that $x_t(w)$ is measurable on $T \times \Omega$ with respect to the product measure $dt \times dP$ where dt is the measure on T we are interested in. Then $x_t(w)$ is a measurable function of t for almost all w. Assuming

$$\int_T E \,|\, x_t(w)\,|\, dt < \infty$$

the integral $\int_T x_t(w) \, dt$ is a measurable function of Ω, i.e., a stochastic variable. This is just Fubini's theorem (see e.g., Halmos [1]).

In the following we shall always assume that Ω has been chosen so that these questions do not arise. For a detailed discussion of these problems we refer to Doob [2].

1.2. Continuity in the Mean

Let us consider a complex-valued stochastic process x_t. We shall assume that the absolute second order moment $E\,|x_t|^2 < \infty$ (we shall usually leave out the argument w). Introduce

$$\left. \begin{aligned} E\,x_t &= m_t \\ E\,(x_s - m_s)\,\overline{(x_t - m_t)} &= r_{s,\,t}. \end{aligned} \right\}$$

In this chapter the *mean value function* m_t is supposed to be identically zero. $r_{s,\,t}$ is called the *covariance function* and in a sense measures the dependence between the values of the process at different t-points.

A covariance function is Hermitian, i.e., $r_{s,\,t} = \bar{r}_{t,\,s}$, *and is nonnegative definite*. This is immediately seen by considering the variance of any linear combination,

$$E\,\Big|\, \sum_{\nu=1}^{n} c_\nu\, x_{t_\nu}\Big|^2 = \sum_{\nu,\,\mu=1}^{n} c_\nu\, \bar{c}_\mu\, r_{t_\nu,\,t_\mu} \geq 0.$$

On the other hand *to each Hermitian and nonnegative matrix* $r_{s,\,t}$ (it is understood that s,t can be discrete or continuous parameters) *there corresponds a stochastic process with* $r_{s,\,t}$ *as its covariance function*. If $r_{s,\,t}$ is real for any set of t-values $t_1, t_2, \ldots, t_n$ the matrix $\{r_{t_\nu,\,t_\mu}; \nu, \mu = 1, 2, \ldots, n\}$ is symmetric and nonnegative definite. Hence there is a normal distribution with this as the covariance matrix. We can define all the finite dimensional probability distributions of the process. Applying Kolmogoroff's method (see section 1.1) we arrive at a process with the desired covariance function. If $r_{s,t}$ takes complex values the same construction is possible, although the process must be allowed to take complex values and the joint distribution of real and imaginary parts must be specified.

A stochastic process is said to be continuous in the mean (continuous i.m.) *at* $t = t_0$ *if* $E|x(t) - x(t_0)|^2 \to 0$ *when* $t \to t_0$ *in the topology of interest.* If this is true for all $t_0 \in T$ the process is called continuous in the mean on T. Such questions do not arise when the process has a discrete t-parameter.

The identity

$$r_{s,t} - r_{s',t'} = r_{s,t} - r_{s',t} + r_{s',t} - r_{s',t'} = E\,(x_s - x_{s'})\,\bar{x}_t + E\,x_{s'} \cdot \overline{(x_t - x_{t'})}$$

holds. But this is less than the following expression in absolute value according to Schwarz' inequality

$$\sqrt{E\,|x_t|^2\,E\,|x_s - x_{s'}|^2} + \sqrt{E\,|x_{s'}|^2\,E\,|x_t - x_{t'}|^2}.$$

As $\sqrt{E\,|x_{s'}|^2} \le \sqrt{E\,|x_s|^2} + \sqrt{E\,|x_s - x_{s'}|^2}$, we see that $r_{s',t'}$ tends to $r_{s,t}$ when (s', t') tends to (s, t).

On the other hand, if the covariance function is continuous at all points of the diagonal $s = t$, then

$$E\,|x_s - x_t|^2 = r_{s,s} + r_{t,t} - 2\,\mathrm{Re}\,r_{s,t},$$

and as $s \to t$ we have $r_{s,s} \to r_{t,t}$ and $r_{s,t} \to r_{t,t}$ which is real and the continuity i.m. follows. *Hence continuity i.m. is equivalent to the continuity of* $r_{s,t}$ *at the points of the diagonal* $s = t$.

Define $||x|| = \sqrt{E\,|x - Ex|^2}$. Note that continuity i.m. is not simply related to the continuity of almost all sample functions. The Poisson process is discontinuous with positive probability over any finite interval but it is continuous i.m. as is easily verified.

1.3. Stochastic Set Functions of Orthogonal Increments

Let Λ be a finite dimensional Euclidean space of points λ. On the Borel field $B\Lambda$ there is defined a σ-finite measure μ. We now take $T = B\Lambda$ and consider a stochastic process $z(s) = z(s, w)$, $s \in B\Lambda$, such that

$$\left.\begin{aligned} &z(s_1 \cup s_2) = z(s_1) + z(s_2) \text{ if } s_1 \cap s_2 = 0 \\ &E\,z(s) = 0 \\ &E\,z(s)\,\overline{z(s')} = \mu\,(s \cap s') \end{aligned}\right\}.$$

1.3

The indication of the dependence of $z(s, w) = z(s)$ on $w \in \Omega$ is dropped for convenience. In particular if s and s' are disjoint the two corresponding stochastic variables are uncorrelated or orthogonal. Because of this we say that $z(s)$ is a *stochastic set function of orthogonal increments* or an orthogonal set function.

We might add that if we ask for independence instead of orthogonality in this definition we get a so-called *differential* stochastic set function. The Wiener process and the Poisson process generate stochastic set functions that are easily seen to be not only orthogonal but also differential.

We are now going to see what meaning we can attach to the expression $\int_\Lambda f(\lambda)\, dz(\lambda)$, where $f(\lambda)$ is a complex-valued function.

Let I be an interval in Λ, i.e., a bounded rectangular parallelepiped and $c_I(\lambda)$ the corresponding characteristic function. We interpret the integral of $c_I(\lambda)$ with respect to $dz(\lambda)$ as $z(I)$. Similarly we put

$$\int_\Lambda \sum_{\nu=1}^{n} \alpha_\nu\, c_{I_\nu}(\lambda)\, d\,z(\lambda) = \sum_{\nu=1}^{n} \alpha_\nu\, z(I_\nu).$$

Assume that $\int_\Lambda |f(\lambda)|^2\, d\mu(\lambda) < \infty$. Then there is a sequence of functions $f_n(\lambda)$ such that

$$\int_\Lambda |f(\lambda) - f_n(\lambda)|^2\, d\mu \to 0 \quad \text{as} \quad n \to \infty$$

where each $f_n(\lambda)$ is of the form $\sum \alpha_\nu c_{I_\nu}(\lambda)$ with the I_ν disjoint. But on putting

$$J_n = \int_\Lambda f_n(\lambda)\, d\,z(\lambda),$$

we have

$$E\,|{}'_n|^2 = \sum |\alpha_\nu|^2\, \mu(I_\nu) = \int_\Lambda |f_n(\lambda)|^2\, d\mu(\lambda).$$

so that

$$E\,|J_n - J_m|^2 = \int_\Lambda |f_n(\lambda) - f_m(\lambda)|^2\, d\mu(\lambda) \to 0 \quad \text{as} \quad n, m \to \infty.$$

But then J_n converges in the mean to a stochastic variable J,

$$E\,|J|^2 = \lim_{n \to \infty} E\,|J_n|^2 = \int_\Lambda |f(\lambda)|^2\, d\mu(\lambda) \quad \text{(see Doob [2])}.$$

26

We shall define $\int_\Lambda f(\lambda)\,dz(\lambda)$ as J and it is easy to verify that J does not depend upon the particular sequence $f_n(\lambda)$ by which we have approximated $f(\lambda)$.

This integral has the usual properties which can be proved easily

$$\int_\Lambda [a\,f(\lambda) + b\,g(\lambda)]\,dz(\lambda) = a\int_\Lambda f(\lambda)\,dz(\lambda) + b\int_\Lambda g(\lambda)\,dz(\lambda) \tag{1}$$

$$\lim_{n\to\infty}\int_\Lambda f_n(\lambda)\,dz(\lambda) = \int_\Lambda f(\lambda)\,dz(\lambda) \tag{2}$$

if and only if

$$\int_\Lambda |f(\lambda) - f_n(\lambda)|^2\,d\mu(\lambda) \to 0 \quad \text{as } n\to\infty.$$

$$E\int_\Lambda f(\lambda)\,dz(\lambda)\,\overline{\int_\Lambda g(\lambda)\,dz(\lambda)} = \int_\Lambda f(\lambda)\,\overline{g(\lambda)}\,d\mu(\lambda). \tag{3}$$

1.4. Orthogonal Representations of Stochastic Processes

As we shall see many important types of processes have a representation in terms of integrals with respect to an orthogonal stochastic set function of the form

$$x_t = \int_\Lambda f(t, \lambda)\,dz(\lambda), \tag{1}$$

where of course $f(t, \lambda)$ has to be quadratically integrable as a function of λ with respect to μ for every value of t. It follows immediately by using property (1.3.3) of the integral that

$$r_{s, t} = E\,x_s\,\bar{x}_t = \int f(s, \lambda)\,\overline{f(t, \lambda)}\,d\mu(\lambda). \tag{2}$$

What is a bit more difficult to prove, but will be very useful, is that *from a covariance representation of the form* (2) *one can deduce the representation* (1) *of the process.*

To prove this let us first assume that the system of functions of λ, $f(t, \lambda)$, when t runs through all values of T, is a basis for $L_2(\Lambda) = \{$the set of functions quadratically integrable with respect to $\mu\}$, i.e., every function $\varphi(\lambda) \in L_2(\Lambda)$ can be approximated in the mean by linear combinations

$$\sum_\nu c_\nu\,f(t_\nu, \lambda),\ t_\nu \in T.$$

If s is a set in Λ of finite μ-measure, then its characteristic function $c_s(\lambda) \in L_2(\Lambda)$. It can then be approximated in the mean by sums

27

$$c_s^{(n)}(\lambda) = \sum_1^n a_\nu^{(n)} f(t_\nu^{(n)}, \lambda).$$

As
$$\int_\Lambda |c_s^{(n)}(\lambda) - c_s^{(m)}(\lambda)|^2 d\mu(\lambda) = E|z_n - z_m|^2$$

where
$$z_n = \sum_{\nu=1}^n a_\nu^{(n)} x_{t_\nu}^{(n)},$$

it follows that the sequence z_n is a Cauchy sequence and hence converges to a stochastic variable which we will denote by $z(s)$. If s_1 and s_2 are disjoint we have

$$E|z(s_1 \cup s_2) - z(s_1) - z(s_2)|^2 = \int_\Lambda |c_{s_1 \cup s_2}(\lambda) - c_{s_1}(\lambda) - c_{s_2}(\lambda)|^2 d\mu(\lambda) = 0.$$

Also we see easily that

$$E z(s_1) \overline{z(s_2)} = \mu(s_1 \cap s_2)$$

so that $z(s)$ is an orthogonal stochastic set function. Put

$$y_t = \int_\Lambda f(t, \lambda) \, dz(\lambda). \tag{3}$$

But

$$E x_t \overline{z(s)} = \lim_{n \to \infty} E x_t \sum_{\nu=1}^n \bar{a}_\nu^{(n)} \bar{x}_{t_\nu}^{(n)}$$

$$= \lim_{n \to \infty} \sum \bar{a}_\nu^{(n)} \int_\Lambda f(t, \lambda) \overline{f(t_\nu^{(n)}, \lambda)} \, d\mu(\lambda) = \int_s f(t, \lambda) \, d\mu(\lambda).$$

Using an approximation procedure again we get

$$E x_t \bar{y}_t = \int_\Lambda |f(t, \lambda)|^2 \, d\mu(\lambda).$$

Then
$$E|x_t - y_t|^2 = 0,$$

so that x_t has the representation (1).

Now we drop the assumption that $f(t, \lambda)$ should form a basis in $L_2(\Lambda)$. If it does not we add all functions orthogonal to every $f(t, \lambda)$, $t \in T$. These new functions we write as $g(t, \lambda)$, $t \in T'$ where T' has no points in common with T. Now we set

$$h(t, \lambda) = \begin{cases} f(t, \lambda) & \text{if } t \in T \\ g(t, \lambda) & \text{if } t \in T'. \end{cases}$$

Let $y_t = x_t$ when $t \in T$ and set y_t equal to the normal process with covariance

$$\int_\Lambda g(s, \lambda) \overline{g(t, \lambda)} \, d\mu(\lambda)$$

independent of x_t for $t \in T'$. Then y_t has covariance

$$\int_\Lambda h(s, \lambda) \overline{h(t, \lambda)} \, d\mu(\lambda), \ s, t \in T \cup T'.$$

$h(t, \lambda)$ is a basis for $L_2(\Lambda)$ when t runs through $T \cup T'$ so that

$$y_t = \int_\Lambda h(t, \lambda) \, dz(\lambda), \ t \in T \cup T'$$

where z is an orthogonal stochastic set function. But

$$x_t = y_t = \int_\Lambda h(t, \lambda) \, dz(\lambda) = \int_\Lambda f(t, \lambda) \, dz(\lambda)$$

when $t \in T$ so that we have the desired representation.

This result gives a representation of the process as the limit of certain linear combinations of the functions of $t f(t, \lambda)$ with weights $dz(\lambda)$ which are stochastic and uncorrelated. This result is due to Karhunen [1] and the proof is essentially that given by Cramér [4]. One should note that the integral (1) should not be interpreted sample function-wise, as in many cases $z(s)$ does not form a completely additive set function with probability one.

1.5. Stationary Processes

So far we have imposed very few essential restrictions upon the processes studied. Our main interest in this book is the class of stationary processes. They arise when the random mechanism producing the process does not change with t. This situation is often met with in technology and in the physical sciences. In other fields, such as economics e.g., it is often assumed to hold if T is not too large and if the systematic component is isolated in an appropriate way.

Let x_t be an n-vector valued process and t a k-vector. Then we say that x_t is *stationary in the strict sense* if the stochastic variables

$$x_{t_1}, x_{t_2}, \ldots, x_{t_m}$$

have the same joint probability distribution as the variables

$$x_{t_1+h}, x_{t_2+h}, \ldots, x_{t_m+h}$$

1.5

for all m, t_1, t_2, ..., t_m and every k-vector h. This means that the simultaneous distributions depend only upon time parameter differences $t_1 - t_2$, $t_1 - t_3$ and so on.

Let T be the set of integers and consider the complex-valued process defined by

$$x_t = \sum_{\nu=1}^{n} c_\nu \, e^{i(t\lambda_\nu + \varphi_\nu)}, \quad t = \cdots -1, 0, 1, \ldots,$$

where the c_ν are real constants, the λ_ν are real constants in the interval $(-\pi, \pi)$ and the φ_ν are independent stochastic variables uniformly distributed in the interval $(-\pi, \pi)$. Consider the joint distribution of x_{t_1+h}, x_{t_2+h}, ..., x_{t_m+h}. They can be written as

$$x_{t_j+h} = \sum_{\nu=1}^{n} c_\nu \, e^{i(t_j\lambda_\nu + \psi_\nu)}, \quad j = 1, 2, \ldots, m,$$

where $\psi_\nu = \varphi_\nu + h\,\lambda_\nu$ and hence the ψ_ν also are uniformly distributed over an interval of length 2π. This implies that the variables x_{t_j+h} have the same joint distribution as x_{t_j} so that the process is strictly stationary. This is called the *model of random phases*. It has an important application in the theory of noise, where the noise current at time t consists of superimposed alternating current components of frequency $\lambda_\nu/2\pi$ cycles per second with constant amplitudes c_ν and phases φ_ν which are supposed to be independent with rectangular distributions. In this application one would naturally use a continuous time parameter instead.

The mean value function is clearly

$$E\,x_t = \sum_{\nu=1}^{n} \frac{1}{2\pi} c_\nu \int_{-\pi}^{\pi} e^{i(t\lambda_\nu + \varphi_\nu)} d\,\varphi_\nu \equiv 0$$

and the covariance function because of the independence of the φ_ν

$$E\,x_s\,\bar{x}_t = \sum_{\nu=1}^{n} c_\nu^2 \frac{1}{2\pi} \int_{-\pi}^{\pi} e^{i(s-t)\lambda_\nu} d\varphi_\nu = \sum_{\nu=1}^{n} c_\nu^2 e^{i(s-t)\lambda_\nu}$$

$$= \int_{-\pi}^{\pi} e^{i(s-t)\lambda} d\,F(\lambda).$$

Here $F(\lambda)$ is the nondecreasing step function

$$F(\lambda) = \sum_{\lambda_\nu \leq \lambda} c_\nu^2.$$

Consider the process $y_t = R\,e\,x_t$. This is the process with physical meaning. Then the mean value

$$E\,y_t = \sum_{\nu=1}^{n} c_\nu\,E\,\cos\,(t\,\lambda_\nu + \varphi_\nu) \equiv 0$$

and the covariance

$$E\,y_s\,y_t = \sum_{\nu=1}^{n} c_\nu^2 \int_{-\pi}^{\pi} \cos\,(s\,\lambda_\nu + \varphi_\nu)\,\cos\,(t\,\lambda_\nu + \varphi_\nu)\,\frac{d\,\varphi_\nu}{2\,\pi}$$

$$= \frac{1}{2} \sum_{\nu=1}^{n} c_\nu^2 \cos\,(s-t)\,\lambda_\nu = \frac{1}{2} \int_{-\pi}^{\pi} \cos\,(s-t)\,\lambda\,d\,F\,(\lambda) \qquad (1)$$

$$= \int_{0}^{\pi} \cos\,(s-t)\,\lambda\,d\,G\,(\lambda),\ G\,(\lambda) = \frac{1}{2} \sum_{\lambda_\nu \le \lambda} c_\nu^2.$$

Let $G(\lambda)$, $0 < \lambda < \pi$, be any nondecreasing bounded function. We can then find a sequence of bounded nondecreasing step functions $G^{(n)}(\lambda)$ with all the mass concentrated at the points $k\,\pi/n$, $k = 0, \ldots, n-1$, such that the total variation of $G^{(n)}(\lambda)$ over every interval approaches that of $G(\lambda)$ over the interval and the mass of $G^{(n)}(\lambda)$ at each of the points $k\,\pi/n$ tends to zero as $n \to \infty$. Consider a sequence of processes $y_t^{(n)}$ of random phases corresponding to $G^{(n)}(\lambda)$ respectively. It is clear that the finite dimensional distributions of $y_t^{(n)}$ converge to the corresponding finite dimensional distributions of the normal process with covariance (1), where $G(\lambda)$ is the arbitrary nondecreasing function spoken of, by a simple application of the central limit theorem. The representation of the covariance function obtained in this case will later be shown to be valid for all stationary processes.

For an example of a stationary process depending upon a continuous t-parameter we consider the following situation. Let a mechanical system of n degrees of freedom be described by the generalized coordinates q_1, q_2, $\cdots$, q_n and the corresponding generalized momenta p_1, p_2, $\ldots$, p_n. Assuming the system to be conservative, the motion is determined by the system of differential equations

$$\left.\begin{array}{l} \dfrac{d\,q_i}{d\,t} = \dfrac{\partial H}{\partial p_i} \\[3mm] \dfrac{d\,p_i}{d\,t} = \dfrac{-\partial H}{\partial q_i} \end{array}\right\} \quad i = 1, 2, \ldots, n,$$

where H is the Hamiltonian and is a function of q_1, q_2, $\ldots$ p_1, p_2, $\ldots$ p_n and t is time. H is supposed to have as many derivatives as are required, so that the system of differential equations has a unique solution for prescribed initial values of p_i and q_i.

The $2n$-space of points $P = (x_1, x_2, \ldots, x_{2n})$, where $x_1 = q_1, \ldots, x_n = q_n$, $x_{n+1} = p_1, \ldots, x_{2n} = p_n$, is called the *phase space* of the system. A system characterized by a point P_s in phase space at $t = s$ is carried into the state corresponding to P_{s+t} after t seconds. This evidently defines a one-parameter group of transformations T_t of the phase space onto itself. We are interested in the behavior of the volume element under these transformations.

Let S be a set of finite Lebesgue measure in phase space. Under the transformation T_t the set is transformed into a set $S_t = T_t S$ with the volume

$$\int_{S_t} dx_1 \ldots dx_{2n} = \int_S J \, dy_1 \ldots dy_{2n},$$

where $T_t(y_1 \ldots y_{2n}) = (x_1 \ldots x_{2n})$ and J is the corresponding Jacobian,

$$J = \frac{\partial(x_1 \ldots x_{2n})}{\partial(y_1 \ldots y_{2n})}.$$

But

$$\frac{\partial J}{\partial t} = \sum_{k=1}^{2n} J_k,$$

where

$$J_k = \frac{\partial(x_1 \ldots x_{k-1}, \dot{x}, x_{k-1}, \ldots x_{2n})}{\partial(y_1 \ldots y_{2n})}$$

and where $\dot{x} = dx_k/dt$. Hence

$$J_k = \sum_{\nu=1}^{2n} \frac{\partial \dot{x}}{\partial x_\nu} \frac{\partial(x_1 \ldots x_{k-1}, x_\nu, x_{k+1}, \ldots x_{2n})}{\partial(y_1 \ldots y_{2n})} = \frac{\partial \dot{x}}{\partial x_k} J,$$

and

$$\frac{\partial J}{\partial t} = J \sum_{k=1}^{n} \frac{\partial^2 H}{\partial p_k \partial q_k} - J \sum_{k=1}^{n} \frac{\partial^2 H}{\partial q_k \partial p_k} = 0$$

so that J does not depend upon t, $J = 1$. The Lebesgue volume is then left unchanged by T_t. *This is Liouville's theorem.*

If we restrict ourselves to a subset of finite volume of the phase space which is time invariant (sometimes this is done by choosing a region between two surfaces of constant energy), we can get a probability measure by norming by the total volume of this subset. Starting out with a uniform *a priori* distribution in the subset, it will clearly remain unchanged as time proceeds. If we are interested in some phase function, i.e., a function of $p_1, \ldots, q_n$, and consider it when t varies it is evidently a strictly stationary stochastic process. Similarly we get strictly stationary vector processes by considering several phase functions simultaneously. In dealing with situations like this, attempts were made to prove the equality of *time averages* and *space averages*, and as a result certain *ergodic* theorems were proved. Such ergodic theorems will be discussed briefly in section 1.7.

In some contexts one meets processes that are not strictly stationary but have the weaker property that the mean value function is identically constant and the covariance function $r_{s,t}$ depends only upon the difference $s - t$, $r_{s,t} = r_{s-t}$. We call such processes weakly stationary processes.

As a simple example we mention the sine functions

$$x_t = \sin 2 \pi t \, \alpha,$$

where t is a positive integer and α is a rectangular stochastic variable in the interval $(0, 1)$. Of course

$$\left. \begin{aligned} & E\, x_t = 0 \\ & E\, x_s\, x_t = \int_0^1 \sin 2 \pi s \alpha \, \sin 2 \pi t \alpha \, d\alpha = \tfrac{1}{2}\, \delta_{s-t} \end{aligned} \right\}$$

which shows the *weak stationarity* of x_t. But x_t is not strictly stationary.

Consider the process $y_t = g(x + t\alpha)$ where x is uniformly distributed on $(0, 1)$, α has distribution function $F(\alpha)$ and g is a quadratically integrable function with period 1. This class of processes is weakly stationary. Here

$$r_\tau = \operatorname{cov}\,(y_t,\, y_{t+\tau}) = \int_{\alpha=-\infty}^{\infty} \int_0^1 g(u)\, g(u + \tau \alpha)\, d\,u\, d\,F(\alpha)$$

and

$$m = E\,y = \int_0^1 g(x)\, d\,x.$$

These processes can also be shown to be strictly stationary just as the random phase model.

1.6. Representations of Stationary Processes

In Sections 1.6–1.9 we consider complex-valued weakly stationary stochastic processes with T as either the set of integers, or the real line, or a finite-dimensional vector space.

We know that $\{r_{\nu-\mu}\}$ forms a nonnegative definite matrix when ν, μ run through all integers. Introduce

$$F_N(\lambda) = \frac{1}{2\pi} \sum_{\nu=-N}^{N}{}' r_\nu \frac{e^{-i\nu\lambda} - e^{+i\nu\pi}}{-i\nu} \left(1 - \frac{|\nu|}{N}\right),$$

where the prime in the summation sign means that the term corresponding to $\nu = 0$ is $r_0(\lambda + \pi)$. Let (λ_1, λ_2) be an interval in $(-\pi, \pi)$. Then

$$F_N(\lambda_2) - F_N(\lambda_1) = \frac{1}{2\pi N} \sum_{\nu,\,\mu=1}^{N} r_{\nu-\mu} \frac{e^{-i(\nu-\mu)\lambda_2} - e^{-i(\nu-\mu)\lambda_1}}{-i(\nu-\mu)}$$

$$= \frac{1}{2\pi N} \int_{\lambda_1}^{\lambda_2} \sum_{\nu,\,\mu=1}^{N} r_{\nu-\mu}\, e^{-i\nu\lambda} e^{i\mu\lambda}\, d\lambda \geq 0.$$

Noting that $F_N(-\pi) = 0$, $F_N(\pi) = r_0$ we see that the $F_N(\lambda)$ are bounded nondecreasing functions in $(-\pi, \pi)$. Then we can extract a subsequence $F_{N_\nu}(\lambda)$ converging to a function $F(\lambda)$ of the same type at all points of continuity of $F(\lambda)$ (see Cramér [3]). But

$$\int_{-\pi}^{\pi} e^{in\lambda}\, dF_{N_\nu}(\lambda) = \begin{cases} r_n\left(1 - \dfrac{|n|}{N_\nu}\right), & |n| \leq N_\nu \\ 0, & |n| > N_\nu. \end{cases}$$

For any fixed n, on letting ν tend to infinity we get

$$r_n = \int_{-\pi}^{\pi} e^{in\lambda}\, dF(\lambda).$$

This is called the *spectral representation of the covariance function* and the theorem is due to Herglotz [1]. It is easily seen that $F(\lambda)$ is unique.

If x_t is real-valued $r_t = r_{-t}$ so that the distribution of the spectrum is symmetric around $\lambda = 0$. Then we can write

$$r_t = 2 \int_{0}^{\pi} \cos t\lambda\, dF(\lambda).$$

When T is the real line and x_t is weakly stationary and continuous in the mean (which is equivalent to r_t being continuous at $t = 0$, see 1.2) it can be proved that

$$r_t = \int_{-\infty}^{\infty} e^{it\lambda}\, dF(\lambda),$$

where $F(\lambda)$ is again a bounded nondecreasing function. Similarly for a real process

$$r_t = 2 \int_{-0}^{\infty} \cos t\lambda\, dF(\lambda).$$

For a proof see Bochner [1]. One may note that these relations are of the same form as that between the distribution function and the characteristic function of a stochastic variable.

In both the discrete and continuous parameter cases $F(\lambda)$ is called the *spectral distribution function* of the process and can be decomposed into three components

$$F(\lambda) = F_a(\lambda) + F_d(\lambda) + F_s(\lambda),$$

where $F_a(\lambda)$ is absolutely continuous, $F_d(\lambda)$ a step function and $F_s(\lambda)$ a continuous function that is constant almost everywhere. We can write

$$\left.\begin{aligned} F_a(\lambda) &= \int_{-\pi}^{\lambda} f(\lambda)\, d\lambda \\ F_d(\lambda) &= \sum_{\lambda_\nu \le \lambda} \Delta F(\lambda_\nu) \end{aligned}\right\},$$

where $f(\lambda) = F'(\lambda) > 0$ is called the *spectral density* of the process and λ_ν are the discontinuity points of $F(\lambda)$ with the corresponding saltuses $\Delta F(\lambda_\nu)$. The third part $F_s(\lambda)$ is called the *singular part* of the decomposition. In the case one usually meets in practice, $f(\lambda)$ is a smooth function, there are at most a small number of saltuses and the singular part is absent.

If T is n-dimensional Euclidean space or the set of all integer lattice points in it, one can obtain a similar representation of the covariance function by the same method. One finds that

$$r_{s-t} = \int_{\Lambda} e^{i(s-t)\cdot\lambda}\, dF(\lambda),$$

where Λ is the n-dimensional Euclidean space in the first case, and the n-cube with sides $(-\pi, \pi)$ in the second case. $F(\lambda)$ defines a bounded measure in both cases and we use the notation $x \cdot y$ to denote the inner product of the two n-vectors x and y.

As we have the representation of the covariance function

$$r_{s,t} = r_{s-t} = \int_{-\pi}^{\pi} e^{is\lambda} e^{-it\lambda}\, dF(\lambda), \quad s,\, t = \cdots -1,\, 0,\, 1,\, \ldots$$

we can apply the representation theorem of section 1.4 with $\Lambda = (-\pi, \pi)$, $f(t, \lambda) = e^{it\lambda}$ and $d\mu = dF$. Then there is an orthogonal set function $z(s)$ defined on the Borel sets of the interval $(-\pi, \pi)$ and such that

$$x_t = \int_{-\pi}^{\pi} e^{it\lambda}\, dz(\lambda), \quad t = \cdots -1,\, 0,\, 1,\, \ldots$$

and
$$E z(s_1)\, \overline{z(s_2)} = \int\limits_{s_1 \cap s_2} d F(\lambda)$$

(Cramér [1]).

In the case of a real process we get the real representation

$$x_t = \int\limits_0^\pi \cos t\lambda\, dz_1(\lambda) + \int\limits_0^\pi \sin t\lambda\, dz_2(\lambda),$$

where $z_1(\lambda)$ and $z_2(\lambda)$ are orthogonal real-valued stochastic set functions with

$$\left. \begin{aligned} E z_1(s_1)\, z_2(s_2) &= 0 \\ E z_1^2(s) = E z_2^2(s) &= 2 \int\limits_s d F(\lambda) \end{aligned} \right\}.$$

A model used extensively but in a more elaborate form in econometrics is the following. Let x_t and y_t be the price and supply of a certain commodity at time $t = \cdots - 1, 0, 1, \ldots$. The price x_t and supply y_t are assumed to be related by difference equations

$$\left. \begin{aligned} x_t &= \alpha - \beta y_t + \eta_t' \\ y_t &= \gamma + \delta x_{t-1} + \eta_t'' \end{aligned} \right\},$$

where $\alpha, \beta, \gamma, \delta$ are real constants and η_t' and η_t'' are sequences of stochastic variables representing the random disturbances that the economic system is exposed to. Solving for x_t we get

$$x_t = \alpha - \beta\gamma - \beta\delta x_{t-1} + \eta_t' - \beta\eta_t''$$

(see Koopmans [2] and Wold [3]). This is a *stochastic difference* equation of order 1. Let us consider the more general case of a difference equation of order p with constant coefficients,

$$a_0 x_{t+p} + a_1 x_{t+p-1} + \cdots + a_p x_t = \eta_t \qquad (1)$$

or
$$L\, x_t = \eta_t,$$

where the linear operator L is defined by

$$L = a_0\, \tau^p + a_1\, \tau^{p-1} + \cdots + a_p\, \tau^0.$$

Here τ stands for the translation operator. We shall assume that the η_t have mean value zero, variance σ^2 and are uncorrelated. A process x_t satisfying such a difference equation is called an *autoregressive* process.

We are interested in finding the stationary (weakly) stochastic processes satisfying (1). It is clear that η_t is weakly stationary so that it can be represented as

$$\eta_t = \int_{-\pi}^{\pi} e^{it\lambda} \, dz_\eta(\lambda).$$

As
$$E \, \eta_s \, \bar{\eta}_t = \sigma^2 \, \delta_{s,t} = \sigma^2 \int_{-\pi}^{\pi} e^{i(s-t)\lambda} \frac{d\lambda}{2\pi}$$

this process has an absolutely continuous spectrum with the constant spectral density $f(\lambda) = \sigma^2/2\pi$. Such a process is called *white noise*. If x_t is a stationary solution of (1) then

$$x_t = \int_{-\pi}^{\pi} e^{it\lambda} \, dz_x(\lambda)$$

$$E \, x_s \, \bar{x}_t = \int_{-\pi}^{\pi} e^{i(s-t)\lambda} \, dF_x(\lambda)$$

and
$$L x_t = \int_{-\pi}^{\pi} \sum_{\nu=0}^{p} a_\nu \, e^{i(p-\nu)\lambda} e^{it\lambda} \, dz_x(\lambda) = \int_{-\pi}^{\pi} e^{it\lambda} \, dz_\eta(\lambda).$$

Put
$$\varphi(z) = \sum_{\nu=0}^{p} a_\nu \, z^{(p-\nu)}.$$

Approximating the function which is 1 for $-\pi \le \lambda \le \mu$, and zero for $\mu < \lambda < \pi$ by the complete system of functions $e^{it\lambda}$, $t = 0, \pm 1, \pm 2, \ldots$ and using property (1.3.2) for integrals with respect to stochastic set functions (see section 1.3), we get

$$\int_{-\pi}^{\mu} \varphi(e^{i\lambda}) \, dz_x(\lambda) = z_\eta(\mu).$$

From this it follows that

$$\int_{-\pi}^{\mu} |\varphi(e^{i\lambda})|^2 \, dF_x(\lambda) = \frac{\sigma^2}{2\pi} (\mu + \pi). \qquad (2)$$

The left hand side is equal to

$$\int_{-\pi}^{\mu} |\varphi(e^{i\lambda})|^2 \, [f_x(\lambda) \, d\lambda + dF_{x,d}(\lambda)].$$

37

The singular part must be absent as the right member of (2) is absolutely continuous and φ is analytic. If $F_x(\lambda)$ had any jumps then $\varphi(e^{i\lambda})$ would have to be zero at these jumps since the right hand side of (2) is continuous. Thus

$$\int_{-\pi}^{\mu} |\varphi(e^{i\lambda})|^2 f_x(\lambda)\, d\lambda = \frac{\sigma^2}{2\pi}(\mu + \pi)$$

and $f_x(\lambda) = (\sigma^2/2\pi)(1/|\varphi(e^{i\lambda})|^2)$. But from this it follows that $\varphi(e^{i\lambda})$ can have no zeroes as $f_x(\lambda)$ would otherwise not be integrable. Hence we have proved that

$$x_t = \int_{-\pi}^{\pi} e^{it\lambda} \frac{1}{\varphi(e^{i\lambda})}\, dz_\eta(\lambda) \tag{3}$$

is the only stationary solution of the difference equation and that it has an absolutely continuous spectrum with the spectral density $f_x(\lambda)$ given above. Note that $\varphi(e^{i\lambda})$ has no real zeros.

Call the zeroes of $\varphi(z)$ in the complex plane $z_1, z_2, ..., z_p$, where the zeroes are enumerated so that $z_1, z_2, ..., z_K$ are inside and $z_{K+1}, ..., z_p$ are outside the unit circle $|z| = 1$. To avoid unnecessary notation we shall assume all zeroes to be simple. Then

$$\frac{1}{\varphi(z)} = \sum_{\nu=1}^{p} \frac{A_\nu}{z - z_\nu} = \sum_{\nu=1}^{K} \frac{A_\nu}{z} \sum_{\mu=0}^{\infty} \left(\frac{z_\nu}{z}\right)^{\mu} - \sum_{\nu=K+1}^{p} \frac{A_\nu}{z_\nu} \sum_{\mu=0}^{\infty} \left(\frac{z}{z_\nu}\right)^{\mu}$$

which is uniformly convergent for $|z| = 1$. Introducing this into (3) we get

$$x_t = \sum_{\nu=1}^{K} A_\nu \sum_{\mu=0}^{\infty} \eta_{t-\mu-1} z_\nu^{\mu} - \sum_{\nu=K+1}^{p} A_\nu \sum_{\mu=0}^{\infty} \eta_{t+\mu} z_\nu^{-\mu-1},$$

so that we have represented the process as a *moving average*

$$x_t = \sum_{\nu=-\infty}^{\infty} b_\nu \eta_{t-\nu}.$$

If all the roots are inside $|z| = 1$, this sum clearly extends over only positive values of ν, so that only the past values $\eta_t, \eta_{t-1}, ...$ are involved.

The covariances can be given a simple form in terms of the b_ν because

$$r_{s,t} = E x_s \bar{x}_t = \sigma^2 \sum_{\nu=-\infty}^{\infty} b_{s-\nu} \bar{b}_{t-\nu}$$

or in matrix form

$$R = \{r_{s-t}; s, t = \cdots -1, 0, 1, \ldots\} = \sigma^2 \, B \, B^*,$$

where
$$B = \{b_{\nu-\mu}; \nu, \mu = \cdots -1, 0, 1, \ldots\}.$$

Here B^* is the conjugate transpose of B.
It is also easily seen that $B = A^{-1}$,

where
$$A = \{a_{\nu-\mu} \text{ if } 0 \le \nu - \mu \le p, = 0 \text{ otherwise}\}.$$

The extension of the above result to a continuous time parameter is fairly obvious. Consider, e.g., a one-dimensional harmonic oscillator subject to friction and exposed to random impulses. The motion is governed by the Langevin equation

$$m \frac{d^2 x_t}{d t^2} + \beta \frac{d x_t}{d t} + \alpha x_t = \eta_t.$$

Here $m > 0$ is the mass of the particle, $\beta > 0$ the friction coefficient and $\alpha > 0$ a constant measuring the elastic force. The η_t are the random shocks and are supposed to form a weakly stationary process with mean zero. As before

$$\left.\begin{array}{l} \eta_t = \displaystyle\int_{-\infty}^{\infty} e^{it\lambda} \, d z_\eta(\lambda) \\[2ex] E \, \eta_x \, \bar{\eta}_t = \displaystyle\int_{-\infty}^{\infty} e^{it\lambda} \, d F_\eta(\lambda) \end{array}\right\}$$

and it is supposed that η_s and η_t are uncorrelated unless $s - t$ is very small compared to the period of the undisturbed particle. This means that the η-spectrum is uniform $= f_\eta$ over a wide range of frequencies. Strictly speaking $f_\eta(\lambda)$ could not be constant for all frequencies as this would imply infinite variance and would not have any physical meaning. Reasoning in the same way as before we get

$$\left.\begin{array}{l} x_t = \displaystyle\int_{-\infty}^{\infty} e^{it\lambda} \frac{1}{-m\lambda^2 + \beta i \lambda + \alpha} \, d z_\eta(\lambda) \\[2ex] f_x(\lambda) = \dfrac{f_\eta}{|-m\lambda^2 + \beta i \lambda + \alpha|^2}, \end{array}\right\}$$

where the second equality is an approximate equality and holds in the large frequency band we have considered. One can also obtain a moving average representation for the process.

We shall derive a general result concerning the representation of a class of weakly stationary stochastic processes as moving averages. For a change the proofs will be carried out for continuous time but the result and derivation are almost the same in the discrete case. First let us note that if we have a moving average with respect to an orthogonal process $\eta(s)$

$$x_t = \int_{-\infty}^{\infty} a(t-s)\, d\,\eta(s) \tag{4}$$

with
$$E\,|\,\eta(s_1) - \eta(s_2)\,|^2 = |\,s_1 - s_2\,|, \quad \int_{-\infty}^{\infty} |\,a(s)\,|^2\, d\,s < \infty, \tag{5}$$

then x_t has an absolutely continuous spectrum. This follows from (see section 1.3)

$$E\, x_s\, \bar{x}_t = \int_{-\infty}^{\infty} a(s-\tau)\,\overline{a(t-\tau)}\, d\,\tau = \int_{-\infty}^{\infty} e^{i(s-t)\lambda}\,|\,\gamma(\lambda)\,|^2\, d\,\lambda.$$

Here we have used Parseval's relation and $\gamma(\lambda)$ is defined as the Fourier-Plancherel transform of $a(\tau)$

$$\gamma(\lambda) = \frac{1}{\sqrt{2\,\pi}}\, \lim_{A\to\infty} \int_{-A}^{A} e^{+i\lambda\tau} a(\tau)\, d\,\tau.$$

The spectral density is $|\,\gamma(\lambda)\,|^2$.

On the other hand if the spectrum is absolutely continuous and $f(\lambda)$ the spectral density we take any measurable square root of it, i.e., a function $\gamma(\lambda)$ satisfying

$$|\gamma(\lambda)|^2 = f(\lambda).$$

As $\gamma(\lambda)$ is quadratically integrable we can define

$$a(\tau) = \frac{1}{\sqrt{2\,\pi}}\, \lim_{A\to\infty} \int_{-A}^{A} e^{-i\lambda\tau} \gamma(\lambda)\, d\,\lambda$$

and we get as before

$$r_{s,t} = \int_{-\infty}^{\infty} a(s-\tau)\,\overline{a(t-\tau)}\, d\,\tau.$$

Applying the representation theorem of section 1.4 we see that there is an orthogonal stochastic set function $\eta(s)$ satisfying (4) and (5).

As an example consider the output current x_t of a vacuum tube. Due to the atomic nature of electricity the current we observe at time t is the result of all the electrons arriving at t or earlier at the anode. The tube and circuit may be characterized by a function $g(t)$ giving the contribution to the current observed at time t due to the arrival of an electron at time 0. $g(t)$ should be assumed integrable together with its square. Assuming the arrivals to happen independently of each other and with an intensity β (the probability of an arrival in the interval $(t, t + \Delta t)$ is $\beta \Delta t$), the number $n(t)$ of arrivals during the time $(0, t)$ forms a Poisson process (see section 1.1).

If the effects of the electrons superimpose in a linear way, the current at time t is

$$x_t = \sum_{t_\nu \leq t} g(t - t_\nu),$$

where t_ν are the time points of the arrivals of the electrons. But this can be written

$$x_t = \int_{-\infty}^{\infty} g(t - \tau) \, dn(\tau) \tag{6}$$

(as $g(t)$ would be zero for negative values of t the integration need only be taken over $(-\infty, t)$). As $n(\tau)$ is a homogeneous stochastic set function with

$$E[n(s_1) - n(s_2)] = \beta(s_1 - s_2)$$
$$E[n(s_1) - n(s_2) - \beta(s_1 - s_2)]^2 = \beta |s_2 - s_1|,$$

we see that (6) is a moving average representation of the current. The only difference from (4) is that here the mean value is not zero but

$$E x_t = \beta \int_{-\infty}^{\infty} g(t - \tau) \, d\tau = \beta \int_0^{\infty} g(\tau) \, d\tau.$$

The current then consists of a d.c. component $\beta \int_0^{\infty} g(\tau) \, d\tau$ plus a *shot noise* current with an absolutely continuous spectrum and a spectral density

$$\frac{\beta}{2\pi} \left| \int_0^{\infty} e^{i\lambda\tau} g(\tau) \, d\tau \right|^2.$$

The covariance

$$r_{s,t} = \beta \int_{-\infty}^{\min(s,t)} g(s - \tau) g(t - \tau) \, d\tau.$$

In the case of discrete time one gets instead the representation

$$x_t = \sum_{\nu = -\infty}^{\infty} a_{t-\nu} \xi_\nu,$$

where the ξ's form white noise and $\sum |a_\nu|^2 < \infty$. The spectral density is

$$f(\lambda) = \frac{\sigma_\xi^2}{2\pi} \left| \sum_{\nu=-\infty}^{\infty} a_\nu e^{-i\nu\lambda} \right|^2.$$

If the ξ's are independent and identically distributed stochastic variables we refer to the ξ process as *pure white noise*. We call x_t a *linear process* if the ξ process is pure white noise.

1.7. Time and Ensemble Averages

So far we have described the stationary processes in terms of means and covariances. They are the averages of the process at one or two time points. Average here means averaging over all possible states, that is over Ω at those times. If we consider the process as an ensemble of possible functions of time, e.g., paths in phase space, one could call the averages *ensemble* (or *phase*) *averages*.

In many cases this is not an operational definition as we have often only one realization of the process at our disposal. It is however intuitively plausible that we would obtain the same result by *averaging over time* instead as the process is stationary and its structure does not change with time. The mathematical counterpart of this is the *ergodic theorem* in its various formulations.

Suppose that we want to measure $m = Ex_t$ of a weakly stationary process with the spectral representation

$$\left. \begin{aligned} x_t - m &= \int_{-\pi}^{\pi} e^{it\lambda} \, dz(\lambda) \\ r_{s,t} &= \int_{-\pi}^{\pi} e^{i(s-t)\lambda} \, dF(\lambda) \\ s, t &= \ldots, -1, 0, 1, \ldots \end{aligned} \right\}$$

Consider the time average

$$\frac{1}{N} \sum_{\nu=1}^{N} (x_\nu - m) = \frac{1}{N} \int_{-\pi}^{\pi} \sum_{\nu=1}^{N} e^{i\nu\lambda} \, dz(\lambda) = \frac{1}{N} \int_{-\pi}^{\pi} e^{i\lambda} \frac{1 - e^{iN\lambda}}{1 - e^{i\lambda}} \, dz(\lambda)$$

$$= \Delta z(0) + \frac{1}{N} \int_{-\pi}^{\pi} e^{i\lambda} \frac{1 - e^{iN\lambda}}{1 - e^{i\lambda}} \, dz_0(\lambda),$$

where $\Delta z(0)$ is the jump (possible zero) of $z(\lambda)$ at 0, and

$$z_0(\lambda) = \begin{cases} z(\lambda), & \lambda < 0 \\ z(\lambda) - \Delta z(0), & \lambda \geq 0. \end{cases}$$

From section 1.3 it follows that

$$E\left|\frac{1}{N}\sum_{\nu=1}^{N} x_\nu - m - \Delta z(0)\right|^2 = \frac{1}{N^2}\int_{-\pi}^{\pi} \frac{\sin^2 \frac{N}{2}\lambda}{\sin^2 \frac{\lambda}{2}}\, dF_0(\lambda) \tag{1}$$

where $F_0(\lambda)$ coincides with $F(\lambda)$ except that a possible discontinuity at $\lambda = 0$ has been removed from $F(\lambda)$. But this expression is at most equal to

$$\frac{1}{N^2}\left\{\int_{-\pi}^{\varepsilon} + \int_{\varepsilon}^{\pi}\right\}\frac{dF_0(\lambda)}{\sin^2\frac{\varepsilon}{2}} + \{F_0(\varepsilon) - F_0(-\varepsilon)\}.$$

Choosing ε so that the second term is sufficiently small and then taking N large we see that the right hand side of (1) tends to zero as $N \to \infty$. Hence *the time average converges in the mean to m plus a stochastic variable of variance $\Delta F(0)$.* If there is no discrete spectral mass at $\lambda = 0$ *the time average converges to the ensemble average.* This is called the *statistical ergodic theorem.* In taking a time average of the process, we are averaging one realization of the process and if $\Delta z(0) \neq 0$, we have an additional term which is of course constant for this realization. One cannot obtain information about the variance of the random term $\Delta z(0) \neq 0$ without considering several realizations of the process. The reader may note that this is a simple version of what is called the weak law of large numbers in probability theory.

In the same way one can show that

$$\frac{1}{N}\sum_{\nu=1}^{N} x_\nu e^{-i\nu\mu} \tag{2}$$

converges in the mean square to $\Delta z(\mu)$. Averages of the form (2) isolate the jumps $\Delta z(\lambda)$ if there are any.

If x_t is strictly stationary and $E|x_t| < \infty$ then one can prove a stronger statement. The time average $\frac{1}{N}\sum_{\nu=1}^{N} x_t$ will converge to a random variable for almost all realizations. This is called the *individual ergodic theorem* (for a proof see Doob [1]).

Taking $\omega = \{x_t, t = \cdots -1, 0, 1, \ldots\}$, and Ω as the space of all such sample sequences, we can define the transformation

$$T\omega = \{x_{t-1}, t = \cdots - 1, 0, 1, \ldots\},$$

i.e., T is the translation operator. From the strict stationarity if follows immediately that $\{T^n\}$ is a group of measure preserving transformations. For each function $L(\omega)$ which is absolutely integrable on Ω with respect to P-measure, $L(T^t\omega)$ is a strictly stationary process and the time average converges to a stochastic variable $\hat{L}$ (see the last paragraph). If it is true that $\hat{L}$ reduces to a constant almost certainly for each $L(\omega)$ then x_t is called an *ergodic process*.

It is clear from the above that if the spectrum of x_t has a jump at $\lambda = 0$ it cannot be ergodic. On the other hand one cannot in general hope to reduce the ergodic property to properties of the spectrum as the later determines only the second order moments. Ergodicity is related to the entire probability structure of the process. However there are two simple cases that have been studied.

If x_t is a normal process one can show that a necessary and sufficient condition for it to be ergodic is that the spectrum be continuous. If x_t is a linear process it has been shown that x_t is an ergodic process. It should be mentioned that in the case of a continuous time parameter the definitions and proofs of this section are quite analogous.

Consider, e.g., the process (1.6.6). As it is a linear process it follows that

$$
\left.
\begin{aligned}
\lim_{T \to \infty} \frac{1}{T} \int_0^T x_t \, dt &= \beta \int_0^\infty g(\tau) \, d\tau = m \\
\lim_{T \to \infty} \frac{1}{T} \int_0^T (x_t - m)^2 \, dt &= \beta \int_0^\infty g^2(\tau) \, d\tau
\end{aligned}
\right\}
$$

with probability one. This is known as Campbell's theorem (see Rice [1]).

1.8. Vector Processes

Let T be n-dimensional Euclidean space and $x_t = (x_t^{(1)}, x_t^{(2)}, \ldots, x_t^{(m)})$ a weakly stationary process taking as values vectors in m-space. Assuming the constant mean value vector to be zero we introduce the covariance matrix

$$
\begin{aligned}
R(t) &= \{r_{j,k}(t)\} \\
&= \{E x_{s+t}^{(j)} \bar{x}_s^{(k)*} \; ; \; j, k = 1, 2, \ldots, m\}, \quad s, t \in T.
\end{aligned}
$$

As before $R(-t) = R(t)^*$; $*$ denotes the conjugate transpose. For any m-vector $\alpha = (\alpha_1, \alpha_2, \ldots, \alpha_m)$ the stochastic process $\alpha \cdot x_t$ is complex-valued and weakly stationary. We can now apply the spectral representation theorem of section 1.6. We then have

$$E\left(\alpha \cdot x_s\right)\overline{\left(\alpha \cdot x_t\right)} = \int_\Lambda e^{i\,(s-t)\cdot\lambda}\,dF_\alpha\,(\lambda) \tag{1}$$

where the spectral distribution function $F_\alpha\,(\lambda)$ depends upon α. We have

$$E\left(\alpha \cdot x_s\right)\overline{\left(\alpha \cdot x_t\right)} = \sum_{\nu,\,\mu=1}^{m} \alpha_\nu\,\bar\alpha_\mu\,r_{\nu,\,\mu}\,(s-t) = \alpha\,R\,(s-t)\,\alpha^*.$$

But then $F_\alpha\,(\lambda) = \alpha\,F\,(\lambda)\alpha^*$, where $F\,(\lambda)$ is a function of λ taking as values Hermitian $m \times m$ matrices. Furthermore the increment over an interval is

$$\alpha\,\Delta\,F\,(\lambda)\alpha^* = \Delta\,F_\alpha\,(\lambda) \ge 0 \tag{2}$$

so that $\Delta\,F\,(\lambda)$ is a nonnegative definite matrix. Equating coefficients of the two quadratic forms in (1) we get

$$r_{j,\,k}\,(s-t) = \int_\Lambda e^{i\,(s-t)\cdot\lambda}dF_{j,\,k}\,(\lambda)$$

where $F_{j,\,k}\,(\lambda)$ is the element corresponding to subscript $(j,\,k)$ of the matrix $F\,(\lambda)$.

Taking $\alpha_j = 1$, $\alpha_\nu = 0$ for $\nu \ne j$, we get from (2)

$$\Delta\,F_{jj}(\lambda) \ge 0.$$

As $F_{jj}\,(\infty) - F_{jj}\,(-\infty) = r_{jj}\,(0) < \infty$ we see that the diagonal elements of $F\,(\lambda)$ are bounded nondecreasing functions.

Setting $\alpha_j = a$, $\alpha_k = b$, $\alpha_\nu = 0$ for $\nu \ne j$, k and using (2) we find that

$$|a|^2\Delta\,F_{jj}(\lambda) + 2\,Re\,ab\,\Delta\,F_{jk}(\lambda) + |b|^2\Delta\,F_{kk}(\lambda) \ge 0$$

for any a, b so that

$$|\Delta\,F_{jk}\,(\lambda)| \le \sqrt{\Delta\,F_{jj}(\lambda)\,\Delta\,F_{kk}}.$$

As $F_{jj}\,(\lambda)$ and $F_{kk}\,(\lambda)$ are of bounded variation, a simple application of Schwarz' inequality shows that all the elements of $F\,(\lambda)$ are of bounded variation. One should note however that for $j \ne k$ the function $F_{jk}\,(\lambda)$ is not necessarily nondecreasing. Hence we have proved the extended spectral representation

$$R\,(s-t) = \int_\Lambda e^{i\,(s-t)\cdot\lambda}\,dF\,(\lambda). \tag{3}$$

45

1.8

$F_{jj}(\lambda)$ is clearly the spectral distribution function of the jth component of x_t. F_{jk} is called the *cross spectral distribution function* of the jth and kth components. This result is due to Cramér [1]. In the discrete case one obtains the analogous representation.

It is easily shown that if $R(s-t)$ is given in the form (3) it can be considered as the covariance function of a stationary process.

Considering each component of the process x_t we find immediately that the process itself can be represented as

$$x_t = \int_\Lambda e^{it\cdot\lambda} \, dz(\lambda), \tag{4}$$

where $z(\lambda)$ is a vector valued stochastic set-function with components $z_1(\lambda)$, $z_2(\lambda)$, ..., $z_n(\lambda)$ and

$$E z_j(s_1) \overline{z_k(s_2)} = \int_{s_1 \cap s_2} dF_{jk}(\lambda).$$

Consider as an example a linear passive electric network consisting of m loops. It is governed by the system of differential equations

$$L \frac{d^2 x_t}{dt^2} + R \frac{dx_t}{dt} + G x_t = \xi_t, \quad -\infty < t < \infty, \tag{5}$$

where the constant matrices L, R and G are determined by the network. ξ_t is an m-vector having as its components the random driving voltages that the loops of the systems are subject to. Similarly the components of x_t represent the charges and we are interested in finding any stationary solution of (5) where the ξ_t represents noise.

If the m different noise sources can be considered as different and essentially independent we have no cross correlation, i.e, $E \xi_j(t) \xi_k(t) = 0$ if $j \neq k$, in which case we say that the m components of the noise are *incoherent*. Then clearly $F_\xi(\lambda)$ reduces to a diagonal matrix. In the general case, however, the cross spectra of the ξ-process may not vanish, in which case we have *coherent noise*.

In any case we represent ξ_t by

$$\xi_t = \int_{-\infty}^{\infty} e^{it\lambda} \, dz_\xi(\lambda),$$

and
$$E \xi_s^{(j)} \xi_t^{(k)} = \int_{-\infty}^{\infty} e^{i(s-t)\lambda} f_{j,k}^{(\xi)}(\lambda) \, d\lambda.$$

46

We have assumed that spectra of the m components are absolutely continuous which implies, as we know, that the cross spectra have the same property.

If x_t is a weakly stationary solution of (5) which then can be represented as (4), we should have (assuming of course that the first and second derivatives in the mean exist)

$$\int_{-\infty}^{\infty} e^{it\lambda} \left[-\lambda^2 L + i\lambda R + G\right] dz_x(\lambda) = \int_{-\infty}^{\infty} e^{it\lambda} dz_\xi(\lambda), \quad -\infty < t < \infty.$$

This implies as in section 1.6 that

$$M_\lambda \, dF_x(\lambda) \, M_\lambda^* = dF_\xi(\lambda) = \{f_{jk}^{(\xi)}(\lambda), \ j, \ k = 1, 2, \ldots, m\} \, d\lambda = f^{(\xi)}(\lambda) \, d\lambda,$$

where
$$M_\lambda = [-\lambda^2 L + i\lambda R + G].$$

Then we see that a necessary and sufficient condition for the existence of a stationary solution is that M_λ be nonsingular for all real λ, i.e., that the undisturbed system have no undamped eigen-oscillation. If this condition is satisfied, the weakly stationary process defined by

$$x_t = \int_{-\infty}^{\infty} e^{it\lambda} M_\lambda^{-1} dz_\xi(\lambda)$$

with the spectral density

$$f^{(x)}(\lambda) = \{f_{j,k}^{(x)}(\lambda), \ j, \ k = 1, 2, \ldots, m\} = M_\lambda^{-1} f^{(\xi)}(\lambda) \, (M_\lambda^{-1})^*$$

is the stationary solution of (5).

In certain applications the covariance structure of the process is characterized by certain symmetry properties in addition to stationarity. Let us first deal with a complex-valued process of a vector argument t in Euclidean n-space Λ such that its covariance function r_t is invariant under rotations of the argument space around the origin.

We have
$$r_t = \int_\Lambda e^{i t \cdot \lambda} dF(\lambda).$$

If 0 is any orthogonal $n \times n$ matrix we have

$$r_t = r_{0t} = \int_\Lambda e^{i \, 0 \, t \cdot \lambda} \, dF(\lambda) = \int_\Lambda e^{it \cdot 0^{-1}\lambda} \, dF(\lambda) = \int_\Lambda e^{it \cdot \mu} \, dF(0\mu),$$

so that $dF(\lambda) = dF(0\lambda)$. This shows that the spectral mass is symmetric with respect to rotations around the origin.

47

1.8

Introduce the distribution function

$$G(u) = \int\limits_{|\lambda| \leq u} dF(\lambda), \quad 0 \leq u < \infty,$$

and

$$K(u, t) = \int e^{it \cdot \lambda} \frac{ds}{s(u)}$$

where the integration is carried out over the surface $|\lambda| = u$, ds is the area element, and $s(u)$ the total area of the surface $|\lambda| = u$

$$s(u) = \frac{2 \pi^{\frac{n}{2}}}{\Gamma\left(\dfrac{n}{2}\right)} u^{n-1}.$$

We have as is easily verified

$$r_t = \int\limits_0^\infty K(u, t) \, dG(u).$$

But

$$\int\limits_{|\lambda| \leq u} e^{it \cdot \lambda} \, d\lambda = (-1)^n \int\limits_0^\pi \cdots \int\limits_0^\pi e^{i \tau u \cos \varphi_1} (\sin \varphi_1)^n (\sin \varphi_2)^{n-1}$$
$$\ldots \sin \varphi_n \, u^n \, d\varphi_1 \ldots d\varphi_n. \quad (6)$$

Since the expression depends only upon length of the vector t we have taken $t = (\tau, 0, 0, \ldots 0)$. Putting

$$\left.\begin{aligned}
\lambda_1 &= u \cos \varphi_1 \\
\lambda_2 &= u \sin \varphi_1 \cos \varphi_2 \\
&\cdots\cdots\cdots\cdots \\
\lambda_n &= u \sin \varphi_1 \ldots \sin \varphi_{n-1} \cos \varphi_n
\end{aligned}\right\}$$

this defines a one-one correspondence between $|\lambda| < u$ and

$$0 \leq \varphi_1 < \pi, \ldots, 0 < \varphi_n < \pi$$

with the Jacobian appearing in the second integral in (6). As

$$\int\limits_0^\pi (\sin \varphi)^n \, d\varphi = \frac{\Gamma\left(\dfrac{n+1}{2}\right)}{\Gamma\left(\dfrac{n+2}{2}\right)} \sqrt{\pi}$$

we get

48

$$\int_{|\lambda|\leq u} e^{it\cdot\lambda}\, d\lambda = (-1)^n \int_0^\pi e^{i\tau u \cos\varphi} u^n \frac{\pi^{\frac{n-1}{2}}}{\Gamma\left(\frac{n+1}{2}\right)} (\sin\varphi)^n\, d\varphi$$

$$= (-1)^n \left(-\frac{2u\pi}{\tau}\right)^{\frac{n}{2}} J_{\frac{n}{2}}(-\tau u) = \left(\frac{2u\pi}{\tau}\right)^{\frac{n}{2}} J_{\frac{n}{2}}(\tau u).$$

Hence by differentiating this with respect to u we get $K(u, t)\, s(u)$ so that

$$(-1)^n K(u, t) = \frac{1}{s(u)} \left\{ \frac{n}{2} \left(\frac{2\pi}{\tau}\right)^{\frac{n}{2}} u^{\frac{n}{2}-1} J_{\frac{n}{2}}(\tau u) + \right.$$

$$\left. + \left(\frac{2u\pi}{\tau}\right)^{\frac{n}{2}} J_{\frac{n-2}{2}}(\tau u)\tau - \left(\frac{2u\pi}{\tau}\right)^{\frac{n}{2}} \frac{n}{2\tau u} J_{\frac{n}{2}}(\tau u)\tau \right\}$$

$$= 2^{\frac{n-2}{2}} u^{-\frac{n-2}{2}} \tau^{-\frac{n-2}{2}} \Gamma\left(\frac{n}{2}\right) J_{\frac{n-2}{2}}(u\tau).$$

(See Whittaker-Watson [1], p. 360). Hence

$$r_t = \frac{2^{\frac{n-2}{2}} \Gamma\left(\frac{n}{2}\right)}{|t|^{\frac{n-2}{2}}} \int_0^\infty u^{-\frac{n-2}{2}} J_{\frac{n-2}{2}}(u\,|t|)\, dG(u),$$

where the integral converges absolutely. Conversely any such representation defines a covariance function. This result is due to Bochner [1].

In certain applications one is interested not in invariance with respect to the whole orthogonal group but to a subgroup of it. A similar but slightly more complicated result can be deduced in this case.

1.9. Operations on Stationary Processes

1.9 A. Linear operations. Let $\mathcal{F}$ be a linear filter through which an input $I(t)$ is passed. We can characterize $\mathcal{F}$ by its *frequency response function* $\gamma(\lambda)$ or its *transient response function* $g(t)$. The function $\gamma(\lambda)$ indicates that the output is equal to $\gamma(\lambda)e^{it\lambda}$ when $I(t) = e^{it\lambda}$. Its absolute value $|\gamma(\lambda)|$ measures the amplification of I at frequency λ and its argument $\arg\gamma(\lambda)$ is the phase shift of $e^{it\lambda}$ on passing through the filter. The function $g(t)$ is the output at time t when $I(t) = \delta_{t_0}$. It is physically plausible that $g(t) = 0$ for $t < 0$ and we shall assume that this is so. If $g(t)$ is integrable

$$\gamma \left(\lambda \right) = \int_0^\infty g \left(t \right) e^{-it\lambda} \, dt.$$

It is sometimes convenient to use filters that do not correspond to a proper function. One may, e.g., be interested in the δ-function and its derivatives.

If the input is a weakly stationary process x_t with the spectral representation

$$x_t = \int_{-\infty}^\infty e^{it\lambda} \, dz \left(\lambda \right),$$

then the output is given by

$$y_t = \int_{-\infty}^\infty e^{it\lambda} \gamma \left(\lambda \right) dz \left(\lambda \right),$$

so that $\qquad dF_y \left(\lambda \right) = \left| \gamma \left(\lambda \right) \right|^2 dF_x \left(\lambda \right).$

In order that these equations have a meaning we clearly have to assume that

$$\int_{-\infty}^\infty \left| \gamma \left(\lambda \right) \right|^2 dF_x \left(\lambda \right) < \infty,$$

i.e., the average output power should be finite.

The situation is similar for vector processes. As an example let x_t be a weakly stationary process taking n-vectors as values and having derivatives in the mean. Suppose that the filter corresponds to the linear operator

$$\alpha = \{L_{ij};\ i,\ j = 1,\ 2,\ \ldots,\ n\},$$

where each element is of the form

$$L_{ij} = \sum_{k=1}^m a_{ijk} \frac{\partial^k}{\partial t^k}.$$

Then $\qquad x_t = \int_\Lambda e^{it\cdot\lambda} \, dz \left(\lambda \right)$

and the filtered process

$$y_t = \int_\Lambda e^{it\cdot\lambda} A \left(\lambda \right) dz \left(\lambda \right)$$

where $A \left(\lambda \right)$ is the $n \times n$ matrix with elements

$$A_{ij}(\lambda) = \sum_{k=1}^{m} a_{ijk} (i\lambda)^k.$$

Hence y_t has a spectral matrix

$$A(\lambda) \, dF(\lambda) \, A^*(\lambda);$$

compare this result with the example given in section 1.8.

Another simple linear operation is the following. Let $x_t = (x_t^{(1)}, \ x_t^{(2)})$ be a weakly stationary two-dimensional process with a spectrum characterised by the matrix of spectral distribution functions $F(\lambda) = \{F_{jk}(\lambda); j, k = 1, 2\}$. Putting $y_t = x_t^{(1)} + x_t^{(2)}$ it is immediately seen that this is also weakly stationary and has the spectral distribution function

$$F_y(\lambda) = F_{11}(\lambda) + 2\, R\, e F_{12}(\lambda) + F_{22}(\lambda).$$

If the components are incoherent

$$F_y(\lambda) = F_{11}(\lambda) + F_{22}(\lambda)$$

i.e., the spectral energies just add.

1.9 B. Amplitude distortion. We are now going to discuss some cases of nonlinear operations. First, consider the so-called *amplitude distorting* filter for which the output is a function $G(x)$ of just the present value of the input

$$y_t = G(x_t),$$

i.e., the filter operates instantaneously. Assume that x_t is a real-valued normal stationary process with discrete time, mean zero and a spectral distribution function $F(\lambda)$. We have

$$R_t = E\, y_s\, y_{s+t} = \int_{-\infty}^{\infty}\!\!\int \frac{1}{2\,\pi\sigma^2\sqrt{1-\varrho^2}}\, e^{-\frac{1}{2\sigma^2(1-\varrho^2)}[x^2 - 2\varrho xy + y^2]} \times$$
$$\times G(x)\, G(y)\, dx\, dy, \quad \varrho = \frac{r_t}{r_0}.$$

Here we have assumed that

$$\int_{-\infty}^{\infty} G^2(x) \frac{1}{\sqrt{2\pi}\,\sigma}\, e^{-\frac{x^2}{2\sigma^2}}\, dx < \infty,$$

so that the new process has finite variance, and that $|\varrho| = |r_t/\sigma^2| < 1$. We have put $\sigma^2 = r_0 = \int_{-\pi}^{\pi} dF(\lambda)$. But then

$$\frac{1}{\sqrt{1-\varrho^2}}\, e^{-\frac{1}{2\,\sigma^2(1-\varrho^2)}\,[x^2-2\varrho\,xy+y^2]} = \sum_{\nu=0}^{\infty} h_\nu\left(\frac{x}{\sigma}\right) h_\nu\left(\frac{y}{\sigma}\right) \varrho^\nu\, e^{-\frac{x^2+y^2}{2\,\sigma^2}}$$

where $h_n(x)$ are the orthonormal Hermite polynomials (see Cramér [3], p. 133)

$$h_n(x) = \frac{(-1)^n}{\sqrt{n!}}\left(\frac{d^n}{dx^n}\, e^{-\frac{x^2}{2}}\right) e^{\frac{x^2}{2}}.$$

Hence

$$R_t = \sum_{\nu=1}^{\infty} g_\nu^2\, \varrho^\nu$$

where

$$g_\nu = \int_{-\infty}^{\infty} h_\nu\left(\frac{x}{\sigma}\right) G(x)\, d\Phi\left(\frac{x}{\sigma}\right)$$

and the change of the order of operations is easily justified.

For the case $\varrho = 1$ we note that the formula still holds as we then get from the Parseval relation

$$R_0 = \int_{-\infty}^{\infty} G^2(x)\, \frac{1}{\sqrt{2\,\pi}\,\sigma}\, e^{-\frac{x^2}{2\,\sigma^2}}\, dx = \sum_{\nu=0}^{\infty} g_\nu^2.$$

The formula holds similarly for $\varrho = -1$.

Introducing the convolutions of $F(\lambda)$ with itself we get

$$F^{*n}(\lambda) = \int_{-\pi}^{\pi} F^{*(n-1)}(\lambda - \mu)\, dF(\mu)$$

($dF(\mu)$ is defined outside $(-\pi, \pi)$ by periodicity). But

$$r_t^n = 2\int_0^{\pi} \cos t\,\mu\, dF^{*n}(\mu).$$

As $\sum_{\nu=0}^{\infty} g_\nu^2 < \infty$ and as $F^{*n}(\pi) - F^{*n}(-\pi) = r_0^n$ we see that

$$F_0(\lambda) = \sum_{n=0}^{\infty} g_n^2\, \frac{F^{*n}(\lambda)}{r_0^n}$$

defines a spectral distribution function in $(-\pi, \pi)$ and we can now immediately verify that

$$R_t = \int_{-\pi}^{\pi} e^{it\lambda}\, dF_0(\lambda).$$

As we usually consider the spectrum as corresponding to the co-variances, we should consider $R_t - (E\,G\,(x_t))^2$. Now

$$E\,y_t = \int\limits_{-\infty}^{\infty} G\,(x)\,h_0\left(\frac{x}{\sigma}\right)\,d\,\Phi\left(\frac{x}{\sigma}\right) = g_0$$

so that the spectral distribution function of y_t is

$$F_y\,(\lambda) = \sum_{n=1}^{\infty} g_n^2\,\frac{F^{*\,n}\,(\lambda)}{r_0^n}\,. \tag{1}$$

Now this is difficult to compute but we can get good approximations in the following way. $F^{*\,n}(\lambda)/r_0^n$ is clearly the nth convolution of a distribution function corresponding to a stochastic variable X in the interval $(-\pi, \pi)$ reduced modulo 2π. To get an asymptotic expression we assume that this stochastic variable X has a frequency function $p(\lambda)$ which is absolutely continuous. Denoting its characteristic function by $\varphi(z) = Ee^{izX}$ we see that the sum $X_1 + X_2 + \cdots + X_n$ reduced modulo 2π has the frequency function $\pi_n(x) = \sum\limits_{k=-n}^{n} p^{*\,n}(x + 2\,\pi k), -\pi < x < \pi$. But according to the Poisson summation formula we have then for $n \geq 2$

$$\pi_n\,(x) = \frac{1}{2\,\pi}\sum_{v=-\infty}^{\infty} \varphi^n\,(v)\,e^{-ivx}. \tag{2}$$

But as

$$|\varphi\,(z)| < C/z,\ |z| > 1$$

we find

$$\sum_{v=A}^{\infty} |\varphi^n\,(v)| \leq C^n\,\frac{A^{-n+1}}{A-1}$$

which tends to zero when $n \to \infty$ if $A > C,\ 1$. As the other terms in (2) tend to zero except the one corresponding to $v = 0$ we see that $\pi_n(x)$ converges uniformly to the constant $1/2\,\pi$.

This enables us to get the approximation wanted by using instead of (1)

$$F_{y\ \text{appr}}\,(\lambda) = \sum_{n=1}^{p} g_n^2\,\frac{F^{*\,n}\,(\lambda)}{r_0^n} + \frac{\lambda + \pi}{2\,\pi}\sum_{n=p+1}^{\infty} g_n^2$$

$$= \sum_{n=1}^{p} g_n^2\left[\frac{F^{*\,n}\,(\lambda)}{r_0^n} - \frac{\lambda}{2\pi}\right] + \frac{\lambda + \pi}{\sigma\,(2\,\pi)^{3/2}}\int\limits_{-\infty}^{\infty} G^2\,(x)\,e^{-\frac{x^2}{2\sigma^2}}\,d\,x - g_0^2\,\frac{\lambda + \pi}{2\,\pi}\,.$$

Taking $p = 1$ or 2 would be adequate for most purposes.

Two cases of special interest will be considered. First let us deal with a *linear rectifier*

$$G(u) = \begin{cases} \alpha u, & u > 0 \\ 0, & u \leq 0. \end{cases}$$

Then

$$\left. \begin{array}{l} g_1 = \dfrac{\alpha \sigma}{2} \\[2ex] g_2 = \dfrac{\alpha \sigma}{2 \sqrt{\pi}} \end{array} \right\}.$$

Using the approximation given above we get

$$F_{y \; \text{appr}} (\lambda) = \frac{\alpha^2}{4} F(\lambda) + \frac{\alpha^2}{4 \pi \sigma^2} \int_{-\pi}^{\pi} F(\mu) \, d F(\lambda - \mu) - \frac{\alpha^2 \sigma^2}{4} \frac{\lambda + \pi}{2 \pi} -$$

$$- \frac{\alpha^2 \sigma^2}{4 \pi} \frac{\lambda + \pi}{2 \pi} + \frac{\alpha^2 \sigma^2}{4 \pi} (\lambda + \pi) - \frac{\alpha^2 \sigma^2}{2 \pi} \frac{\lambda + \pi}{2 \pi}.$$

As a second example consider a square law device $G(u) = \alpha u^2$. Then

$$g_\nu = 0 \text{ for } \nu \neq 0, \, 2$$
$$g_2 = \alpha \sigma^2 \sqrt{2}$$

and we then get from (1) the exact relation

$$F_y (\lambda) = 2 \alpha^2 \int_{-\pi}^{\pi} F(\mu) \, d F(\lambda - \mu).$$

Compare with Rice [1].

Now let $x_t = (x_t^{(1)}, x_t^{(2)})$ be a stationary real-valued normal process with the matrix of spectral distribution functions $F(\lambda) = \{F_{jk}(\lambda); \, j, \, k = 1, \, 2\}$. Consider the filter

$$\mathcal{F} = \begin{pmatrix} G & 0 \\ 0 & I \end{pmatrix},$$

where G is the amplitude distorting operator introduced above, and I is the identity filter. Compute the cross correlation coefficient between $G(u)$ and v where u and v have a simultaneous normal distribution with means zero, variances σ^2 and correlation coefficient ϱ. We get

$$E G(u) v = E G(u) \, E[v \,|\, u] = E G(u) \, u \varrho$$

$$= \varrho \frac{1}{\sqrt{2 \pi} \, \sigma} \int_{-\infty}^{\infty} u \, G(u) \, e^{-\frac{u^2}{2 \sigma^2}} \, d u = \varrho \, \sigma \, g_1.$$

Applying this to the two components of x_t we easily find the matrix of spectral distribution functions of the new process $y_t = \mathcal{F} x_t$

$$F_y(\lambda) = \begin{cases} F_G(\lambda) & \dfrac{g_1}{\sigma} F_{12}(\lambda) \\[2ex] \dfrac{g_1}{\sigma} F_{21}(\lambda) & F_{22}(\lambda) \end{cases},$$

where $F_G(\lambda)$ is given by (1) (see Bussbang, [1]). Note that if $G(u)$ is symmetric then the two components of the noise y_t are incoherent. Also note that a similar result holds for all linear processes.

Considering the same process x_t let us now define y_t as the one dimensional process $x_t^{(1)} \cdot x_t^{(2)}$. We have

$$E y_t = r_{1.2}(0)$$

and

$$E y_s\, y_{s+t} = E\, x_s^{(1)}\, x_{s+t}^{(2)}\, E\, x_s^{(2)}\, x_{s+t}^{(1)} + E\, x_s^{(1)}\, x_{s+t}^{(1)}\, E\, x_s^{(2)}\, x_{s+t}^{(2)} + \; + E\, x_s^{(1)}\, x_s^{(2)}\, E\, x_{s+t}^{(1)}\, x_{s+t}^{(2)t}$$

$$= r_{1,\,2}(t)\, r_{1,\,2}(-t) + r_{1,\,1}(t)\, r_{2,\,2}(t) + [r_{1,\,2}(0)]^2.$$

The covariances of y_t are then given by the two first terms of this expression. The spectral distribution function of y_t can then be written in terms of convolutions

$$F_y(\lambda) = \int_{-\pi}^{\pi} F_{12}(\mu)\, d F_{21}(\lambda - \mu) + \int_{-\pi}^{\pi} F_{11}(\mu)\, d F_{22}(\lambda - \mu).$$

1.9 C. Rounding off. Consider a normal stationary process x_t with spectral distribution function $F(\lambda)$. After rounding off we obtain a new process y_t. If the rounding off unit is h we have $y_t = G[x_t]$, where $G(x) = \nu h$ if $\nu h \leq x < (\nu + 1)h$. We are interested in the change of the spectrum caused by this operation.

If $F_r(\lambda)$ is the spectral distribution function of the new process we have (see formula (1.9 B 1))

$$F_r(\lambda) = \sum_{k=1}^{\infty} g_k^2 \frac{F^{*k}(\lambda)}{r_0^k} \tag{3}$$

with

$$g_k = \int_{-\infty}^{\infty} h_k\left(\frac{x}{\sigma}\right) G(x)\, d\Phi\left(\frac{x}{\sigma}\right)$$

and

$$r_0 = \sigma^2 = \int_{-\pi}^{\pi} d F(\lambda).$$

1.9

Writing $G(x) = x - \dfrac{h}{2} + \Delta_h(x)$ we get

$$g_k = \sigma\,\delta_{k1} + \int\limits_{-\infty}^{\infty} \Delta_h(x)\,h_k\left(\frac{x}{\sigma}\right) d\,\Phi\left(\frac{x}{\sigma}\right).$$

Now

$$\int\limits_{-\infty}^{\infty} \Delta_h(x)\,g(x)\,d\,x = -\sum_{\nu=-\infty}^{\infty}\ \int\limits_{\nu h}^{(\nu+1)h} [x-(\nu+\tfrac{1}{2})\,h]\,[g((\nu+\tfrac{1}{2})\,h) +$$

$$+ (x-(\nu+\tfrac{1}{2})\,h)\,g'((\nu+\tfrac{1}{2})h) + R_\nu]\,d\,x$$

where
$$R_\nu = \frac{(x-(\nu+\tfrac{1}{2})\,h)^2}{2}\,g''((\nu+\theta)h).$$

Hence
$$g_k = \sigma\,\sigma_{k1} - \frac{h^3}{12}\sum_{\nu=-\infty}^{\infty} [g'((\nu+\tfrac{1}{2})\,h)+o\,(1)],$$

with
$$g(x) = h_k\left(\frac{x}{\sigma}\right)\frac{d\,\Phi\left(\frac{x}{\sigma}\right)}{d\,x}.$$

Now it is easy to see that

$$g_k = \sigma\,\delta_{k1} + o\,(h^2),\quad k=1,\,2,\,\ldots.$$

The order terms $o\,(h^2)$ do not hold uniformly in k, so that we cannot conclude that $F_r(\lambda) - F(\lambda) = o\,(h^2)$. In fact we know that

$$\int\limits_{-\pi}^{\pi} d\,F_r(\lambda) = \int\limits_{-\pi}^{\pi} d\,F(\lambda) + \frac{h^2}{12}\,(1+o\,(1)),$$

which is simply Sheppard's correction (see, e.g., Cramér [3], pp. 361–2). But for any $p>0$ we have by integrating (3)

$$\int\limits_{-\pi}^{\pi} d\,F_r(\lambda) = \sum_{k=1}^{\infty} g_k^2 = \sigma^2 + o\,(h^2) + \sum_{p+1}^{\infty} g_k^2 = \sigma^\circ + \frac{h^2}{12}\,(1+o\,(1))$$

and we get

$$\sum_{p+1}^{\infty} g_k^2 = \frac{h^2}{12}\,(1+o\,(1)).$$

Using the limit relation proved in section 1.9 B we see that

56

$$F_r(\lambda) = F(\lambda) + \frac{h^2}{12} \frac{\lambda + \pi}{2\pi} (1 + o(1)).$$

This means that by rounding off we superimpose incoherent white noise of spectral density $h^2/24\pi$ on the original process for small values of the rounding off unit h. See also Tukey [1].

1.9 D. Periodic sampling. Let x_t, $-\infty < t < \infty$, be a weakly stationary process with a spectral density $f(\lambda)$. In many cases it is not possible or convenient to observe x_t for each $t \in T$, but only at some points t_ν. If these are chosen as lattice points $t_\nu = \nu h$ we say that x_t has been *sampled periodically*. Denoting the covariances of the new process by $r_{\nu h}$ we have

$$r_{\nu h} = E\, x_s\, x_{s + \nu h} = \int_{-\infty}^{\infty} e^{i\nu h\lambda} f(\lambda)\, d\lambda = \int_{-\pi}^{\pi} e^{i\nu\lambda} f_h(\lambda)\, d\lambda,$$

where
$$f_h(\lambda) = \frac{1}{h} \sum_{-\infty}^{\infty} f\left(\frac{\lambda + 2n\pi}{h}\right), \quad -\pi < \lambda < \pi.$$

The sum converges for almost every λ to an integrable function in $(-\pi, \pi)$. Hence the new spectral density is $f_h(\lambda)$. The spectral density corresponding to a certain λ is put together from contributions from the frequencies $\lambda/h + 2n\pi/h$. If h is small only the term for $n = 0$ matters but otherwise we note that generally it is not possible to reconstruct $f(\lambda)$ completely even if we know $f_h(\lambda)$ exactly. Hence if we want to use periodic sampling to get information concerning the spectrum we must choose h so small that the range of frequencies we believe are significant are included in the interval $(-\pi/h, \pi/h)$. In some cases of interest, however, random noise originating perhaps from rounding off errors or from the physical device used masks the higher frequencies so that little is gained by making h very small. Note that if the spectrum of the process (assumed real-valued) is included in the range $(-\pi/h, \pi/h)$ the spectrum is determined by the covariances $r_{\nu h}$. If the process and its first k derivatives are observed at points νh the spectrum can be reconstructed from the covariance structure if it is in the range $(-\pi(k+1)/h, \pi(k+1)/h)$.

If we observe instead certain mean values taken at periodic time points,

$$y_\nu = \frac{1}{h} \int_{(\nu - \frac{1}{2})h}^{(\nu + \frac{1}{2})h} x_t\, dt$$

we find easily that the y-process has the spectral density

$$f_y(\lambda) = \frac{4}{h}\sin^2\frac{\lambda}{2}\sum_{n=-\infty}^{\infty}\frac{f\left(\dfrac{\lambda+2n\pi}{h}\right)}{(\lambda+2n\pi)^2}.$$

1.9 E. Random sampling. Sometimes we may sample the process at time points t chosen at random. Let x_t be a real-valued stationary process. Consider a sequence $\ldots z_{-1},\,z_0\,z_1,\,\ldots$ of independent positive stochastic variables with the same distribution. Put

$$t_\nu = t_{\nu-1} + z_\nu,\ \nu = \cdots - 1,\,0,\,1,\,\ldots\,.$$

To determine the probability distributions of t_ν we either fix t_0 as 0 say, or we can let it have some arbitrary probability distribution. Then

$$y_\nu = x_{t_\nu},\ \nu = \cdots - 1,\,0,\,1,\,\ldots$$

is also stationary, with the covariances

$$E\,y_\nu\,y_\mu = E\,x_{t_\nu}\,x_{t_\mu} = E\,[E\,(x_{t_\nu}\,x_{t_\mu}\,|\,t_\nu,\,t_\mu\ \text{fixed})] = E\,r_{t_\nu-t_\mu}.$$

But as

$$r_{t_\nu-t_\mu} = \int_{-\infty}^{\infty} e^{i(t_\nu-t_\mu)\lambda}\,d\,F(\lambda)$$

we get

$$E\,y_\nu\,y_\mu = \int_{-\infty}^{\infty} [\varphi(\lambda)]^{|\nu-\mu|}\,d\,F(\lambda), \tag{4}$$

where $\varphi(\lambda)$ is the characteristic function $\varphi(\lambda) = E\,e^{i\lambda z}$.

To determine the spectrum of the new process define

$$P_\lambda(a) = \frac{1}{2\pi}\int_{-\pi}^{\lambda}\frac{1-|a|^2}{|1-a\,e^{-il}|^2}\,d\,l$$

if $|a| < 1$, and $P_\lambda(a)$ as the distribution function on $(-\pi,\,\pi)$ having all its mass at the point $\lambda = \theta$ where $a = e^{i\theta}$, $-\pi < \theta \le \pi$. In any case $P_\lambda(a)$ is a distribution function in λ. Also

$$\int_{-\pi}^{\pi} e^{i\nu\lambda}\,d\,P_\lambda(a) = \begin{cases} a^\nu & \nu \ge 0 \\ \bar{a}^{|\nu|}, & \nu < 0. \end{cases}$$

We can always define a bounded nondecreasing function

$$G(\lambda) = \int_{-\infty}^{\infty} P_\lambda[\varphi(x)]\,d\,F(x).$$

$G(\lambda)$ is the spectral distribution function of y_ν as for $\nu \geq 0$

$$\int_{-\pi}^{\pi} e^{i\nu\lambda} \, dG(\lambda) = \int_{-\pi}^{\pi} \int_{-\infty}^{\infty} e^{i\nu\lambda} \, dP_\lambda \, [\varphi(x)] \, dF(x)$$

$$= \int_{-\infty}^{\infty} [\varphi(x)]^\nu \, dF(x) = E \, y_{k+\nu} \, y_k .$$

If $z = h\,\xi$, where $E\,\xi = 1$, it is of interest to consider $G(h\,\lambda)$ and its limit when $h \to 0$. Consider the characteristic function

$$\int_{-\pi/h}^{\pi/h} e^{iy\lambda} \, d_\lambda \, G(\lambda h) = \int_{-\pi}^{\pi} e^{iy\lambda/h} \, dG(\lambda)$$

of $G(\lambda h)$. Letting $r = y/h$ be an integer we see that

$$\int_{-\pi}^{\pi} e^{iy\lambda/h} \, dG(\lambda) = \int_{-\infty}^{\infty} [\varphi(x\,h)]^{y/h} \, dF(x).$$

But $\varphi(x\,h) = 1 + i\,x\,h + o(h)$ when $|x| < h^{-1/2}$. On letting $r \to \infty$, the limiting value is

$$\int_{-\infty}^{\infty} e^{iyx} \, dF(x).$$

But we get the same limiting value no matter how $h \to 0$. If $y/(r+1) < h < y/r$

$$\left| \int_{-\pi}^{\pi} (e^{ir\lambda} - e^{iy\lambda/h}) \, dG(\lambda) \right| \leq \int_{-\pi}^{\pi} |\lambda| \, dG(\lambda).$$

But $G(\lambda)$ tends to the distribution function with all its mass at zero when $h \to 0$ so that the difference tends to zero and the same limiting value is obtained no matter how $h \to 0$. The limit of the characteristic function of $G(h\,\lambda)$ is thus the characteristic function of $F(\lambda)$. Thus $G(h\lambda)$ approaches $F(\lambda)$ as $h \to 0$ as one might expect intuitively.

1.10. Harmonizable Stochastic Processes

Although we are mainly concerned with stationary processes in this book we will just briefly discuss a more general class of processes.

Suppose that $z(s)$ is an additive stochastic set function defined for each bounded Borel set on the real axis, not necessarily orthogonal, but such that

1.10

$$E \, z \, (x) = 0$$

$$E \, z \, (s_1) \, \overline{z \, (s_2)} = \int\limits_{\lambda \in s_1} \int\limits_{\mu \in s_2} d \, F \, (\lambda, \, \mu) \Bigg\} \tag{1}$$

where $F(\lambda, \mu)$ is a function of bounded variation. Also we assume that $F(\lambda, \mu)$ defines a *nonnegative definite* set function, i.e.,

$$\int\limits_{-\infty}^{\infty} \int c \, (\lambda) \, \overline{c \, (\mu)} \, d \, F \, (\lambda, \, \mu) \geq 0$$

for each continuous function $c(\lambda)$ vanishing outside some finite interval. Then one can define integrals of the type

$$x_t = \int\limits_{-\infty}^{\infty} e^{it\lambda} \, d \, z \, (\lambda) \tag{2}$$

and show that such a process has the covariance function

$$r_{s, \, t} = E \, x_s \, \bar{x}_t = \int\limits_{-\infty}^{\infty} \int e^{is\lambda - it\mu} \, d \, F \, (\lambda, \, \mu). \tag{3}$$

Conversely if a process has a covariance of the type in (3), where $F(\lambda, \mu)$ is nonnegative definite, one can show that the process can be represented in the form (2), with $z(s)$ having the properties (1). These processes are called *harmonizable*. The weakly stationary processes form a subset of this class and correspond to $F(\lambda, \mu)$ having all its mass concentrated on the main diagonal $\lambda = \mu$. For a more detailed study of these processes see Loève [1] and Cramér [4].

CHAPTER 2

STATISTICAL QUESTIONS WHEN THE SPECTRUM
IS KNOWN (LEAST SQUARES THEORY)

2.0. Introduction

This chapter is devoted to linear problems when the spectrum (or the covariance function) of the stationary process is known; we especially study the question of how to construct the optimal linear predictor. Our exposition is based upon the original paper by Kolmogoroff [2] and Doobs' book [2]. Wiener [1] should be consulted for a somewhat different approch via generalized harmonic analysis. The two methods are equivalent for many practical purposes. A third approach using the theory of Toeplitz forms is also possible (see Grenander [3]).

This chapter is somewhat more formal than the rest of the book and uses mathematical machinery that may be unfamiliar to the reader. To make the exposition complete in this respect we have added an Appendix where the reader will find statements and proofs of some results in complex variable theory used in this chapter.

It should be noted that we seldom know the spectrum *a priori* and usually have to estimate it from observed realisations of the process. How this should be done is studied in Chapters 4 and 8.

2.1. Preliminaries

Let x_t, $E\,x_t \equiv 0$, $t \in T$, be a weakly stationary (see section 1.5) stochastic process. In many statistical contexts, a set of stochastic variables x_t, $t \in I \subset T$, has been observed and one wishes to estimate a stochastic variable x_t, $t \in T - I$, by a *linear combination* of the observed stochastic variables that is *best in the sense of smallest mean square error*. This problem can be rephrased in a convenient geometric language.

Consider the set of all finite linear combinations $\sum c_\nu x_{t_\nu}, t_\nu \in T$, where the c_ν are complex constants. This is a *linear manifold* M, that is, given elements y, $z \in M$ and complex numbers α, β

$$\alpha y + \beta z$$

is also in M. Add to M all stochastic variables that are limits in the mean square of elements of M. We then obtain the *closed linear manifold* $\mathcal{M}$. Let the *inner product* of two elements x, $y \in \mathcal{M}$ be

$$(x, y) = E x \bar{y}.$$

The *length* of an element $x \in \mathcal{M}$ can then be defined as

$$\|x\| = \sqrt{E |x|^2}.$$

Clearly the length of an element x is zero if and only if $x = 0$ with probability one. Random variables equal with probability one are to be identified with each other.

The inner product (x, y) is a linear function of x for fixed y and

$$\overline{(x, y)} = (y, x).$$

The Schwarz inequality implies that

$$|(x, y)| \leq \|x\| \cdot \|y\|.$$

The *distance* between two elements x, y is defined as

$$\|x - y\|.$$

This distance satisfies the *triangle inequality*, that is, given the elements x, y

$$\|x + y\| \leq \|x\| + \|y\|.$$

This is simply Minkowski's inequality (see e.g. Titchmarsh [1]). We then have a linear vector space $\mathcal{M}$ that is complete in the norm. This means that if $x_n \in \mathcal{M}$ and is a Cauchy sequence, that is, $\|x_n - x_m\| \to 0$ when n, $m \to \infty$, then the limit in the mean square of x_n belongs also to $\mathcal{M}$ as is easily seen.

Consider the closed linear manifold $\mathcal{N}$ generated by the stochastic variables x_t, $t \in I \subset T$. This is a linear vector space complete in the norm and is a subspace of $\mathcal{M}$. The case of greatest interest is that in which $\mathcal{N}$ is a proper subspace of $\mathcal{M}$, that is, $\mathcal{N} \neq \mathcal{M}$. We shall refer to $\mathcal{N}$ as the *observed space*. We wish to *estimate* an element $x \in \mathcal{M}$ but not necessarily in $\mathcal{N}$ by an element $x_e \in \mathcal{N}$ which is best in the sense of smallest mean square error, that is,

$$\|x - x_e\| = \min_{y \in \mathcal{N}} \|x - y\|.$$

Let $\delta = \min \|x - y\|$. We shall show that *there is an element $x_e \in \mathcal{N}$ such that*

$$\|x - x_e\| = \delta.$$

Let y_n be a sequence of elements of $\mathcal{N}$ such that $\|x - y_n\| \to \delta$. It follows from the parallellogram law (for any x, $y \in \mathcal{M}$, $\|x - y\|^2 + \|x + y\|^2 = 2\|x\|^2 + 2\|y\|^2$) that

$$\|y_n - y_m\|^2 = 2\|y_n - x\|^2 + 2\|y_m - x\|^2 - 4\|\tfrac{1}{2}(y_n + y_m) - x\|^2.$$

But $\tfrac{1}{2}(y_n + y_m) \in \mathcal{N}$ so that

$$\|\tfrac{1}{2}(y_n + y_m) - x\|^2 \geq \delta^2$$

and $$\|y_n - y_m\|^2 \leq 2\|y_n - x\|^2 + 2\|y_m - x\|^2 - 4\delta^2.$$

As n, $m \to \infty$ the right side of this inequality tends to zero so that y_n is a Cauchy sequence. Because of the completeness of $\mathcal{M}$ and $\mathcal{N}$ there is an $x_e \in \mathcal{N}$ such that $y_n \to x_e$ and by continuity of the norm $\|x_e - x\| = \delta$.

We shall also show that $x - x_e$ *is orthogonal to* $\mathcal{N}$. The element $x_e + \alpha y \in \mathcal{N}$ for every $y \in \mathcal{N}$ and every complex number α. Thus

$$\|x - x_e - \alpha y\| \geq \delta$$

and

$$0 \leq \|x - x_e - \alpha y\|^2 - \|x - x_e\|^2$$
$$= -\bar{\alpha}(x - x_e, y) - \alpha(y, x - x_e) + |\alpha|^2 \cdot \|y\|^2.$$

Let $\alpha = \beta(x - x_e, y)$ where β is a real number. Then

$$0 \leq -2\beta |(x - x_e, y)|^2 + \beta^2 |(x - x_e, y)|^2 \cdot \|y\|^2.$$

This cannot be true for small positive values of β unless $(x - x_e, y) = 0$. Thus $x - x_e \perp \mathcal{N}$. This implies that *any* $x \in \mathcal{M}$ *can be written in the form* $x = z_1 + z_2$ *where* $z_1 \in \mathcal{N}$, $z_2 \perp \mathcal{N}$. It is easily seen that this representation is unique. The element $z_1 = x_e$ of $\mathcal{N}$ is called the *projection of* x *on* $\mathcal{N}$ and is the unique element of $\mathcal{N}$ such that $\|x - z_1\| = \min\limits_{y \in \mathcal{N}} \|x - y\|$.

In some problems, it is convenient to introduce another linear vector space isomorphic to the space $\mathcal{M}$ generated by the stochastic process x_t. By an isomorphism we mean a mapping that takes each element of one space into a corresponding element of the second and vice versa, that is linear, and that preserves the norm of the elements mapped. In heuristic language we could say that these spaces are two different representations of the same geometry. The isomorphism is here considered for a process with an integral-valued parameter but it is quite analogous for other parameter sets. This isomorphism is implied by the spectral representation of a stationary process obtained in section 1.6. Using this representation we see that $\mathcal{M}$ consists of elements of the form

$$x = \int\limits_{-\pi}^{\pi} \sum_{t=-n}^{n} c_t\, e^{it\lambda}\, dz\,(\lambda),$$

where n is finite and the c's are complex numbers, as well as all limits in the mean of these elements. Since

$$\|x\|^2 = E\,|x|^2 = \int\limits_{-\pi}^{\pi} \Big|\sum_{t=-n}^{n} c_t\, e^{it\lambda}\Big|^2\, dF\,(\lambda),$$

where $F(\lambda)$ is the spectral distribution function of the process, it follows that $\mathcal{M}$ *consists of all elements of the form*

$$\int\limits_{-\pi}^{\pi} g\,(\lambda)\, dz\,(\lambda),$$

where $$\int\limits_{-\pi}^{\pi} |g\,(\lambda)|^2\, dF\,(\lambda) < \infty.$$

Consider the space $L_2(dF)$ of all functions $g(\lambda)$ quadratically integrable with respect to $dF(\lambda)$. Functions $g(\lambda)$ differing only on a set of F-measure zero are to be identified with each other. The inner product of two elements $h,\, g \in L_2(dF)$ is defined as

$$(h, g) = \int\limits_{-\pi}^{\pi} h\,(\lambda)\, \overline{g\,(\lambda)}\, dF\,(\lambda).$$

$L_2(dF)$ is a linear vector space complete in the norm

$$\|g\| = \sqrt{(g,g)}.$$

If $x = \int\limits_{-\pi}^{\pi} h\,(\lambda)\, dz\,(\lambda)$ *is an element of* $\mathcal{M}$, *it is clear that a 1–1 correspondence is set up between the elements of* $\mathcal{M}$ *and* $L_2(dF)$ *by making* $x \in \mathcal{M}$ *correspond to* $h(\lambda) \in L_2(dF)$. In particular, x_n corresponds to $e^{in\lambda}$. The mapping is obviously linear. The inner product is left invariant under the mapping since

$$(x,\, y) = E\,x\bar{y} = \int\limits_{-\pi}^{\pi} h\,(\lambda)\, \overline{g\,(\lambda)}\, dF\,(\lambda) = (h,g),$$

where $x = \int\limits_{-\pi}^{\pi} h(\lambda) dz(\lambda)$, $y = \int\limits_{-\pi}^{\pi} g(\lambda) dz(\lambda)$ are any two elements of $\mathcal{M}$. *This correspondence is thus an isomorphism* and the two spaces have the same geometrical character. The problems of this chapter are geometrical problems since they are least square problems. When considering a least squares problem in $\mathcal{M}$, it may sometimes be more convenient to solve the corresponding problem in $L_2(dF)$. The solution of the problem in $\mathcal{M}$ will be the isomorph of the solution of the corresponding problem in $L_2(dF)$.

We now derive a simple and useful inequality. Suppose that the spaces $L_2(dF)$, $L_2(dG)$ are given with $0 \le dG(\lambda) \le dF(\lambda)$. Let $\mathcal{N}(dF)$, $\mathcal{N}(dG)$ be the closed linear submanifolds of $L_2(dF)$ and $L_2(dG)$, respectively, generated by the set $\{e^{in\lambda};\ n \in I\}$ where I is an index set. Let the function $h(\lambda)$ be an element of both $L_2(dG)$, $L_2(dF)$. Consider the errors of approximation

$$\sigma_F^2 = \inf_{a \,\varepsilon\, \mathcal{N}(dF)} \int\limits_{-\pi}^{\pi} |h(\lambda) - a(\lambda)|^2 dF(\lambda)$$

$$\sigma_G^2 = \inf_{a \,\in\, \mathcal{N}(dG)} \int\limits_{-\pi}^{\pi} |h(\lambda) - a(\lambda)|^2 dG(\lambda).$$

$\mathcal{N}(dF) \subset \mathcal{N}(dG)$ since $dG(\lambda) \le dF(\lambda)$. It is then clear that

$$\sigma_G^2 \le \sigma_F^2,$$

since the function minimizing the error of approximation in $L_2(dF)$ gives an error which cannot be less than that resulting when it is used as an approximation in $L_2(dG)$.

2.2. Prediction

Consider a weakly stationary process x_t, $Ex_t \equiv 0$, $t = \ldots, -1, 0, 1, \ldots$. Assume that we have observed x_{n-m}, x_{n-m+1}, $\ldots$, x_n, $m > 0$, and that we wish to estimate $x_{n+\nu}$, $\nu > 0$, by a linear combination of the observed stochastic variables that is best in the sense of smallest mean square error. We want to predict ν *steps ahead*. We shall not consider this problem but rather the limiting one in which $m = +\infty$. It will be shown that the solution given is the limit in the appropriate sense (mean square) of the solution for large m when $m \to \infty$.

Let $\mathcal{M}\{\ldots\}$ denote the closed linear manifold generated by the elements in braces. The symbols $\cap$ and $\cup$ are used to denote intersection and union of sets respectively. For convenience, we introduce the following linear manifolds

$$\mathfrak{M}_{m,n} = \mathfrak{M}\{x_t; \ n-m \le t \le n\}$$

$$\mathfrak{M}_n = \mathfrak{M}\{x_t; \ t \le n\} \qquad\qquad {}_n\mathfrak{M} = \{e^{it\lambda}; \ t \le n\}$$

$$\mathfrak{M}_{-\infty} = \bigcap_{-\infty}^{\infty} \mathfrak{M}_n \qquad\qquad {}_{-\infty}\mathfrak{M} = \bigcap_{-\infty}^{\infty} {}_n\mathfrak{M}$$

$$\mathfrak{M}_\infty = \mathfrak{M}\{x_t; \ -\infty < t < \infty\} \qquad {}_\infty\mathfrak{M} = \mathfrak{M}\{e^{it\lambda}; \ -\infty < t < \infty\}.$$

From the comments of section 2.1 it is clear that the solution of the first prediction problem mentioned above is the projection z_m of $x_{n+\nu}$ on the manifold $\mathfrak{M}_{m,n}$ and the solution of the limiting problem is the projection z of $x_{n+\nu}$ on the manifold $\mathfrak{M}_n$. The corresponding errors of prediction are

$$\| z_m - x_{n+\nu} \| = \min_{y \in \mathfrak{M}_{m,n}} \| y - x_{n+\nu} \| = \delta_m$$

$$\| z - x_{n+\nu} \| = \min_{y \in \mathfrak{M}_n} \| y - x_{n+\nu} \| = \delta.$$

The following brief discussion shows that the *prediction error* $\delta_m \to \delta$ *as* $m \to \infty$ *and that the predictor* $z_m \to z$ *in the mean square as* $m \to \infty$. Now $\mathfrak{M}_{m,n} \subset \mathfrak{M}_{m',n}$ if $m \le m'$ and $\mathfrak{M}_n = \bigcup_m \mathfrak{M}_{m,n}$. There is then a sequence of points $y_m \in \mathfrak{M}_{m,n}$ such that $\| y_m - z \| \to 0$ as $m \to \infty$. But then

$$\| y_m - x_{n+\nu} \| \to \delta$$

as $m \to \infty$. Thus $\delta_m \to \delta$ as $m \to \infty$ and an argument of section 2.1 implies that

$$\| z - z_m \| \to 0 \quad \text{as } m \to \infty.$$

We shall now concentrate on the limiting prediction problem where $m = \infty$ and discuss it in some detail. Let $\varphi_{n,\nu}$ denote the predictor of $x_{n+\nu}$ given $x_n, x_{n-1}, \dots$ and let $\phi_\nu(\lambda)$ correspond to $\varphi_{0,\nu}$ in the isomorphism between $\mathfrak{M}_\infty$ and ${}_\infty\mathfrak{M}$. But then $e^{in\lambda}\phi_\nu(\lambda)$ corresponds to $\varphi_{n,\nu}$. The error of prediction

$$\sigma_\nu^2 = E\,|x_{n+\nu} - \varphi_{n,\nu}|^2 = \int_{-\pi}^{\pi} |e^{i\nu\lambda} - \phi_\nu(\lambda)|^2\, dF(\lambda).$$

The *error of prediction does not decrease when we predict further ahead*, that is

$$0 \le \sigma_1^2 \le \sigma_2^2 \le \cdots .$$

This is so because $\mathfrak{M}_{n+1} \supset \mathfrak{M}_n$. But then it can be seen that *the errors of prediction* σ^2 *are either all zero or all positive*. When the prediction errors are zero, the manifolds $\mathfrak{M}_n$ are all the same and equal to the manifold $\mathfrak{M}_\infty$ generated by the process x_n. A positive error of prediction implies that each manifold $\mathfrak{M}_n$ is a proper subspace of the next manifold $\mathfrak{M}_{n+1}$.

We first consider a process with an absolutely continuous spectral distribution function so that

$$F(\lambda) = \int\limits_{-\pi}^{\lambda} f(x)\,dx,$$

where $f(\lambda) = F'(\lambda)$. We also assume that

$$\int\limits_{-\pi}^{\pi} \log f(\lambda)\,d\lambda > -\infty.$$

The predictor will be obtained and the prediction error will be shown to be positive. Since $\frac{1}{2}\log f(\lambda)$ is integrable, it has a Fourier development

$$\tfrac{1}{2}\log f(\lambda) \sim \sum_{-\infty}^{\infty} a_n\,e^{in\lambda},$$

where
$$a_n = \frac{1}{4\,\pi}\int\limits_{-\pi}^{\pi}\log f(\lambda)\,e^{-in\lambda}\,d\lambda,\quad a_{-n} = \bar{a}_n.$$

Consider the function

$$g(z) = a_0 + 2\sum_{1}^{\infty} a_n\,z^n.$$

The function $g(z)$ is analytic in the unit circle $|z| < 1$ and its real part

$$R\,e\,g(r\,e^{i\lambda}) = \sum_{-\infty}^{\infty} a_n\,r^{|n|}\,e^{in\lambda}$$

is the harmonic function with boundary value $\frac{1}{2}\log f(\lambda)$. This statement is made more precise later on. Let

$$c(z) = \sum_{j=0}^{\infty} c_j\,z^j,$$

where
$$\sum_{j=0}^{\infty} \bar{c}_j\,z^j = e^{g(z)}\,\sqrt{2\,\pi},\quad |z| < 1.$$

Note that the function $c(z)$ is analytic in the unit circle $|z| < 1$ and has no zeros there, since $g(z)$ is analytic in the unit circle. Moreover

$$\int_{-\pi}^{\pi} |c(re^{-i\lambda})|^2 \, d\lambda = 2\pi \int_{-\pi}^{\pi} e^{2\,Reg(re^{i\lambda})} \, d\lambda$$

$$= 2\pi \int_{-\pi}^{\pi} \exp\left\{\frac{1}{2\pi} \int_{-\pi}^{\pi} \frac{1-r^2}{1-2r\,\cos(\theta-\lambda)+r^2} \log f(\theta)\, d\theta\right\} d\lambda$$

$$\leq 2\pi \int_{-\pi}^{\pi} f(\theta) \frac{1}{2\pi} \int_{-\pi}^{\pi} \frac{1-r^2}{1-2r\,\cos(\theta-\lambda)+r^2} \, d\lambda \, d\theta$$

$$= 2\pi \int_{-\pi}^{\pi} f(\theta)\, d\theta$$

(this is Jensen's inequality, see e.g. Hardy, Littlewood and Polya [1]) so that $c(z) \in H_2$ (see appendix on complex variable theory). The boundary value

$$c(e^{-i\lambda}) = \sum_{j=0}^{\infty} c_j e^{-ij\lambda} = \lim_{r\to 1-} c(re^{-i\lambda}), \qquad \sum_{j=0}^{\infty} |c_j|^2 < \infty.$$

exist almost everywhere and is such that

$$\frac{1}{2\pi} |c(e^{-i\lambda})|^2 = f(\lambda).$$

Consider the function

$$e^{i\lambda\nu} \sum_{j=\nu}^{\infty} c_j e^{-ij\lambda} / c(e^{-i\lambda}).$$

The fact that $c(z) \neq 0$ when $|z| < 1$ implies that this function in an element of ${}_0\mathcal{M}$ as $1/c(z)$ is analytic in $|z| < 1$. On the other hand

$$e^{i\nu\lambda}\left(1 - \frac{\sum_{j=\nu}^{\infty} c_j e^{-ij\lambda}}{c(e^{-i\lambda})}\right)$$

is orthogonal to ${}_0\mathcal{M}$ as the inner product of these two functions

$$\int_{-\pi}^{\pi} \sum_{j=\nu}^{\infty} c_j e^{-ij\lambda} \frac{\overline{\left(c(e^{-i\lambda}) - \sum_{j=\nu}^{\infty} c_j e^{-ij\lambda}\right)}}{|c(e^{-i\lambda})|^2} f(\lambda)\, d\lambda$$

$$= \int_{-\pi}^{\pi} \sum_{j=\nu}^{\infty} c_j e^{-ij\lambda} \overline{\left(c(e^{-i\lambda}) - \sum_{j=\nu}^{\infty} c_j e^{-ij\lambda}\right)} d\lambda = 0.$$

But then it is clear that

$$\phi_\nu(\lambda) = e^{i\nu\lambda} \sum_{j=\nu}^{\infty} c_j e^{-ij\lambda} / c(e^{-i\lambda}).$$

Note that the errors of prediction are positive since

$$\sigma_1^2 = \int_{-\pi}^{\pi} |e^{i\lambda} - \phi_1(\lambda)|^2 f(\lambda)\, d\lambda - c_0^2$$

$$= 2\pi \exp\left\{ \frac{1}{2\pi} \int_{-\pi}^{\pi} \log f(\lambda)\, d\lambda \right\} > 0.$$

We have shown that *if x_t is a process with an absolutely continuous spectral distribution function*

$$F(\lambda) = \int_{-\pi}^{\lambda} f(x)\, dx,$$

where

$$\int_{-\pi}^{\pi} \log f(\lambda)\, d\lambda > -\infty,$$

then the errors of prediction are positive. In particular the error of prediction one step ahead is

$$\sigma_1^2 = 2\pi \exp\left\{ \frac{1}{2\pi} \int_{-\pi}^{\pi} \log f(\lambda)\, d\lambda \right\} > 0.$$

The predictor

$$\varphi_{n,\nu} = \int_{-\pi}^{\pi} e^{in\lambda} \phi_\nu(\lambda)\, dz(\lambda)$$

$$= \int_{-\pi}^{\pi} e^{i(n+\nu)\lambda} \frac{\sum_{j=\nu}^{\infty} c_j e^{-ij\lambda}}{c(e^{-i\lambda})}\, dz(\lambda),$$

where $z(\lambda)$ is the stochastic set function corresponding to the process x_t and

$$c(e^{-i\lambda}) = \sum_{j=0}^{\infty} c_j e^{-ij\lambda} = \lim_{r\to 1-} c(r e^{-i\lambda})$$

$$= \lim_{r\to 1-} \sqrt{2\pi} \exp\left\{ \frac{1}{4\pi} \int_{-\pi}^{\pi} \frac{e^{-i\theta} + r e^{-i\lambda}}{e^{-i\theta} - r e^{-i\lambda}} \log f(\theta)\, d\theta \right\}.$$

Let us now reconsider the prediction problem assuming only that the prediction error is positive and see what conclusions we can draw concern-

69

ing the structure of the observed process. Since the prediction errors are positive, $\sigma_1 > 0$. Define the stochastic variables ξ_n by

$$x_n - \varphi_{n-1,\,1} = \sigma_1 \xi_n.$$

Since $\varphi_{n-1,1}$ is the projection of x_n on $\mathcal{M}_{n-1}$, ξ_n is orthogonal to $\mathcal{M}_{n-1}$. $\mathcal{M}_n$ is generated by $\mathcal{M}_{n-1}$ and ξ_n. The process $\{\xi_n\}$ is an orthonormal process

$$E\,\xi_n\,\bar{\xi}_m = \delta_{n-m}.$$

Define the constants γ_m by

$$\gamma_m = E\,x_n\,\bar{\xi}_{n-m} \quad (\gamma_0 = \sigma_1).$$

Let
$$u_n = \sum_{m=0}^{\infty} \gamma_m\,\xi_{n-m}, \qquad v_n = x_n - u_n.$$

Note that $\gamma_m\,\xi_{n-m}$ is the projection of x_n on the manifold $\mathcal{M}_{n-m} - \mathcal{M}_{n-m-1}$. This manifold is the orthogonal complement of $\mathcal{M}_{n-m-1}$ in $\mathcal{M}_{n-m}$. The processes $\{u_n\}$ and $\{v_n\}$ are both stationary. The stochastic variable $v_n \in \mathcal{M}_{-\infty}$ and consequently it is orthogonal to the process $\{\xi_n\}$. It is therefore orthogonal to the process $\{u_n\}$. It is clear from the construction given above that the predictor

$$\varphi_{n-\nu,\,\nu} = \sum_{m=\nu}^{\infty} \gamma_m\,\xi_{n-m} + v_n.$$

Note that if the observed process were $\{u_n\}$ instead of $\{x_n\}$, the corresponding predictor would be

$$\sum_{m=\nu}^{\infty} \gamma_m\,\xi_{n-m}.$$

It is of some interest to consider the function

$$\gamma(z) = \sum_{j=0}^{\infty} \gamma_j\,z^j.$$

This function is analytic in the unit circle $|z| < 1$ since $\sum |\gamma_j|^2 < \infty$. We shall show that $\gamma(z)$ has no zeros in $|z| < 1$. Assume that there were a zero z_0, $|z_0| < 1$. It is clear that $z_0 \neq 0$ for if it were, we would have $\gamma(0) = \gamma_0 = \sigma_1 = 0$ contrary to our assumption that the error of prediction is positive. Now consider the element

$$x = \sum_{j=0}^{\infty} z_0^j\,\xi_{n-j}.$$

The element x is in $\mathfrak{M}\{u_j; j \leq n\}$ but not in $\mathfrak{M}\{u_j; j \leq n-1\}$. On the other hand, if z_0 were a zero of $\gamma(z)$, we would have

$$E u_n \bar{x} = \sum \gamma_j z_0^j = 0.$$

But this implies that x is in $\mathfrak{M}\{u_j; j \leq n-1\}$, a contradiction.

We can also show that $\log|\gamma(e^{-i\lambda})|$ is integrable. Since $\gamma(z)$ is analytic in $|z| < 1$ and has no zeros there, it follows that $\log \gamma(z)$ is analytic in the unit circle $|z| < 1$. But then

$$\log \gamma(0) = \frac{1}{2\pi i} \int\limits_{|z|=r} \frac{\log \gamma(z)}{z} \, dz, \qquad 0 < r < 1,$$

and on taking real parts of both sides, we have

$$\log|\gamma(0)| = \frac{1}{2\pi} \int\limits_{-\pi}^{\pi} \log|\gamma(r e^{i\lambda})| \, d\lambda.$$

But

$$\frac{1}{2\pi} \int\limits_{|\gamma(e^{i\lambda})| \geq 1} \log|\gamma(e^{i\lambda})| \, d\lambda \leq \infty$$

since $0 \leq \log \gamma \leq \gamma$ when $\gamma \geq 1$ and $\gamma(e^{i\lambda})$ is quadratically integrable. Using Fatou's lemma we have

$$-\frac{1}{2\pi} \int\limits_{|\gamma(e^{i\lambda})| < 1} \log|\gamma(e^{i\lambda})| \, d\lambda \leq -\log|\gamma(0)| + \frac{1}{2\pi} \int\limits_{|\gamma(e^{i\lambda})| \geq 1} \log|\gamma(e^{i\lambda})| \, d\lambda$$

so that $\log|\gamma(e^{i\lambda})|$ is integrable. In particular, this implies that $\gamma(e^{i\lambda})$ is not zero for almost all λ.

Since $\{u_n\}$, $\{v_n\}$, $\{\xi_n\}$ are stationary they have spectral representations

$$u_n = \int\limits_{-\pi}^{\pi} e^{in\lambda} dz_u(\lambda), \quad v_n = \int\limits_{-\pi}^{\pi} e^{in\lambda} dz_v(\lambda), \quad \xi_n = \int\limits_{-\pi}^{\pi} e^{in\lambda} dz_\xi(\lambda)|,$$

where

$$E|dz_u(\lambda)|^2 = dF_u(\lambda), \quad E|dz_v(\lambda)|^2 = dF_v(\lambda), \quad E|dz_\xi(\lambda)|^2 = \frac{d\lambda}{2\pi}.$$

The linear representation of the process $\{u_n\}$ in terms of the process $\{\xi_n\}$ implies that $\{u_n\}$ has the spectral density (its spectral distribution function is absolutely continuous)

$$\frac{1}{2\pi}\,|\gamma\,(e^{-i\lambda})|^2.$$

As we have seen, this last expression is positive almost everywhere. But the processes $\{u_n\}^*$ and $\{v_n\}$ are orthogonal so that $z_u(\lambda)$ and $z_v(\lambda)$ are orthogonal. Now

$$z_u(\lambda) = \int_{-\pi}^{\lambda} \gamma\,(e^{-i\mu})\,d z_\xi(\mu)$$

so that

$$z(\lambda) = \int_{-\pi}^{\lambda} [\gamma\,(e^{-i\mu})\,d z_\xi(\mu) + d z_v(\mu)].$$

Since $\xi_n \in \mathfrak{M}_\infty$ there is an element $\Phi(\lambda) \in L_2(dF)$ such that

$$\xi_n = \int_{-\pi}^{\pi} \Phi(\lambda)\,[\gamma\,(e^{-i\lambda})\,d z_\xi(\lambda) + d z_v(\lambda)] = \int_{-\pi}^{\pi} e^{in\lambda}\,d z_\xi(\lambda).$$

On comparing integrands we see that

$$\Phi(\lambda)\,\gamma\,(e^{-i\lambda}) = e^{in\lambda}$$

for almost all λ (Lebesgue measure) while

$$\Phi(\lambda) = 0$$

for almost all λ (F_v measure). Since $\gamma\,(e^{-i\lambda})$ is not zero almost everywhere (Lebesgue measure) the conditions on $\Phi(\lambda)$ mentioned above cannot be satisfied unless $F_v(\lambda)$ increases only on a set of Lebesgue measure zero. Call the set of increase of F_v S. But then the spectral density of the process x_n

$$f(\lambda) = F'(\lambda) = \frac{1}{2\pi}\,|\gamma\,(e^{-i\lambda})|^2.$$

The spectral distribution function of the process v_n

$$F_v(\lambda) = F(\lambda) - \int_{-\pi}^{\lambda} F'(\mu)\,d\mu$$

consists of the singular part and the jumps of $F(\lambda)$.
   The error of prediction ν steps ahead

$$\sigma_\nu^2 = \sum_{j=0}^{\nu-1} |\gamma_j|^2$$

is the same for both the x process and the u process. In particular $\sigma_1^2 = \gamma_0^2 > 0$. Since $\log|\gamma(z)|$ is a harmonic function in $|z| < 1$, it is clear that

$$\log|\gamma(re^{i\lambda})| = \frac{1}{2\pi} \int_{-\pi}^{\pi} \frac{R^2 - r^2}{R^2 - 2Rr\cos(\theta - \lambda) + r^2} \log|\gamma(Re^{i\theta})|\, d\theta$$

$$\leq \frac{1}{2\pi} \int_{-\pi}^{\pi} \frac{1 - r^2}{1 - 2r\cos(\theta - \lambda) + r^2} \log|\gamma(e^{i\theta})|\, d\theta$$

$$= \tfrac{1}{2} \log 2\pi + \frac{1}{4\pi} \int_{-\pi}^{\pi} \frac{1 - r^2}{1 - 2r\cos(\theta - \lambda) + r^2} \log f(-\theta)\, d\theta$$

$$= \log|c(re^{i\lambda})|$$

by Fatou's lemma. Thus $\log|c(re^{i\lambda})/\gamma(re^{i\lambda})|$ is a nonnegative harmonic function in $|z| < 1$. Now u_n is a process with an absolutely continuous spectral distribution function

$$F_u(\lambda) = \int_{-\pi}^{\lambda} f(\mu)\, d\mu,$$

where $\int_{-\pi}^{\pi} \log f(\lambda)\, d\lambda > -\infty$. But the error of prediction one step ahead is

$$\sigma_1^2 = c_0^2 = \gamma_0^2 > 0,$$

and so $\log|c(0)/\gamma(0)|^2 = 0$. A nonnegative harmonic function which is zero at an interior point is zero everywhere. Thus,

$$\log|c(z)| = \log|\gamma(z)|$$

when $|z| < 1$. The functions $c(z)$ and $\gamma(z)$ can only differ by a constant factor $e^{i\alpha}$ where α is real. Since $c(0) = \gamma(0) > 0$, it is clear that this factor is one, that is

$$c(z) = \gamma(z)$$

and in particular
$$c(e^{-i\lambda}) = \gamma(e^{-i\lambda}).$$

Now

$$x_n - \varphi_{n-\nu,\nu} = \sum_{j=0}^{\nu-1} c_j\, \xi_{n-j} = \int_{-\pi}^{\pi} e^{i(n-\nu)\lambda}(e^{i\nu\lambda} - \phi_\nu(\lambda))\, dz(\lambda)$$

$$= \int_{-\pi}^{\pi} e^{i(n-\nu)\lambda}(e^{i\nu\lambda} - \phi_\nu(\lambda))\, d(z_u(\lambda) + z_v(\lambda))$$

$$= \int_{-\pi}^{\pi} e^{i(n-\nu)\lambda}(e^{i\nu\lambda} - \phi_\nu(\lambda))\, dz_u(\lambda)$$

so that

$$\sigma_\nu^2 = \sum_{j=0}^{\nu-1} |c_j|^2 = \int_{-\pi}^{\pi} |e^{i\nu\lambda} - \phi_\nu(\lambda)|^2 \, d F_u(\lambda) + \int_{-\pi}^{\pi} |e^{i\nu\lambda} - \phi_\nu(\lambda)|^2 \, d F_v(\lambda)$$

$$= \int_{-\pi}^{\pi} |e^{i\nu\lambda} - \phi_\nu(\lambda)|^2 \, d F_u(\lambda).$$

The function $\phi_\nu(\lambda)$ is in the closed linear manifold $_0\mathcal{M}$ with weight function $d F(\lambda)$ and hence in both manifolds with weight functions $d F_u(\lambda)$, $d F_v(\lambda)$ respectively. From the equation above, it follows that we must have

$$\phi_\nu(\lambda) = \begin{cases} e^{i\nu\lambda} \sum_{j=\nu}^{\infty} c_j e^{-ij\lambda} \big/ c(e^{-i\lambda}) & \lambda \notin S \\ e^{i\nu\lambda} & \lambda \in S, \end{cases}$$

where S is the set of Lebesgue measure zero on which $F_v(\lambda)$ increases.
We have thus seen that *the prediction error is positive if and only if*

$$\int_{-\pi}^{\pi} \log F'(\lambda) \, d\lambda > -\infty.$$

If the prediction error is positive, the predictor is

$$\varphi_{n,\nu} = \int_{-\pi}^{\pi} e^{in\lambda} \phi_\nu(\lambda) \, dz(\lambda)$$

$$= \int_{-\pi}^{\pi} e^{i(n+\nu)\lambda} \frac{\sum_{j=\nu}^{\infty} c_j e^{-ij\lambda}}{c(e^{-i\lambda})} \, dz(\lambda),$$

where

$$c(e^{-i\lambda}) = \sum_{j=0}^{\infty} c_j e^{-ij\lambda} = \sqrt{2\pi} \lim_{r\to 1-} \exp\left\{ \frac{1}{4\pi} \int_{-\pi}^{\pi} \frac{e^{-i\theta} + r e^{-i\lambda}}{e^{-i\theta} - r e^{-i\lambda}} \log F'(\theta) \, d\theta \right\}.$$

Then the prediction error

$$\sigma_\nu^2 = \sum_{j=0}^{\nu-1} |c_j|^2.$$

In any case the error of prediction one step ahead is

$$\sigma_1^2 = 2\pi \exp\left\{ \frac{1}{2\pi} \int_{-\pi}^{\pi} \log F'(\lambda) \, d\lambda \right\}.$$

In the previous discussion, a process $\{x_n\}$ with positive prediction errors is decomposed into two processes $\{u_n\}$, $\{v_n\}$ orthogonal to each other. The process

$$x_n = u_n + v_n$$

and $\{(x_n, u_n, v_n)\}$ is a stationary vector process. Both the processes $\{u_n\}$, $\{v_n\}$ belong to $\mathcal{M}_\infty$. The process u_n has the same prediction errors σ_v^2 as the process x_n. The manifolds $\mathcal{M}\{u_m; m \le n\}$ have only the zero element in common. A process u_n such that $\cap_n \mathcal{M}\{u_m; m \le n\} = \{0\}$ is called purely nondeterministic. The process v_n can be seen to have prediction errors $\sigma_v^2 = 0$ so that all the manifolds $\mathcal{M}\{v_m; m \le n\}$ are the same. If a process v_n is such that all the manifolds $\mathcal{M}\{v_m; m \le n\}$ are the same, it is said to be purely deterministic.

From our discussion of the prediction problem, it is clear that a process u_n is purely nondeterministic if and only if its spectral distribution function

$$F_u \lambda) = \int\limits_{-\pi}^{\lambda} f(x)\, dx$$

is absolutely continuous and

$$\int\limits_{-\pi}^{\pi} \log f(\lambda)\, d\lambda > -\infty.$$

It is also clear that $\int\limits_{-\pi}^{\pi} \log f(\lambda)\, d\lambda > -\infty$ ($f(\lambda)$ integrable) if and only if there is a function $a(z) \in H_2$ such that $a(z) \neq 0$ when $|z| < 1$ and

$$\frac{1}{2\pi}|a(e^{-i\lambda})|^2 = f(\lambda).$$

We can even remove the restriction that $a(z) \neq 0$ when $|z| < 1$. The theorem of F. Riesz (see appendix on complex variable theory) indicates that if $a(z)$ does have zeros in $|z| < 1$, they can be removed so as to obtain a function $b(z) \in H_2$, $b(z) \neq 0$ when $|z| < 1$ and still satisfying

$$\frac{1}{2\pi}|b(e^{-i\lambda})|^2 = f(\lambda).$$

In the discussion of this section a purely nondeterministic process u_n was shown to have a one-sided moving average representation

$$u_n = \sum_{j=0}^{\infty} c_j\, \xi_{n-j}$$

75

in terms of an orthonormal process ξ_n where $\mathcal{M}\{\xi_m;\ m \leq n\} = \mathcal{M}\{u_m;\ m \leq n\}$. The coefficients c_j are those of the function

$$c(z) = \sum_{j=0}^{\infty} c_j z^j = \sqrt{2\pi}\ \exp\left\{\frac{1}{4\pi}\int_{-\pi}^{\pi}\frac{e^{-i\theta}+z}{e^{-i\theta}-z}\ \log f(\theta)\ d\theta\right\}.$$

Note that among all functions $a(z) \in H_2$ with $a(0) > 0$ and such that

$$\frac{1}{2\pi}\ |a(e^{-i\lambda})|^2 = f(\lambda),$$

$c(z)$ is the one with maximal absolute value. This can be seen from some of the earlier discussion. It can be seen that the representation given above for a purely nondeterministic process u_n is unique except for a factor of absolute value one.

The discussion also implies that *a process v_n is purely deterministic if and only if*

$$\int_{-\pi}^{\pi}\ \log F'(\lambda)\ d\lambda = -\infty.$$

Thus v_n may have an absolutely continuous spectral distribution function

as long as $\int_{-\pi}^{\pi}\ \log f(\lambda)\,d\lambda = -\infty$.

Let $x_n = \int_{-\pi}^{\pi} e^{in\lambda}\,dz(\lambda)$ be a stationary process with positive prediction errors, $E\,|dz(\lambda)|^2 = dF(\lambda)$. We shall show that *there is* then *a unique decomposition of $x_n = u_n + v_n$ into a purely nondeterministic process $\{u_n\}$ and a purely deterministic process $\{v_n\}$ orthogonal to each other, both belonging to $\mathcal{M}_\infty$, and such that $\{(x_n, u_n, v_n)\}$ is a stationary vector process*. This decomposition is the one constructed in the discussion of the prediction problem (see Wold [1]). Since $\{u_n\}$ belongs to $\mathcal{M}_\infty$, it follows that u_n has the representation

$$u_n = \int_{-\pi}^{\pi} h(\lambda,\ n)\,dz(\lambda).$$

The stationarity of $\{(x_n,\ u_n,\ v_n)\}$ implies that

$$E\,x_n\,\bar{u}_m = \int_{-\pi}^{\pi} e^{in\lambda}\,\overline{h(\lambda,\ m)}\,dF(\lambda) = E\,x_{n-m}\,\bar{u}_0$$

$$= \int_{-\pi}^{\pi} e^{i(n-m)\lambda}\,\overline{h(\lambda,\ 0)}\,dF(\lambda)$$

so that

$$\int_{-\pi}^{\pi} e^{in\lambda} \, \overline{[h(\lambda, m) - e^{im\lambda} h(\lambda, 0)]} \, dF(\lambda) \equiv 0$$

for all n. But then

$$h(\lambda, m) = e^{im\lambda} h(\lambda, 0)$$

almost everywhere (Lebesgue measure) since $F'(\lambda) > 0$ almost everywhere. Thus

$$u_m = \int_{-\pi}^{\pi} e^{im\lambda} h(\lambda) \, dz(\lambda), \quad h(\lambda) = h(\lambda, 0).$$

In the same way, using the fact that $x_n = u_n + v_n$, we can show that

$$v_m = \int_{-\pi}^{\pi} e^{im\lambda} (1 - h(\lambda)) \, dz(\lambda).$$

The orthogonality of the processes $\{u_n\}$, $\{v_n\}$ implies that

$$\int_{-\pi}^{\pi} e^{im\lambda} h(\lambda) \, \overline{(1 - h(\lambda))} \, dF(\lambda) = 0.$$

The function $h(\lambda)$ must be either zero or one almost everywhere with respect to F measure and in particular almost everywhere with respect to Lebesgue measure. Let S be the set on which $h(\lambda) = 0$. The set S must be of zero Lebesgue measure, since u_n is purely nondeterministic and thus has a spectral density which is positive almost everywhere (Lebesgue measure). The absolutely continuous spectral distribution function of u_n is thus

$$F_u(\lambda) = \int_{-\pi}^{\lambda} F'(x) \, dx$$

and the spectral distribution function of v_n is

$$F_v(\lambda) = F(\lambda) - \int_{-\pi}^{\lambda} F'(x) \, dx.$$

The set of increase of $F_v(\lambda)$ is S. This is the decomposition carried out in the discussion of the prediction problem.

It is worthwhile noting that this decomposition of x_n into a purely nondeterministic and a purely deterministic process is no longer unique if the condition that $\{u_n\}$, $\{v_n\}$ be in $\mathcal{M}_\infty$ is omitted. There are then in general an infinite number of such decompositions. The terminology purely non-deterministic and purely deterministic is very suggestive but should not be taken too literally. The problems considered in this chapter are all linear least squares problems. It is interesting to contrast the linear prediction problem with the general prediction problem in which there is no restriction of linearity on the estimates. The problem of predicting x_{n+1} given x_n, x_{n-1}, ... is that of finding the quadratically integrable stochastic variable $f(x_n, x_{n-1}, \ldots)$ defined on the sample space of x_n, x_{n-1}, ... such that

$$E\left| x_{n+1} - f(x_n, x_{n-1}, \ldots) \right|^2$$

is minimized. The set of all quadratically integrable $f(x_n, x_{n-1}, \ldots)$ is a closed linear submanifold of the closed linear manifold of quadratically integrable stochastic variables defined on the sample space of the process $\{x_n\}$. But the unique minimizing $f(x_n, x_{n-1}, \ldots)$ must be such that

$$x_{n+1} - f(x_n, x_{n-1}, \ldots)$$

is orthogonal to this submanifold, and so we must have

$$f(x_n, x_{n-1}, \ldots) = E(x_{n+1} | x_n, x_{n-1}, \ldots).$$

Perhaps one should call a process $\{x_n\}$ such that

$$x_{n+1} = E(x_{n+1} | x_n, x_{n-1}, \ldots)$$

purely deterministic. The process

$$x_n = e^{in\xi}$$

where ξ is a stochastic variable with distribution function $F(\lambda)$ would be purely deterministic in this new sense. It would be purely deterministic in the linear sense if and only if

$$\int_{-\pi}^{\pi} \log F'(\lambda)\, d\lambda = -\infty.$$

It is important to *note that if a process $\{x_n\}$ is normal, the solutions of the linear least squares problem and the corresponding general least squares problem are identical.*

We now consider the prediction problem in the simple case of an autoregressive scheme. Let $\{x_n\}$ be a stationary process with an absolutely continuous spectral distribution whose spectral density

$$f(\lambda) = \frac{1}{2\pi} \frac{1}{\left|\sum\limits_{j=0}^{p} b_j\, e^{-ij\lambda}\right|^2}, \quad b_0 \neq 0. \tag{1}$$

The polynomial $\sum\limits_{j=0}^{p} b_j z^j$ cannot vanish when $|z| = 1$ since $f(\lambda)$ is integrable. We can suppose that all the roots of the polynomial have modulus greater than one. For if

$$\sum_{j=0}^{p} b_j z^j = (z - z_0) \sum_{j=0}^{p-1} a_j z^j,$$

had the root z_0 of modulus less than one, we could consider instead $(z\bar{z}_0 - 1) \sum\limits_{j=0}^{p-1} a_j z^j$ which has the same absolute value on $|z| = 1$ but one zero less in $|z| < 1$. By iterating this procedure we can remove all roots of modulus less than one and preserve the absolute value of the function on $|z| = 1$. Now x_n has the spectral representation

$$x_n = \int_{-\pi}^{\pi} e^{in\lambda}\, dz(\lambda).$$

Consider the stochastic variable

$$\xi_n = \int_{-\pi}^{\pi} \sum_{j=0}^{p} b_j\, e^{-ij\lambda}\, e^{in\lambda}\, dz(\lambda) = \sum_{j=0}^{p} b_j x_{n-j}.$$

The process $\{\xi_n\}$ is orthonormal since

$$E\,\xi_n\,\bar{\xi}_m = \frac{1}{2\pi} \int_{-\pi}^{\pi} e^{i(n-m)\lambda}\, d\lambda = \delta_{n-m}$$

Moreover

$$E\,x_n\,\bar{\xi}_m = \frac{1}{2\pi} \int_{-\pi}^{\pi} \frac{e^{i(n-m)\lambda}}{\sum\limits_{j=0}^{p} b_j\, e^{-ij\lambda}}\, d\lambda = 0$$

when $m > n$ since the roots of $\sum\limits_{j=0}^{p} b_j z^j$ are of modulus greater then one. The stochastic variable $\bar{\xi}_n$ is orthogonal to $\mathfrak{M}_{n-1}$. Thus

$$x_{n+1} = -\frac{1}{b_0}\,(b_1 x_n + \cdots + b_p x_{n-p+1}) + \frac{\xi_{n+1}}{b_0}$$

where ξ_{n+1} is orthogonal to $\mathfrak{M}_n$. A process with an absolutely continuous spectrum where $f(\lambda)$ is given by (1) is therefore an autoregressive scheme. The linear predictor

$$\varphi_{n,1} = -\frac{1}{b_0}(b_1 x_n + \cdots + b_p x_{n-p+1})$$

and the predictors $\varphi_{n,\nu}$ can be obtained by iterating this procedure. The error of prediction

$$\sigma_1^2 = \frac{1}{|b_0|^2}.$$

We shall only state some of the corresponding results for the prediction problem when the process x_t is a continuous parameter weakly stationary process. A detailed discussion of some aspects of this problem may be found in the papers of K. Karhunen [1, 2] and in J. L. Doob's book [2] on stochastic processes. The process x_t has the spectral representation

$$x_t = \int_{-\infty}^{\infty} e^{it\lambda} \, dz(\lambda), \ E\, dz(\lambda)\, \overline{dz(\mu)} = \delta_{\lambda\mu}\, dF(\lambda).$$

Let $\mathfrak{M}_t$ as before denote

$$\mathfrak{M}_t = \mathfrak{M}\{x_\tau; \tau \leq t\},$$

where the parameters are now continuous. Given that x_u, $u \leq t$, has been observed, the best linear least squares predictor $\varphi_{t,\tau}$ of $x_{t+\tau}$, $\tau > 0$, is the projection of $x_{t+\tau}$ on $\mathfrak{M}_t$. The prediction error

$$\sigma_\tau^2 = E\,|\varphi_{t,\tau} - x_{t+\tau}|^2$$

and as before either $\sigma_\tau^2 = 0$ for all $\tau \geq 0$ or $\sigma_\tau^2 > 0$ for all $\tau > 0$. The first case we again call that of a purely deterministic process. If the process x_t has positive prediction errors and is such that $\cap\, \mathfrak{M}_t = \{0\}$, we call it purely nondeterministic. The prediction errors of a process x_t are now positive if and only if

$$\int_{-\infty}^{\infty} \frac{\log F'(\lambda)}{1+\lambda^2}\, d\lambda \geq -\infty.$$

If a process $\{x_t\}$ has positive prediction errors, there is a unique decomposition of the process

$$x_t = u_t + v_t$$

into a purely nondeterministic process $\{u_t\}$ and a purely deterministic process $\{v_t\}$ orthogonal to each other where $\{(x_t, u_t, v_t)\}$ is a stationary vector process and u_t and v_t belong to $\mathcal{M}_\infty$. Here

$$u_t = \int_{-\infty}^{\infty} e^{it\lambda}\, d\,z_u\,(\lambda),\ E\,d\,z_u\,(\lambda)\,\overline{d\,z_u\,(\mu)} = \delta_{\lambda\mu}\,d\,F_u\,(\lambda)$$

$$v_t = \int_{-\infty}^{\infty} e^{it\lambda}\, d\,z_v\,(\lambda),\ E\,d\,z_v\,(\lambda)\,\overline{d\,z_v\,(\mu)} = \delta_{\lambda\mu}\,d\,F_v\,(\lambda),$$

where

$$F_u\,(\lambda) = \int_{-\infty}^{\lambda} F'\,(x)\,d\,x$$

$$F_v\,(\lambda) = F\,(\lambda) - \int_{-\infty}^{\lambda} F'\,(x)\,d\,x.$$

Let

$$c\,(w) = \sqrt{2\,\pi}\,\exp\left\{-\frac{1}{2\,\pi\,i}\int_{-\infty}^{\infty} \frac{1+\lambda w}{\lambda - w}\,\frac{\log F'\,(\lambda)}{1+\lambda^2}\,d\,\lambda\right\}.$$

The function $c\,(w)$ is a function of the complex variable $w = u + i\,v$ that is analytic and nonzero in the halfplane $v < 0$. Moreover

$$\int_{-\infty}^{\infty} |\,c\,(u + i\,v)\,|^2\,d\,u \le M,$$

for all $v < 0$. The limit

$$c\,(u) = \lim_{v\to 0-} c\,(u + i\,v)$$

exists for allmost all u and

$$\int_{-\infty}^{\infty} |\,c\,(u+i\,v) - c\,(u)\,|^2\,d\,u \to 0$$

as $v \to 0-$. One can show that

$$\frac{1}{2\,\pi}\,|\,c\,(u)\,|^2 = f\,(u) = F'\,(u)$$

almost everywhere. The Fourier transform

$$c^*\,(t) = \frac{1}{2\,\pi}\int_{-\infty}^{\infty} e^{itu}\,c\,(u)\,d\,u$$

of $c(u)$ vanishes for $t < 0$. The process u_t has the one-sided moving average representation

$$u_t = \int_{-\infty}^{t} c^*(t-u)\, d\xi(u), \quad \int_{0}^{\infty} |c^*(u)|^2\, d u < \infty,$$

in terms of a process $\xi(u)$ where $E d\xi(u)\overline{d\xi(v)} = \delta_{uv} d u$ and $\xi(u) - \xi(v) \in \mathfrak{M}\{u_\tau;\, \tau \le t\}$ if $u,\, v \le t$. Except for a multiplicative constant of absolute value one, it can be shown that this is the unique one-sided moving average representation of u_t in terms of a process $\xi(u)$ of the type described above. The predictor

$$\varphi_{t,\,\tau} = \int_{-\infty}^{t} c^*(t+\tau-u)\, d\xi(u) + v_{t+\tau}$$

and the prediction error is

$$\sigma_\tau^2 = \int_{0}^{\tau} |c^*(s)|^2\, d s.$$

Some discussion of multidimensional linear least squares prediction can be found in J. L. Doob's book on stochastic processes.

2.3. Interpolation

Several interpolation problems are considered in this section. At times for convenience a restriction will be imposed on the spectrum of the process studied.

Let x_n be a discrete parameter process, $n = \cdots,\, -1, 0, 1, \ldots$. Assume that the entire time series has been observed except at the time point $n = 0$. Thus x_n, $n \ne 0$, *has been observed*. We would like to *estimate* x_0 by that linear combination of the observed stochastic variables which is best in the sense of smallest mean square error. Let us assume that $F(\lambda)$ is absolutely continuous and that $1/f(\lambda)$ is integrable, where $f(\lambda)$ is the spectral density of the process. The process x_n has the spectral representation

$$x_n = \int_{-\pi}^{\pi} e^{in\lambda}\, d z(\lambda).$$

Let the linear estimate of x_0 be

$$x_0^* = \int_{-\pi}^{\pi} c(\lambda)\, d z(\lambda).$$

The estimate x_0^* is the projection of x_0 on the manifold $\mathfrak{M} \{x_n;\ n \neq 0\}$ and so $x_0 - x_0^*$ is orthogonal to this manifold, that is

$$E (x_0 - x_0^*)\, \bar{x}_n = \int_{-\pi}^{\pi} (1 - c\,(\lambda))\, e^{-in\lambda} f\,(\lambda)\, d\,\lambda = 0, \quad n \neq 0.$$

It is clear that $c\,(\lambda)$ will satisfy these conditions if and only if it is of the form

$$c\,(\lambda) = 1 - \frac{k}{f\,(\lambda)}\,,$$

where k is a constant. But the error of interpolation

$$\sigma^2 = E\,|x_0 - x_0^*|^2 = \int_{-\pi}^{\pi} |1 - c\,(\lambda)|^2 f\,(\lambda)\, d\,\lambda$$

$$= |k|^2 \int_{-\pi}^{\pi} \frac{d\,\lambda}{f\,(\lambda)} = \int_{-\pi}^{\pi} (1 - c\,(\lambda))\, f\,(\lambda)\, d\,\lambda = 2\,\pi\,k$$

since $c\,(\lambda)$ is an element of the closed linear manifold generated by $e^{in\lambda}$, $n \neq 0$, with weight function $f\,(\lambda)$. The number k is real and given by

$$k = \frac{2\,\pi}{\displaystyle\int_{-\pi}^{\pi} \frac{d\,\lambda}{f\,(\lambda)}}\,.$$

The error of interpolation

$$\sigma^2 = 4\,\pi^2 \Big/ \int_{-\pi}^{\pi} \frac{d\,\lambda}{f\,(\lambda)}\,.$$

A slightly more general problem would be that in which x_n, $n = 0, 1, \cdots, N$ *are not observed* and one again wishes to obtain the best linear least squares *estimate of x_0* in terms of the observed stochastic variables. An argument analogous to that given above indicates that the error of interpolation

$$\sigma^2 = E\,|x_0 - x_0^*|^2 = \frac{4\,\pi^2}{\displaystyle\max_{c_0 = 1} \int_{-\pi}^{\pi} \left|\sum_{j=0}^{N} c_j\, e^{ij\lambda}\right|^2 \frac{d\,\lambda}{f\,(\lambda)}}\,. \tag{2}$$

The interpolator

$$x_0^* = \int_{-\pi}^{\pi} c\,(\lambda)\, d\,z\,(\lambda),$$

where
$$1 - c(\lambda) = \frac{\sigma^2}{2\pi} \sum_{j=0}^{N} c_j e^{ij\lambda} \frac{1}{f(\lambda)}.$$

Here $c_0 = 1$ and the c_j's, $0 < j \leq N$, are the numbers maximizing the expression in the denominator of (2). If $1/f(\lambda)$ is not integrable, it can be seen that the error of interpolation $\sigma^2 = 0$. We can approximate $f(\lambda)$ by

$$f_N(\lambda) = \begin{cases} f(\lambda) \text{ if } f(\lambda) > \dfrac{1}{N} \\ \dfrac{1}{N} \text{ if } f(\lambda) \leq \dfrac{1}{N}. \end{cases}$$

A process with spectral density $f_N(\lambda)$ has positive error of interpolation. But as $N \to \infty$, the error of interpolation tends to zero. However, the error of interpolation for the process $\{x_n\}$ is less than the error for a process with spectral density $f_N(\lambda)$. Thus $\sigma^2 = 0$.

The following interpolation problem might arise when one is observing a continuous parameter process at discrete time points. *Let x_t be a continuous time parameter* weakly stationary stochastic process ($-\infty < t < \infty$). The process has the spectral representation

$$x_t = \int_{-\infty}^{\infty} e^{it\lambda} dz(\lambda),$$

where
$$r_t = E x_{\tau+t} \bar{x}_\tau = \int_{-\infty}^{\infty} e^{it\lambda} dF(\lambda).$$

Suppose that *the process has been observed at the time points* $n = \cdots, -1, 0, 1, \ldots$ and that *we wish to estimate x_t where t is not an integer.* Let the best linear least squares estimate of x_t be

$$x_t^* = \int_{-\infty}^{\infty} c(\lambda) dz(\lambda).$$

The function $c(\lambda)$ has period 2π since it is an element of the linear closed manifold generated by $e^{in\lambda}$ where n is integral. Since x_t^* is the best linear least squares estimate of x_t in terms of the x_n, n integral, we must have

$$E(x_t - x_t^*) \bar{x}_n = \int_{-\infty}^{\infty} [e^{it\lambda} - c(\lambda)] e^{-in\lambda} dF(\lambda) = 0$$

for all integral n. This can be written in the more convenient form

84

$$\int_0^{2\pi} e^{-in\lambda}\left[e^{it\lambda}\,dF_1(\lambda) - c(\lambda)\,dF_2(\lambda)\right] \equiv 0$$

for all integral n, where

$$F_1(\lambda) = \Sigma e^{2n\pi it}[F(\lambda + 2n\pi) - F(2n\pi)]$$
$$F_2(\lambda) = \Sigma [F(\lambda + 2n\pi) - F(2n\pi)]$$

since $c(\lambda)$ has period 2π. But this cannot be satisfied unless

$$c(\lambda) = e^{it\lambda}\frac{dF_1(\lambda)}{dF_2(\lambda)}$$

and the *error of interpolation* is then

$$\sigma^2 = \int_0^{2\pi}\left|1 - \frac{dF_1(\lambda)}{dF_2(\lambda)}\right|^2 dF(\lambda).$$

If ΔF_1 and ΔF_2 vanish simultaneously on the same set S then $c(\lambda)$ is undefined on this set and can be set equal to any function square integrable with respect to dF on S (for example a constant). The contribution to the error from this set S is of course zero.

2.4. Filtering of Stationary Processes

The problem of *filtering* usually consists in designing a filter to be applied to a process which has been disturbed by noise so as to recover the original process as closely as possible. Let us call the undisturbed process *the signal* s_t and *the noise* n_t. The process (s_t, n_t), $t = \cdots, -1, 0, 1, \ldots$, is supposed to be stationary with a known spectral matrix $F(\lambda)$.

Let us consider the simplest version of this problem when there is no internal noise generated in the filter. We now have to decide what class of filters is most suitable for our purpose. Let us confine ourselves to linear filters. Among these we could consider all acting upon the past of the input $s_t + n_t$. Sometimes one may use filters utilizing the whole series $s_t + n_t$ for $-\infty < t < \infty$. A usual situation is one in which we have a parameter class $\mathcal{F}_\alpha$ of filters available, where α is a finite dimensional vector. We can think of s_t and n_t as voltages and of $\mathcal{F}_\alpha$ as a passive network with a finite number of meshes, α corresponding to its variable elements.

If $\mathcal{F}_\alpha$ has the frequency response function $\varphi_\alpha(\lambda)$, then the mean square error of the filter is given by

$$\sigma_\alpha^2 = \int\limits_{-\pi}^{\pi} d\,G_\alpha\,(\lambda) = E\,|\,s_t - \mathcal{F}_\alpha\,(s_t + n_t)\,|^2,$$

where $G_\alpha(\lambda)$ is the spectral distribution function of the error $s_t - \mathcal{F}_\alpha(s_t + n_t)$. But we have

$$d\,G_\alpha(\lambda) = |\,\varphi_\alpha(\lambda) - 1\,|^2\,d\,F_{11}(\lambda) + |\,\varphi_\alpha(\lambda)\,|^2\,d\,F_{22}(\lambda) +$$

$$+ 2\,Re\,\{[\varphi_\alpha(\lambda) - 1]\overline{\varphi_\alpha(\lambda)}\,d\,F_{12}(\lambda)\}.$$

When the noise and signal are incoherent, the cross-spectrum vanishes and

$$\sigma_\alpha^2 = \int\limits_{-\pi}^{\pi} \{|\,\varphi_\alpha(\lambda) - 1\,|^2\,d\,F_{11}(\lambda) + |\,\varphi_\alpha(\lambda)\,|^2\,d\,F_{22}(\lambda)\}.$$

We should choose α so that σ_α^2 is minimized.

As in prediction and interpolation problems, one of the crucial points in filtering is that *we seldom know the spectral matrix $F(\lambda)$ a priori*. The question of estimating a spectrum from empirical data will be discussed in detail in Chapters 4, 5 and 6.

2.5. Treatment of Linear Hypotheses with Specified Spectrum

Let $y_t = x_t + m_t$ be a process observed at $t = 1, 2, \ldots, n$ with mean value $m_t = E\,y_t$ and stationary random component x_t, $E\,x_t \equiv 0$. In many cases one assumes that the means $m_t = E\,y_t$ are given as linear expressions in unknown parameters $\gamma_1, \gamma_2, \ldots, \gamma_s$ $(s < n)$

$$m = \Phi\,\gamma,$$

where
$$m = \begin{pmatrix} m_1 \\ \vdots \\ m_n \end{pmatrix}, \qquad \gamma = \begin{pmatrix} \gamma_1 \\ \vdots \\ \gamma_s \end{pmatrix}$$

and Φ is an $n \times s$ matrix of known constants and of rank s. An example is that of a polynomial or trigonometric regression. Denote the covariance matrix of the process x_t by R.

We want to find good linear estimates $c = \begin{pmatrix} c_1 \\ c_2 \\ \vdots \\ c_s \end{pmatrix}$ of the γ's. One possibility

is to use the method of least squares, that is, to minimize

$$(x - \Phi c)^* (x - \Phi c)$$

with respect to c. Let $\Phi^*\Phi$ be a nonsingular matrix. Then

$$(x - \Phi c)^*(x - \Phi c) = x^*(I - \Phi(\Phi^*\Phi)^{-1}\Phi^*)x + ((\Phi^*\Phi)^{\frac{1}{2}}c - (\Phi^*\Phi)^{-\frac{1}{2}}\Phi^*x)^*$$
$$\times ((\Phi^*\Phi)^{\frac{1}{2}}c - (\Phi^*\Phi)^{-\frac{1}{2}}\Phi^*x)$$

so that the *least squares estimate*

$$c_L = (\Phi^*\Phi)^{-1}\Phi^*x.$$

By $(\Phi^*\Phi)^{\frac{1}{2}}$ we mean the unique positive definite square root of the positive definite matrix $\Phi^*\Phi$, which has been assumed to be non-singular. The estimate c_L is unbiased since

$$Ec_L = (\Phi^*\Phi)^{-1}\Phi^*\Phi\gamma = \gamma.$$

One might go further and ask for an estimate c_0 optimal in the sense that among all linear unbiased estimates it has minimum variance. A linear unbiased estimate a with covariance matrix M_a is said to be *minimum variance* if $M_a \le M_b$ for all linear unbiased estimates b. We say that $M_a \le M_b$ if $M_b - M_a$ is nonnegative definite.

Assuming R to be nonsingular, *we shall show that*

$$c_0 = (\Phi^*R^{-1}\Phi)^{-1}\Phi^*R^{-1}x$$

is a minimum variance linear unbiased estimate of γ. It is unbiased since

$$Ec_0 = (\Phi^*R^{-1}\Phi)^{-1}\Phi^*R^{-1}\Phi\gamma = \gamma.$$

Now if $c = Lx$ is an unbiased estimate of γ, it is clear that we must have

$$L\Phi = I.$$

In showing that c_0 is minimum variance we shall prove and then make use of what might be called a Schwarz inequality for matrices. Note that the covariance matrix of $c = Lx$ is

$$LRL^*.$$

Let l^*, ϕ be two $n x s$ matrices such that ll^* is nonsingular. Let λ, μ be any two s vectors. Then

$$(\lambda l + \mu\phi^*)(\lambda l + \mu\phi^*)^* \ge 0$$

and expanding we have

$$\lambda ll^*\lambda^* + \lambda l\phi\mu^* + \mu\phi^*l^*\lambda^* + \mu\phi^*\phi\mu^* \ge 0.$$

2.5

Let $A = ll^*$, $B = l\phi$, $C = \phi^*\phi$. The above inequality can then be rewritten as

$$\lambda A \lambda^* + \lambda B \mu^* + \mu B^* \lambda^* + \mu C \mu^* = (\lambda A^{\frac{1}{2}} + \mu B^* A^{-\frac{1}{2}})(\lambda A^{\frac{1}{2}} + \mu B^* A^{-\frac{1}{2}})^* +$$
$$+ \mu [C - B^* A^{-1} B] \mu^* \geq 0.$$

On setting $\lambda = -\mu B^* A^{-1}$, we can see that

$$C \geq B^* A^{-1} B$$

or $$\phi^* \phi \geq (l\phi)^*(ll^*)^{-1}(l\phi).$$

Note that there is equality if and only if there exist vectors λ, μ one of which is not the zero vector such that $\lambda l + \mu \phi^* = 0$. On setting $\phi = R^{\frac{1}{2}} L^*$, $l = \Phi^* R^{-\frac{1}{2}}$ we find that

$$E (c - \gamma) (c - \gamma)^* = L R L^*$$
$$\geq (L\Phi)(\Phi^* R^{-1} \Phi)^{-1}(L \Phi)^*$$
$$= (\Phi^* R^{-1} \Phi)^{-1}$$
$$= E (c_0 - \gamma)(c_0 - \gamma)^*$$

since $L \Phi = I$, proving that c_0 is minimum variance.

In the discussion above we never made use of the assumption that x_t is stationary. It is only introduced because that is the case of greatest interest for us. The estimates c_0 are sometimes called Markov estimates. One should note that if the process is normal c_0 is the maximum likelihood estimate and is efficient. Tests and confidence regions based on c_0 can then be constructed in the usual way.

When x_t is white noise we have $R = \sigma^2 I$ so that $c_L = c_0$. The least squares estimates are strictly speaking not as good as the estimates c_0 when the process is not white noise. On the other hand the Markov estimates require knowledge of the covariances which are in general not given. We shall see in Chapter 7, however, that in many practical cases the least squares estimates are almost as good as the Markov estimates.

Before closing this section, we shall briefly discuss the existence of consistent estimates of regression coefficients. *We shall say that an estimate is consistent if it converges in the mean square to the true value as $n \rightarrow \infty$.* For simplicity we deal only with the case $s = 1$ so that there is just one unknown regression coefficient m to estimate

$$E y_t = m \varphi_t.$$

The regression variable φ_t is assumed to be of the Fourier-Stieltjes form

88

$$\varphi_t = \int\limits_{-\pi}^{\pi} e^{it\lambda}\, d\mu\,(\lambda)$$

where $\mu\,(\lambda)$ is of bounded variation in $(-\pi, \pi)$ but not necessarily real. Assume that $y_t,\ t = -n,\ -n+1, \ldots,\ n-1,\ n$, has been observed. Consider the unbiased estimate

$$c = \sum_{t=-n}^{n} c_t\, y_t.$$

Introduce the polynomial

$$P_n\,(z) = \sum_{t=-n}^{n} c_t\, z^t.$$

The estimate c is unbiased if

$$1 = \sum_{t=-n}^{n} c_t\, \varphi_t = \int\limits_{-\pi}^{\pi} P_n\,(e^{i\lambda})\, d\mu\,(\lambda).$$

The variance is

$$D^2\,[c] = \int\limits_{-\pi}^{\pi} |\,P_n\,(e^{i\lambda})\,|^2\, d F\,(\lambda).$$

Dividing the integration interval $(-\pi, \pi)$ into a sufficiently fine grid $-\pi < \lambda_1^{(p)} < \lambda_2^{(p)} < \cdots < \lambda_p^{(p)} < \pi$ we get from the Schwarz inequality

$$1 \leq \left[\int\limits_{-\pi}^{\pi} |\,P_n\,(e^{i\lambda})\,|\,|\,d\mu\,(\lambda)\,| \right]^2$$

$$\leq [\sum_{\nu} |\,P_n\,(e^{i\lambda_\nu^{(p)}})\,|\,|\,\Delta\mu\,(\lambda_\nu^{(p)})\,|]^2 + \varepsilon$$

$$\leq \sum_{\nu} |\,P_n\,(e^{i\lambda_\nu^{(p)}})\,|^2\, \Delta F\,(\lambda_\nu^{(p)}) \sum_{\nu} \frac{|\,\Delta\mu\,(\lambda_\nu^{(p)})\,|^2}{\Delta F\,(\lambda_\nu^{(p)})} + \varepsilon,$$

where $\Delta\mu\,(\lambda_\nu^{(p)})$, $\Delta F\,(\lambda_\nu^{(p)})$ denote the μ and F mass in the νth interval and ε can be made arbitrarily small by taking a sufficiently fine division. We know that

$$H_p = \sum \frac{|\,\Delta\mu\,(\lambda_\nu^{(p)})\,|^2}{\Delta F\,(\lambda_\nu^{(p)})}$$

is nondecreasing (see e.g. Wintner [1]) when the division is made finer. Denoting the limit (finite or infinite) by

$$H = \int\limits_{-\pi}^{\pi} \frac{|\,d\mu\,(\lambda)\,|^2}{d F\,(\lambda)},$$

2.5

the *Hellinger integral*, we see that

$$D^2[c] \geq \frac{1}{H}.$$

This is really the greatest lower bound of $D^2[c]$. To see this, introduce the step function

$$\varphi_p(\lambda) = H_p^{-1} \frac{\overline{\Delta \mu(\lambda_\nu^{(p)})}}{\Delta F(\lambda_\nu^{(p)})}, \quad \lambda_\nu^{(p)} \leq \lambda \leq \lambda_{\nu+1}^{(p)}.$$

This can be uniformly approximated (except for small intervals around discontinuities) by trigonometric polynomials of high order. As

$$\left.\begin{array}{c} \displaystyle\int_{-\pi}^{\pi} \varphi_p(\lambda) \, d\mu(\lambda) = 1 \\[2em] \displaystyle\int_{-\pi}^{\pi} |\varphi_p(\lambda)|^2 \, dF(\lambda) = H_p^{-1} \end{array}\right\}$$

we see that

$$\inf D^2[c] = \frac{1}{H}.$$

There is a consistent estimate of the regression coefficient if and only if the Hellinger integral of $\mu(\lambda)$ with respect to $F(\lambda)$ diverges. In the case of a constant mean value, $\mu(\lambda)$ is constant except for a jump at $\lambda = 0$ and we have a consistent estimate if and only if there is no spectral mass at $\lambda = 0$.

We can apply the solution given above to the first interpolation problem considered in section 2.3. On setting $\mu(\lambda) = \lambda/2\pi$ we see that the minimization problem is in this case equivalent to minimizing

$$E\left|x_0 - \sum_{t \neq 0} c_t x_t\right|^2.$$

The greatest lower bound is then

$$\frac{4\pi^2}{\displaystyle\int_{-\pi}^{\pi} \frac{(d\lambda)^2}{dF(\lambda)}}$$

which we obtained in section 2.3 via another method. This result is due to Kolmogoroff [2].

CHAPTER 3

STATISTICAL ANALYSIS OF PARAMETRIC MODELS

3.0. Introduction

From this point on we shall deal with statistical problems arising when the covariance structure of the process is not completely known. In the present chapter we discuss some of the techniques that have been suggested in the last two or three decades and that have been studied most intensively. These techniques have in common the fact that they are based on the a priori assumption of *finite parameter models*; usually a moving average or autoregressive scheme of low order plus a regression component.

3.1. Periodogram Analysis

One of the simplest models that has been proposed for time series analysis is the *scheme of hidden periodicities,*

$$x_t = \sum_{\nu=1}^{p} (a_\nu \cos \lambda_\nu t + b_t \sin \lambda_\nu t) + \xi_t,$$

where a_ν, b_ν and λ_ν are real constants with $0 < \lambda_\nu \leq \pi$, and where ξ_t is pure white noise. We wish to detect the *periods* $2\pi/\lambda_\nu$ that have been masked by the random disturbances ξ_t. For this purpose the following statistic has been proposed

$$I_n(\lambda) = \frac{1}{2\pi n} \left| \sum_{t=1}^{n} x_t e^{-it\lambda} \right|^2 = \frac{1}{4\pi} A^2(\lambda) + \frac{1}{4\pi} B^2(\lambda),$$

where

$$\left. \begin{aligned} A(\lambda) &= \sqrt{\frac{2}{n}} \sum_{t=1}^{n} x_t \cos t\lambda \\ B(\lambda) &= \sqrt{\frac{2}{n}} \sum_{t=1}^{n} x_t \sin t\lambda \end{aligned} \right\}. \tag{1}$$

$I_n(\lambda)$ is called the *periodogram* and is clearly suggested by a Fourier analysis treating the time series as if it were just the undisturbed trigonometric sum.

Writing x_t in the complex form

$$x_t = \sum_{\nu=1}^{p} \alpha_\nu e^{it\lambda_\nu} + \xi_t$$

3.1

we get

$$\frac{1}{\sqrt{n}} \sum_{t=1}^{n} x_t\, e^{-it\lambda} = \frac{1}{\sqrt{n}} \sum_{\nu=1}^{p} \alpha_\nu\, e^{i\,(\lambda_\nu - \lambda)}\, \frac{e^{in(\lambda_\nu - \lambda)} - 1}{e^{i\,(\lambda_\nu - \lambda)} - 1} + \frac{1}{\sqrt{n}} \sum_{\nu=1}^{p} \xi_t\, e^{-it\lambda}.$$

The second term has mean zero and variance 1. The first term evidently tends to zero if $\lambda \neq \lambda_\nu, \nu = 1, 2, \ldots p$; otherwise it is of the order $\sqrt{n}$. Hence we can expect, for large samples, that the periodogram have high peaks at the frequencies λ_ν and otherwise be of moderate size. On computing the periodogram one could then infer that its great peaks correspond to *real* periods.

Naturally the question of the statistical significance of these periods arises, and we shall mention a test due to R. A. Fisher [1]. It has been observed that the periodogram often has a very irregular appearance and many research workers were tempted to attribute real meaning to the many peaks of the periodogram. In Fisher's test the null hypothesis is that the process has no period, that is $x_t = \xi_t$, and that the ξ's are normally distributed with unknown mean m and standard deviation σ.

Let the number of observed values be odd, say $n = 2m + 1$, and consider m values of the periodogram at the points $l_r = 2\pi r/(2m + 1), r = 1, 2, \ldots . m$. Because of the orthogonality of the trigonometric coefficients in (1), the stochastic variables

$$\left. \begin{array}{l} A\,(l_r), \quad r = 1, 2, \ldots m \\ B\,(l_r), \quad r = 1, 2, \ldots m \end{array} \right\}$$

are $2m$ independent normal variables with mean zero and variance σ^2. Hence

$$\frac{s_r}{\sigma^2} = \frac{A^2\,(l_r) + B^2\,(l_r)}{\sigma^2}; \quad r = 1, 2, \ldots m\,;$$

are independent χ^2-variables. The joint frequency function of $s_1, s_2, \ldots s_m$ is then

$$c^m\, e^{-c \sum_1^m z_\nu}$$

for $z_1, z_2, \ldots z_m \geq 0$ and 0 otherwise. Let y_r be the rth largest value of $s_1, s_2, \ldots s_m$. Introduce

$$g = \frac{y_1}{y_1 + y_2 + \cdots y_m}.$$

92

We shall derive the characteristic function of the variable $h = 1/g$. As the distribution of h does not depend upon the scale factor c, we can take it as 1. We then get

$$\varphi(t) = E\, e^{ith}$$

$$= m\binom{m-1}{r-1} \int\limits_{y_1=0}^{\infty} \int\limits_{y_2=y_1}^{\infty} \cdots \int\limits_{y_r=y_1}^{\infty} \int\limits_{y_{r+1}=0}^{y_1} \cdots \int\limits_{y_m=0}^{y_1} e^{it\frac{\Sigma y_\nu}{y_1} - \Sigma y_\nu}\, dy_1\, dy_2 \cdots dy_m$$

$$= \frac{m!}{(m-r)!\,(r-1)!} \int\limits_{y=0}^{\infty} \frac{e^{r(it-y)}\,[1 - e^{it-y}]^{m-r}}{\left[1 - \dfrac{it}{y}\right]^{m-1}}\, dy.$$

g has an absolutely continuous distribution with the frequency function

$$-\frac{1}{2\pi}\frac{m!}{(m-r)!\,(r-1)!} \int\limits_{t=-\infty}^{\infty} e^{-\frac{it}{g}}\frac{1}{g^2} \int\limits_{y=0}^{\infty} \frac{e^{r(it-y)}\,[1 - e^{it-y}]^{m-r}}{\left[1 - \dfrac{it}{y}\right]^{m-1}}\, dy\, dt,$$

as the integrand is bounded by the expression

$$\frac{e^{-ry}\,[1 + e^{-y}]^{m-r}}{\left[1 + \dfrac{t^2}{y^2}\right]^{\frac{m-1}{2}}},$$

which is integrable if $m > 2$. Developing $[1 - e^{it-y}]^{m-r}$ and using

$$\int\limits_{-\infty}^{\infty} \frac{e^{itx}}{(K+it)^\mu}\, dt = \begin{cases} \dfrac{2\pi e^{-Kx}}{(\mu-1)!}\, x^{\mu-1}, & x > 0, \quad K > 0 \\ 0, & x < 0, \quad K > 0, \end{cases}$$

we get

$$\frac{m!\,(m-1)}{(m-r)!\,(r-1)!} \sum\limits_{j=r}^{[1/g]} (-1)^{j-r}\binom{m-r}{j-r}(1-jg)^{m-2}.$$

Integrating this between x and $1/r$ we obtain

$$P(g > x) = \frac{m!}{(r-1)!} \sum\limits_{j=r}^{[1/x]} \frac{(-1)^{j-r}}{j\,(m-j)!\,(j-r)!}(1-jx)^{m-1}.$$

The most important case is that of the greatest value of $s_1, s_2, \ldots s_m$, i.e. $r = 1$. We then have

$$P\left(g>x\right)=m\left(1-x\right)^{m-1}-\frac{m\left(m-1\right)}{2}\left(1-2\,x\right)^{m-1}+$$

$$+\frac{m\left(m-1\right)\left(m-2\right)}{3\cdot2}\left(1-3\,x\right)^{m-1}-\cdots,\tag{2}$$

where the summation should extend as long as the terms inside the brackets are positive.

The practical application of this is as follows. Compute the values of the periodogram $s_1,\ s_2,\ \dots s_m$ and $g=(\max s_\nu)/(s_1+s_2+\cdots s_m)$. If $g<g_p$, where g_p is some appropriate percentile of the distribution given by (2), we accept the hypothesis that no period is present in the data. If $g>g_p$, we reject the hypothesis. Intuitively one would then believe that $2\,\pi/l_\nu$ is a real period if l_ν corresponds to max s_ν. Although this would not be in strict accordance with formal statistical theory, it is the way one usually proceeds in practice.

Once we have decided the order of the trigonometric polynomial and its frequencies λ_ν one may wish to estimate the coefficients $a_\nu,\ b_\nu$. As the correlation matrix of ξ_t is known (it is the identity matrix) we can use section 2.6 to get the minimum variance estimates. We have in this case (where the λ's are some of the l_ν's)

$$c=(\alpha_1,\ \alpha_2,\ \dots\ \alpha_p)_{p\times1}$$

$$\Phi=(e^{it\lambda_\nu};\ t=1,\ 2,\ \dots\ n,\ \nu=1,\ 2,\ \dots\ p)_{n\times p}.$$

Hence

$$\Phi^*\Phi=\left\{\sum_{t=1}^{n}e^{-it\lambda_j}\,e^{it\lambda_k};\ j,\ k=1,\ 2,\ \dots\ p\right\}_{p\times p}=n\,I$$

and the minimum variance estimates are

$$c_\nu=\alpha_\nu^*=\frac{1}{n}\sum_{t=1}^{n}e^{-it\lambda_\nu}\,x_t.$$

Confidence intervals for α_ν can be obtained in the standard way when ξ_t is normal pure white noise with known or unknown variance (Cramér [3], p. 550).

3.2. The variate difference method

Another scheme that has been proposed is

$$x_t=\sum_{\nu=0}^{p}\alpha_\nu\,t^\nu+\xi_t=m_t+\xi_t,$$

where the regression coefficients α_ν are unknown. If p is known, we can use the minimum variance estimates to estimate α_ν in the same way as we did in section 3.1.

However if p is not known, it has to be estimated and for this purpose the so-called *variate difference method* has been suggested (see Tintner [1]). Introduce the difference operator of order q

$$y_t = \Delta^q x_t = x_{t+q} - \binom{q}{1} x_{t+q-1} + \binom{q}{2} x_{t+q-2} - \cdots (-1)^q x_t.$$

We have
$$E y_t = \Delta^q m_t$$

and
$$D^2[y_t] = \sum_{\nu=0}^{q} \binom{q}{\nu}^2 \cdot D^2[\xi_t] = \binom{2q}{q} \cdot D^2[\xi_t].$$

This is used in the following way. First the empirical variance of the original sample x_t is computed. Then the first differences of the series x_t are found and their empirical variance is divided by $\binom{2}{1} = 2$. Then the second differences are found and their empirical variance is now divided by $\binom{4}{2} = 6$, and so on.

The series of numbers obtained after a while (when we reach the pth difference) should stabilize except for random fluctuations. The order of the difference when this happens can be taken as an estimate of p and

$$\frac{D^2[y_t]}{\binom{2q}{q}}$$

is an estimate of the variance of the disturbance ξ_t.

3.3. Effect of Smoothing of Time Series (Slutzky's Theorem)

In the older literature on time series analysis one very often finds techniques in which the sample is first smoothed by a series of linear operations of simple type. The smoothing is supposed to eliminate the random fluctuations. The resulting series is then subjected to some analysis, say Fourier analysis, to isolate the periodic components. The danger of such a procedure is pointed out by a theorem of Slutzky [1] (see also Moran [1]).

Let L be a finite linear operator

$$L u_t = a_0 u_{t+p} + a_1 u_{t+p-1} + \cdots + a_p u_t$$

with the frequency response function

95

$$\varphi(\lambda) = \sum_{\nu=0}^{p} a_\nu e^{-i\nu\lambda}$$

corresponding to the filter L. Suppose that the process x_t is stationary with the spectral distribution function $F(\lambda)$. Then Lx_t is a stationary process with the spectral distribution function

$$\int_{-\pi}^{\lambda} |\varphi(l)|^2 \, dF(l).$$

Consider the normed process

$$y_t = \frac{Lx_t}{D[Lx_t]}.$$

Its spectral distribution function is

$$G(\lambda) = \frac{\int_{-\pi}^{\lambda} |\varphi(l)|^2 \, dF(l)}{\int_{-\pi}^{\pi} |\varphi(l)|^2 \, dF(l)}. \tag{1}$$

Consider a finite linear operator M with the frequency response function $m(\lambda)$. The function $|m(\lambda)|^2$ is continuous. Assume that it has a unique absolute maximum, say at $\lambda = \lambda_0$. The case of several maxima can be treated in a similar way. Put $L = M^n$ and assume that $\lambda = \lambda_0$ is a point in the spectrum of x_t. We clearly have $\varphi(\lambda) = m(\lambda)^n$ and (1) defines a sequence of distribution functions in $(-\pi, \pi)$. Suppose that $-\pi < \lambda < \lambda_0$. Then

$$\int_{-\pi}^{\pi} |m(\lambda)|^{2n} \, dF(\lambda) \geq [F(\lambda_0 + \varepsilon) - F(\lambda_0 - \varepsilon)][|m(\lambda_0)| - \delta]^{2n},$$

where $\varepsilon, \delta > 0$. On the other hand

$$\int_{-\pi}^{\lambda} |m(\lambda)|^{2n} \, dF(\lambda) \leq [F(\lambda) - F(-\pi)][|m(\lambda_0)| - \delta']^{2n}$$

where $\delta' > \delta$. If λ_0 is a point of increase of the spectral distribution function $F(\lambda)$ so that $F(\lambda_0 + \varepsilon) > F(\lambda_0 - \varepsilon)$, it follows that $G(\lambda)$ tends to zero when n tends to infinity. One can similarly show that $G(\lambda)$ tends to one when $\lambda > \lambda_0$ and n increases. Hence the behaviour of y_t over any fixed finite interval will approximate that of the harmonic with frequency λ_0 if n is sufficiently large.

96

Slutzky considers two linear operators,

$$\left. \begin{array}{l} M\,u_t = u_{t+1} + u_t \\ N\,u_t = u_{t+1} - u_t \end{array} \right\}.$$

Let $L = M^\mu N^\nu$ and let μ and ν tend to infinity with $\nu/\mu = \alpha$, $0 < \alpha < 1$. Clearly in this case

$$\varphi(\lambda) = (1 + e^{i\lambda})^\mu (1 - e^{i\lambda})^\nu.$$

The function $|\varphi(\lambda)|^2$ has an absolute maximum at $\lambda = \lambda_0$, where

$$\cos \lambda_0 = \frac{\mu - \nu}{\mu + \nu} = \frac{1 - \alpha}{1 + \alpha}.$$

One can now again prove that the smoothed series converges to a harmonic with frequency λ_0 (see Moran [1], p. 76).

These results indicate that although smoothing can be used to eliminate random disturbances it also may introduce periodicities which are not present in the original process. It should also be pointed out that existing periods or peaks in the spectral density may be obliterated by a smoothing operation.

3.4. Serial Correlation Coefficients for Normal White Noise

A property common to both schemes treated in 3.1 and 3.2 is that the disturbance is pure white noise. In most cases one does not have any a priori knowledge concerning this. A need was felt for techniques to determine whether a given time series could be regarded as a sample from a pure white noise process. In this section we shall review briefly a few of the many results in this direction.

Assume x_t to be a normally distributed process with unknown mean value m. We want to test the hypothesis that x_t is white noise. It is clear that one intuitively plausible statistic to consider is the *first serial correlation coefficien* (of lag one)

$$b = \frac{c_1'}{c_0'},$$

where $$c_p' = \sum_{\nu=1}^{n-p} (x_\nu - \bar{x})(x_{\nu+p} - \bar{x}), \quad p \geq 0.$$

One could consider serial correlation coefficients of higher lag but we shall not discuss them here.

The distribution of b under the null hypothesis can not be obtained in closed form. Because of this difficulty one is led to consider instead the *circular serial correlation coefficient*

$$\hat{b} = \frac{\hat{c}_1}{\hat{c}_0},$$

where

$$\hat{c}_p = \sum_{\nu=1}^{n} (x_\nu - \bar{x})(x_{\nu+p} - \bar{x}), \quad p \geq 0,$$

and we have assumed the circular definition $x_{\nu+n} = x_\nu$. Consider the two quadratic forms

$$\hat{C} = x^* \hat{C} x,$$
$$\gamma = x^* V x,$$

where

$$\hat{C} = \left\{ \begin{pmatrix} 0 & \frac{1}{2} & 0 & \dots & 0 & \frac{1}{2} \\ \frac{1}{2} & 0 & \frac{1}{2} & \dots & 0 & 0 \\ 0 & \frac{1}{2} & 0 & \dots & 0 & 0 \\ & & \cdot & \cdot & \cdot & \\ \frac{1}{2} & 0 & 0 & \dots & \frac{1}{2} & 0 \end{pmatrix} - \frac{1}{n} \begin{pmatrix} 1 & 1 & \dots & 1 \\ 1 & 1 & \dots & 1 \\ & \cdot & \cdot & \cdot & \\ 1 & 1 & \dots & 1 \end{pmatrix} \right\}.$$

$$V = I - \frac{1}{n} \begin{pmatrix} 1 & 1 & \dots & 1 \\ 1 & 1 & \dots & 1 \\ & \cdot & \cdot & \cdot & \\ 1 & 1 & \dots & 1 \end{pmatrix}$$

Now $\hat{b} = \hat{C}/\gamma$. Now $\hat{C}V = V\hat{C}$ so that there is an orthogonal transformation taking both $\hat{C}$ and V into diagonal form at the same time.

Let us now derive expressions for the eigenvalues of a *circular matrix*

$$A = \begin{pmatrix} a_1 & a_2 & a_3 & \dots & a_n \\ a_n & a_1 & a_2 & \dots & a_{n-1} \\ & \cdot & \cdot & \cdot & \cdot & \cdot \\ a_2 & a_3 & a_4 & \dots & a_1 \end{pmatrix}.$$

Now $A = \sum_{s=1}^{n} a_s J^{s-1}$, where

$$J = \begin{pmatrix} 0 & 1 & \dots & 0 & 0 \\ 0 & 0 & \dots & 0 & 0 \\ & \cdot & \cdot & \cdot & \cdot \\ 0 & 0 & \dots & 0 & 1 \\ 1 & 0 & \dots & 0 & 0 \end{pmatrix}.$$

The eigenvalues of J are $w_k = e^{2\pi i k/n}$. The eigenvalues of A are then

$$\lambda_j = \sum_{\nu=1}^{n} a_\nu w_j^{\nu-1} = \sum_{\nu=1}^{n} a_\nu e^{\frac{2\pi i (\nu-1) j}{n}}.$$

In the first case take

$$a_\nu = \begin{cases} -\dfrac{1}{n}, & \nu \neq 2, n \\[2mm] \dfrac{1}{2} - \dfrac{1}{n}, & \nu = 2, n. \end{cases}$$

The eigenvalues of $\hat{C}$ are

$$\lambda_j = -\frac{1}{n} \sum_{\nu=1}^{n} w_j^{\nu-1} + \tfrac{1}{2}(w_j + w_j^{-1}) = \cos\frac{2\pi j}{n}, \qquad j = 1, 2, \dots n-1 \Bigg\}$$
$$\lambda_n = 0.$$

The eigenvalues of V are

$$\mu_j = 1, \qquad j = 1, 2, \dots n-1 \Bigg\}$$
$$\mu_n = 0.$$

The eigenvalues λ_n and μ_n correspond to the same eigenvector

$$\left(\frac{1}{\sqrt{n}}, \frac{1}{\sqrt{n}}, \dots \frac{1}{\sqrt{n}} \right)$$

as is immediately verified. Hence

$$\hat{C} = \sum_{j=1}^{n-1} y_j^2 \cos\frac{2\pi j}{n} \Bigg\}$$
$$\gamma = \sum_{j=1}^{n-1} y_j^2 \Bigg\}, \qquad (1)$$

where $(y_1, y_2, \dots y_n)$ is the transform of $(x_1, x_2, \dots x_n)$ under the orthogonal transformation so that they still are independent normal variables with mean zero and common standard deviation.

Let us now compute the distribution of $\hat{b}$ when n is odd. For n even the same method can be used and we refer to R. L. Anderson [1] for the result. Consider

$$P(\hat{b} > \alpha) = P(\hat{C} - \alpha \gamma > 0).$$

The quadratic form $Q = x^*(\hat{C} - \alpha V)x$ has the characteristic function (see Cramér [3], p. 233)

$$\varphi(t) = |I - 2it(\hat{C} - \alpha V)|^{-\frac{1}{2}} = \prod_{k=1}^{n-1} [1 - 2it(\lambda_k - \alpha)]^{-\frac{1}{2}}.$$

The eigenvalues are equal in pairs, $\lambda_k = \lambda_{n-k}$ for $k = 1, 2, \ldots n-1$ (see formula (1)). We have

$$\varphi(t) = \prod_{k=1}^{\frac{n-1}{2}} [1 - 2it(\lambda_k - \alpha)]^{-1}.$$

Q then has the frequency function $(n \geq 3)$

$$f(u) = \frac{1}{2\pi} \int_{-\infty}^{\infty} e^{-iut} \varphi(t) dt = \frac{1}{2} \sum_{\lambda_k > \alpha} e^{\frac{u}{2(\alpha - \lambda_k)}} \frac{(\lambda_k - \alpha)^{\frac{n-3}{2}}}{a_k} \frac{1}{\lambda_k - \alpha}$$

by a simple application of the calculus of residues. We have put

$$a_k = \prod_{j=1, j \neq k}^{\frac{n-1}{2}} (\lambda_k - \lambda_j).$$

Hence
$$P(\hat{b} > \alpha) = \int_0^{\infty} f(u) du = \sum_{\lambda_k > \alpha} (\lambda_k - \alpha)^{\frac{n-3}{2}} \frac{1}{a_k}.$$

This can be used to get a one- or two-sided test of significance for the null hypothesis. For tables see R. L. Anderson [1].

Madow [1] has derived the distribution of $\hat{b}$ under the alternative hypothesis that $y_t = x_t - m$ is a first order autoregressive scheme so that its frequency function is (again using the circular definition)

$p(x_1, x_2, \ldots x_n \,|\, A, B)$

$$= \text{const. } \exp\left\{ -\frac{1}{2} \left[A \sum_{\nu=1}^{n} (x_\nu - m)^2 + 2B \sum_{\nu=1}^{n} (x_{\nu+1} - m)(x_\nu - m) \right] \right\},$$

where $A = (1 + \varrho^2)/\sigma^2$, $B = -\varrho/\sigma^2$ when y_t satisfies the stochastic difference equation

$$\left. \begin{array}{l} y_{t+1} - \varrho y_t = \xi_t, \quad |\varrho| < 1. \\ E\,\xi_t = 0, \quad D[\xi_t] = \sigma. \end{array} \right\}.$$

Note that the sample mean $\bar{x}$ is independent of γ, $\hat{b}$ whatever the values of A and B. Under the null hypothesis γ and $\hat{b}$ are independent. This is most easily seen by a geometric argument. The conditional distribution of $\hat{b}$ given

100

γ (see formula (1)) does not depend on γ and the independence follows. γ has a χ^2-distribution with $n-1$ degrees of freedom. Hence γ, $\hat{b}$ have the joint frequency function

$$g(\gamma, \hat{b}) = \text{const. } \gamma^{\frac{n-3}{2}} e^{-\frac{\gamma}{2}} \sum_{\lambda_k > b} (\lambda_k - \hat{b})^{\frac{n-5}{2}} \frac{1}{a}$$

under the null hypothesis.

It is clear that $(\hat{b}, \gamma)$ is a sufficient statistic for (A, B) in the sense that

$$p(x_1, x_2, \ldots x_n \mid A, B) = q(\hat{b}, \gamma \mid A, B) \, r(x_1, x_2, \ldots x_n \mid \hat{b}, \gamma),$$

where $r(x_1, x_2, \ldots x_n)$ does not depend upon A and B. Hence

$$q(\hat{b}, \gamma \mid A, B) = q(\hat{b}, \gamma \mid 1, 0) \text{ const. } \frac{e^{-\frac{1}{2}(A\gamma + 2B\hat{b}\gamma)}}{e^{-\frac{1}{2}\gamma}}$$

$$= \text{const. } \gamma^{\frac{n-3}{2}} e^{-\frac{1}{2}\gamma(A+2B\hat{b})} \sum_{\lambda_k > b} (\lambda_k - \hat{b})^{\frac{n-5}{2}} \frac{1}{a_k}.$$

Integrating over $0 < \gamma < \infty$ we get the marginal frequency function of $\hat{b}$

$$\text{const. } \left(\frac{A}{2} + B\hat{b}\right)^{-\frac{n-1}{2}} \sum_{\lambda_k > \hat{b}} (\lambda_k - \hat{b})^{\frac{n-5}{2}} \frac{1}{a_k},$$

which is the desired expression.

3.5. Approximate Distributions of Quadratic Forms

The only reason for dealing with the circular coefficient $\hat{b}$ instead of with b is that it does not seem possible to get an explicit expression for the distribution of b. Let us compute the eigenvalues of the quadratic form C appearing in the numerator of the noncircular serial correlation coefficient. We have

$$C = \begin{pmatrix} 0 & \frac{1}{2} & 0 & \ldots & 0 & 0 \\ \frac{1}{2} & 0 & \frac{1}{2} & \ldots & 0 & 0 \\ \cdot & \cdot & \cdot & \cdot & \cdot & \cdot \\ 0 & 0 & 0 & \ldots & \frac{1}{2} & 0 \end{pmatrix}.$$

For simplicity we have assumed that the mean value of x_t is zero. Set

$$|C - \lambda I| = \begin{pmatrix} -\lambda & \frac{1}{2} & 0 & \ldots & 0 \\ \frac{1}{2} & -\lambda & \frac{1}{2} & \ldots & 0 \\ 0 & 0 & 0 & \ldots & -\lambda \end{pmatrix} = \Delta_n.$$

3.5

As
$$\Delta_n = -\lambda\,\Delta_{n-1} - \tfrac{1}{4}\,\Delta_{n-2}$$

we have
$$\Delta_n = \alpha\,\xi_1^n + \beta\,\xi_2^n, \tag{1}$$

where ξ_1, ξ_2 are roots of the equation

$$\xi^2 + \lambda\,\xi + \tfrac{1}{4} = 0. \tag{2}$$

Then

$$\left.\begin{aligned}
\Delta_1 &= -\lambda = \xi_1 + \xi_2 = \alpha\,\xi_1 + \beta\,\xi_2 \\
\Delta_2 &= \lambda^2 - \tfrac{1}{4} = \xi_1^2 + \xi_2^2 + \xi_1\,\xi_2 = \alpha\,\xi_1^2 + \beta\,\xi_2^2
\end{aligned}\right\},$$

where we have just used the relation between roots and coefficients of equation (2). Then solving for α, β and using (1) we find

$$\Delta_n = \frac{\xi_1^{n+1} - \xi_2^{n+1}}{\xi_1 - \xi_2}.$$

As $\xi_1\,\xi_2 = \tfrac{1}{4}$ we can define w by setting

$$\left.\begin{aligned}
\xi_1 &= -\frac{w}{2} \\
\xi_2 &= -\frac{1}{2w}
\end{aligned}\right\}.$$

Then $\lambda = (w + w^{-1})/2$ and $\Delta_n = 0$, $n > 0$, implies that

$$\frac{w^{n+1} - w^{-n-1}}{w - w^{-1}} = 0.$$

Thus
$$w^{2(n+1)} = 1, \quad n > 0.$$

Hence
$$\lambda_k = \cos\frac{\pi}{n+1}\,k, \; k = 1, 2, \ldots n. \tag{3}$$

Note that all these eigenvalues are different, in contrast to the circular case discussed in the last section. The characteristic function will now not reduce to a rational function and we can scarcely hope for an explicit inversion of it.

There are various ways in which to obtain approximations. The simplest (and crudest) way is to compute the first two moments of the statistic and use the normal approximation. A closer approximation has been suggested by Koopmans in an important paper [1]. He observed that the eigenvalues of the form in question were distributed asymptotically as the values of cos

πx, $0 < x < 1$, and used this to approximate the characteristic function. Whittle used the same idea in more complicated situations (Whittle [1]).

It has been pointed out (see Grenander [3]) that this method is an application of a general theorem of Szegö [1] on the asymptotic distribution of the eigenvalues of Toeplitz forms, which we are going to prove.
Consider a *Toeplitz matrix*

$$T_n = \{c_{\nu-\mu}; \, \nu, \mu = 1, 2, \ldots n\},$$

where

$$c_\nu = \frac{1}{2\pi} \int\limits_{-\pi}^{\pi} e^{i\nu x} g(x) \, dx.$$

Here $g(x)$ is a measurable bounded function $|g(x)| \le M < \infty$. Denote the eigenvalues by $\lambda_{1,n}, \lambda_{2,n}, \ldots \lambda_{n,n}$. The quadratic form

$$\tau_n = x^* T_n x = \sum_{\nu,\mu=1}^{n} c_{\nu-\mu} x_\nu \bar{x}_\mu = \int\limits_{-\pi}^{\pi} \left| \sum_{\nu=1}^{n} x_\nu e^{i\nu x} \right|^2 g(x) \, dx$$

is Hermitian so that the λ's are real and the norm of τ_n $||\tau_n|| \le M$ so that $|\lambda_{\nu,n}| \le M$. For any n we can talk about the (discrete) distribution of the eigenvalues in the interval $(-M, M)$.

Let α be a real variable, $|\alpha| < 1/M$. Then $(1/2\pi)[1 + \alpha g(x)] > 0$ and it can be considered as the spectral density of a stationary process y_t, which then has the covariance matrix

$$R_n = I_n + \alpha T_n.$$

We know that the residual variance

$$\sigma_\nu^2 = \min_{b_1, b_2, \ldots, b_\nu} E \left| y_t - b_1 y_{t-1} - b_2 y_{t-2} \ldots b_\nu y_{t-\nu} \right|^2 \tag{4}$$

can be expressed in terms of covariance determinants (see Cramér [3], p. 305)

$$\sigma_\nu^2 = \frac{|R_{\nu+1}|}{|R_\nu|}.$$

But

$$|R_\nu| = \prod_{j=1}^{\nu} [1 + \alpha \lambda_{j,\nu}].$$

On the other hand (see section 2.2)

$$\lim_{\nu \to \infty} \sigma_\nu^2 = 2\pi \exp \left\{ \frac{1}{2\pi} \int\limits_{-\pi}^{\pi} \log \frac{[1 + \alpha g(x)]}{2\pi} \, dx \right\}.$$

3.5

As

$$\lim_{n\to\infty} \log \sigma_n^2 = \lim_{n\to\infty} \frac{1}{n} \sum_{\nu=1}^{n} \log \sigma_\nu^2 = \lim_{n\to\infty} \frac{\log |R_{n+1}| - \log |R_1|}{n}$$

$$= \lim_{n\to\infty} \frac{1}{n} \sum_{\nu=1}^{n} \log [1 + \alpha \lambda_{\nu,n}]$$

we have

$$\lim_{n\to\infty} \frac{1}{n} \sum_{j=1}^{n} \log [1 + \alpha \lambda_{j,n}] = \frac{1}{2\pi} \int_{-\pi}^{\pi} \log [1 + \alpha g(x)] \, dx.$$

Introducing

$$s_{n,p} = \sum_{\nu=1}^{n} \lambda_{\nu,n}^p$$

and using

$$\log (1 + x) = \sum_{p=1}^{\infty} (-1)^{p-1} \frac{x^p}{p}$$

which converges for $|x| < 1$, we have for $|\alpha| < 1/M$

$$\lim_{n\to\infty} \sum_{p=1}^{\infty} \frac{(-1)^{p-1}}{p} \frac{s_{n,p}}{n} \alpha^p$$

$$= \frac{1}{2\pi} \int_{-\pi}^{\pi} \left\{ \sum_{p=1}^{\infty} \frac{(-1)^{p-1}}{p} g^p(x) \alpha^p \right\} dx$$

$$= \sum_{p=1}^{\infty} \frac{(-1)^{p-1}}{p} \frac{1}{2\pi} \int_{-\pi}^{\pi} g^p(x) \alpha^p \, dx$$

because of the uniform convergence.

Set

$$\left. \begin{array}{l} f_n(z) = \displaystyle\sum_{p=1}^{\infty} \frac{(-1)^{p-1}}{p} \frac{s_{n,p}}{n} z^p \\[3mm] f(z) = \displaystyle\sum_{p=1}^{\infty} \frac{(-1)^{p-1}}{p} \frac{1}{2\pi} \int_{-\pi}^{\pi} g^p(x) z^p \, dx. \end{array} \right\}$$

For $|z| < 1/2M$ the sequence $f_n(z)$ is uniformly bounded. Further, for every real z in the interval $(-1/M, 1/M)$ $f_n(z)$ converges to $f(z)$. It then follows from Vitali's theorem (see Titchmarsh [1], p. 168) that the series converges uniformly in $|z| < 1/2M$. Then

$$\lim_{n\to\infty} \frac{s_{n,p}}{n} = \frac{1}{2\pi} \int_{-\pi}^{\pi} g^p(x) \, dx, \quad p = 1, 2, \dots .$$

Now we have a sequence of distributions in the finite interval $(-M, M)$. As the moments converge, the same is true of the distributions. The limiting moments belong to the stochastic variable $g(x)$ where x is uniformly distributed in $(-\pi, \pi)$. Hence we have proved that *the eigenvalues of a Toeplitz form behave asymptotically like the ordinates of the function $g(x)$ with equidistributed x.*

The case of circulants is considerably easier than that of Toeplitz forms. Consider the symmetric circulant matrix A of section 3.4. The symmetry condition implies that $a_2 = a_n$, $a_3 = a_{n-1}$ and so on. Hence (see section 3.4)

$$\lambda_{j,n} = a_1 + 2 a_2 \cos \frac{2\pi j}{n} + 2 a_3 \cos \frac{3\pi j}{n} + \cdots .$$

This series has a finite number of terms and the last term depends on whether n is odd or even. The eigenvalues are clearly the equidistributed ordinates of the partial sums corresponding to the Fourier series

$$h(x) \sim a_1 + 2 \sum_2^\infty a_\nu \cos \nu x.$$

If the a_ν's had been defined as Fourier coefficients of a bounded real function $g(x)$ symmetric about zero

$$a_\nu = \frac{1}{2\pi} \int_{-\pi}^{\pi} e^{i(\nu-1)x} g(x) \, dx$$

we would have $\qquad\qquad h(x) = g(x),$

the analogue of the above theorem.

C in the present section is a Toeplitz matrix corresponding to $g(x) = \cos \pi x$ and (3) agrees with the theorem just proved.

One should note that ratios of quadratic forms Q_1/Q_2 can be treated by considering the difference $Q_1 - u\, Q_2$ as in section 3.4. These results can be used to get approximations to the moments of interest and they can be used to approximate the distribution by a Pearson curve or Gram-Charlier series. Without going into details we refer to the papers of Koopmans, Rubin, Dixon, Whittle, Leipnik in the bibliography. Proper care should be used in applying these approximations as we know very little about the order of the error except in some special cases (see Eklind-Jung [1]).

Dixon [1] considers the somewhat more general case of testing one autoregressive scheme against another. The hypothesis to be tested is that the process is an autoregressive scheme of order $r \geq 0$ with unspecified coefficients. The alternative hypothesis is chosen as an autoregressive scheme of order $m > r$ still without specifying the coefficients. As such a scheme of the rth order is Markoffian of the rth order it follows that the residual variance σ_ν^2 (see formula (4)) decreases at first but is constant for $\nu > r$. Remembering the expression of σ_ν^2 as the ratio between two covariance determinants, it would be intuitively plausible to use as a test statistic

$$U = \frac{D_{m+1}}{D_m} \frac{D_r}{D_{r+1}},$$

where D_ν denotes the empirical covariance determinant of order ν. We reject the null hypothesis if $U < U_0$. Dixon uses the normal approximation to choose U_0. Whittle [1] has suggested using the approximations of the eigenvalue distribution just described. Dixon uses the circular statistics while Whittle uses the noncircular ones. Also see Hsu [1] who suggests using the Cornish-Fisher form of the Charlier series to get asymptotic expansions for the distributions of statistics of this type.

The methods described in this and the last section have been elaborated in various directions by various authors. We do not pursue this topic any further because we believe that the discussion above gives an accurate picture of the ideas upon which these techniques are based. An interesting observation of Durbin and Watson [1] allows one to use modified noncircular statistics. The reader is also referred to the papers of Hannan [1], Champernowne [1] and Wise [1].

3.6. Testing Autoregressive Schemes and Moving Averages

In this section we will study how to test the hypotheses that the process is an autoregressive scheme or a moving average of some specified order. In the last section we discussed briefly a test designed for the first case, and one of the two tests we discuss here is an alternative test for this hypothesis.

Consider a real autoregressive scheme of order k

$$x_{t+k} + a_1 x_{t+k-1} + \cdots + a_k x_t = \varepsilon_{t+k}, \tag{1}$$

where the ε's are independent with the same distribution. We also assume that the roots of the characteristic equation

$$z^k + a_1 z^{k-1} + \cdots + a_k = 0$$

are all of modulus less than one. Then we know that x_t can be expressed as

106

an infinite moving average of the ε's with the summation extending only over past values of the time parameter.

Note that if this condition concerning the modulus of the roots is fulfilled, the parameters $a_1, a_2, \cdots a_k$ can be estimated consistently (see section 3.7).

We know that the spectral density is

$$f(\lambda) = \frac{\sigma_\varepsilon^2}{2\pi} \left| \sum_{\nu=0}^{k} a_\nu e^{i\nu\lambda} \right|^{-2}, \quad a_0 = 1,$$

so that the correlation coefficients

$$\varrho_\nu = \frac{\sigma_\varepsilon^2}{2\pi i V} \int\limits_{|z|=1} z^{-\nu} \frac{1}{\varphi(z)\,\varphi(z^{-1})} \frac{dz}{z},$$

where

$$\varphi(z) = \sum_{\nu=0}^{k} a_\nu z^\nu,$$

and V is the variance of the process x_t. This means that ϱ_ν is the νth coefficient of the Laurent series of $\sigma_\varepsilon^2/V \varphi(z)\,\varphi(z^{-1})$. For convenience we take $\sigma_\varepsilon^2 = 1$.

On defining the quantity

$$P_\nu = \sum_{j=-\infty}^{\infty} \varrho_j \varrho_{\nu-j}$$

we see that it corresponds in the same way to the function

$$V^{-2} [\varphi(z)\,\varphi(z^{-1})]^{-2}.$$

Similarly, we define A_j by

$$\varphi^2(z) = \sum_{j=-\infty}^{\infty} A_j z^j.$$

Then

$$B_t = \sum_{j=-\infty}^{\infty} A_j P_{t-j}$$

corresponds to the function $\varphi^2(z)/V^2 [\varphi(z)\,\varphi(z^{-1})]^2 = \varphi^{-2}(z^{-1})V^{-2}$, which has no poles for $|z| > 1$ so that

$$B_t = 0, \quad t > 0.$$

Considering

$$C_t = \sum_{j=-\infty}^{\infty} A_j \varrho_{t-j}$$

we see that it corresponds to $\varphi^2(z)/V \varphi(z)\,\varphi(z^{-1}) = \varphi(z)/V \varphi(z^{-1})$ so that

$$C_t = 0, \quad t > k.$$

3.6

As a test statistic we shall use

$$R_s = \sum_{j=-\infty}^{\infty} A_j \varrho^*_{s-j},$$

where ϱ^*_s is the sth empirical correlation coefficient. It is easy to prove that

$$\left.\begin{aligned}
E \varrho^*_s &\sim \varrho_s \\
\text{cov}\,[\varrho^*_s,\ \varrho^*_t] &\sim \frac{1}{n}\{P_{t-s}+P_{t+s}+2\varrho_t\,\varrho_s\,P_0-2\varrho_s\,P_t-2\varrho_t P_s\}
\end{aligned}\right\} \qquad (2)$$

as $n\to\infty$ (see Bartlett [1], p. 30). Hence

$$E\,R_s = \sum_{j=0}^{2k} E\,A_j \varrho^*_{s-j} \to \sum_{j=0}^{2k} A_j \varrho_{s-j} = 0,\ \ s=k+1,\ k+2\ldots.$$

Now

$$\text{cov}\,(\varrho^*_s,\ R_t) \sim \frac{1}{n}\sum_{j=0}^{2k} A_j\,\{P_{t-s-j}+P_{t-j+s}+2\varrho_s\,\varrho_{t-j}\,P_0-$$

$$-2\varrho_{t-j}\,P_s-2\varrho_s\,P_{t-j}\} = \frac{1}{n}\sum_{j=0}^{2k} A_j\,P_j$$

if $s=t$ and $=0$ if $t>s$. Hence

$$\text{cov}\,(R_s,\ R_t) = \sum_{j=0}^{2k} A_j\,\text{cov}\,(\varrho^*_{s-j},\ R_t) \sim 0$$

if $t>s$ and

$$\sim \frac{1}{n}\sum_{j=0}^{2k} A_j\,P_j$$

if $t=s$.

This result is due to Quenouille [1] who suggests the following application. If x_t satisfies (1) then the quadratic forms $R_{k+1},\ R_{k+2}\ \ldots\ R_q$ are asymptotically normally distributed (this can be reduced to an application of the central limit law) and independent with the mean zero and variance $\frac{1}{n}\sum_{j=0}^{2k} A_j\,P_j$. Further $\varrho^*_1, \varrho^*_2, \ldots \varrho^*_k$ are asymptotically normal with means $\varrho_1, \varrho_2, \ldots \varrho_k$ and independent of $R_{k+1},\ R_{k+2},\ \ldots\ .$

Consider first the case when the coefficients of the difference equation are specified. Then we can test the corresponding hypothesis by using e.g.

108

$$\chi_f^2 = R_{k+1}^2 + R_{k+2}^2 + \cdots + R_{k+f}^2$$

which has a χ^2-distribution asymptotically with f degrees of freedom under the null hypothesis. As a critical region we can choose

$$\chi_f^2 > \text{const.}$$

When the order of the autoregressive scheme but not the coefficients are specified, we first estimate a_1, a_2, ... a_k using the statistics ϱ_1^*, ϱ_2^*, ... ϱ_k^* (see section 3.7) and then proceed as above. The estimation does not disturb the significance level of the test, at least not for large samples, because of the asymptotic independence of the two sets of statistics.

The simplest case is $k = 1$,

$$x_{t+1} - \varrho\, x_t = \varepsilon_t,$$

and as the characteristic equation should have no roots outside the unit circle $|\varrho| < 1$ and we have

$$(1 - \varrho z)^2 = \sum_{j=0}^{2k} A_j\, z^j,$$

$$A_0 = 1, \qquad A_1 = -2\varrho, \qquad A_2 = \varrho^2$$

so that
$$R_s = \varrho_s^* - 2\varrho\, \varrho_{s-1}^* + \varrho^2\, \varrho_{s-2}^*.$$

We might use ϱ_1^* as an estimate of ϱ.

Wold [2] has developed a test for the hypothesis that the process is a moving average of order h with coefficients $1, b_1, b_2, \ldots b_h$

$$x_t = \varepsilon_t + b_1 \varepsilon_{t-1} + \cdots b_h\, \varepsilon_{t-h},$$

where ε_t is pure white noise as before. It has the autocorrelation coefficients

$$\left.\begin{aligned}
&\varrho_0 = 1\\[4pt]
&\varrho_1 = \frac{1}{K}\,[b_1 + b_2 b_1 + b_3 b_2 + \cdots b_h\, b_{h-1}]\\[4pt]
&\varrho_2 = \frac{1}{K}\,[b_2 + b_3 b_1 + b_4 b_2 + \cdots + b_h\, b_{h-2}]\\[4pt]
&\cdot\ \cdot\ \cdot\ \cdot\ \cdot\ \cdot\ \cdot\ \cdot\ \cdot\ \cdot\ \cdot\ \cdot\ \cdot\ \cdot\ \cdot\\[4pt]
&\varrho_h = \frac{b_h}{K}\\[4pt]
&\varrho_\nu = 0,\ \ \nu > h\\[4pt]
&K = 1 + b_1^2 + b_2^2 + \cdots + b_h^2.
\end{aligned}\right\} \tag{3}$$

3.6

Consider the symmetric matrix

$$P = \{\varrho_{i-k};\ i,\ k = 1,\ 2,\ \dots\ n\}.$$

As the covariance matrix P is a positive definite matrix, it can be written as (see Wintner [1], p. 28)

$$P = Y Y^*,$$

where $Y = \{y_{ik};\ i,\ k = 1,\ 2,\ \dots\ n\}$ is triangular and nonsingular

$$\left.\begin{array}{l} y_{ii} > 0 \\ y_{ik} = 0,\ i < k. \end{array}\right\}$$

P cannot be singular as it is the covariance matrix of a process with a continuous spectral density positive almost everywhere. If

$$0 = z^* P z = \sum_{\nu,\ \mu = 1}^{n} z_\nu \bar{z}_\mu \varrho_{\nu-\mu} = \int_{-\pi}^{\pi} \left| \sum_{1}^{n} z_\nu\, e^{i\nu\lambda} \right|^2 f(\lambda)\, d\lambda,$$

then $f(\lambda) \sum_{1}^{n} z_\nu\, e^{i\nu\lambda} = 0$ a.e., which implies that $z = 0$. Then

$$Z = \{z_{ik};\ i,\ k = 1,\ 2,\ \dots\ n\} = Y^{-1}$$

exists and is also triangular. Form the statistics

$$\left.\begin{array}{l} R_{h+i} = z_{i,\,1}\, \varrho_{h+1}^* + z_{i,\,2}\, \varrho_{h+2}^* + \cdots + z_{i,\,i}\, \varrho_{h+i}^* \\ i = 1,\ 2\ \dots\ . \end{array}\right\}$$

For large samples we have

$$E R_{h+i} \sim 0.$$

Formula (2) gives us

$$\text{cov}\ (\varrho_{h+i}^*,\ \varrho_{h+k}^*) \sim \frac{1}{n}\, P_{i-k}$$

so that
$$\text{cov}\ (R_{h+i},\ R_{h+k}) = \frac{1}{n} \sum_{\nu,\ \mu = 1}^{n} z_{i,\,\nu}\, z_{k,\,\mu}\, P_{\nu-\mu}.$$

But the sum is the $(i,\ k)$th element in the matrix

$$Z P Z^* = Y^{-1} Y Y^* Y^{*-1} = I.$$

To test the hypothesis in question we form $R_{h+1},\ R_{h+2},\ \dots\ R_{h+f}$ and

$$\chi_f^2 = n\,[R_{h+1}^2 + R_{h+2}^2 + \cdots + R_{h+f}^2].$$

Under the null hypothesis this has a χ^2-distribution with f degrees of freedom and it is reasonable to use a critical region of the type $\chi^2 > \text{const}$.

The reader might object that the derivations given in this section are not quite complete. To give rigorous derivations would carry us too far into a direction that we do not intend to follow, but we believe that the results are correct as limit theorems as $n \to \infty$ when f is kept fixed.

3.7. Estimation and the Asymptotic Distribution of the Coefficients of an Autoregressive Scheme

Let x_t be a stationary autoregressive scheme satisfying the difference equation

$$x_t = \alpha_1 x_{t-1} + \alpha_2 x_{t-2} + \cdots + \alpha_p x_{t-p} + \alpha_0 + \varepsilon_t,$$

where the stochastic variables ε_t are independent and identically distributed with mean value zero and the roots of the equation

$$z^p - \alpha_1 z^{p-1} - \cdots - \alpha_p = 0 \tag{1}$$

have modulus less than one. Here the order p of the autoregressive scheme is assumed known. It will be adequate to assume that the first four moments of the ε_t exist.

The process x_t is not assumed to be normal. It is not unreasonable to try as estimates of the parameters of the process $\alpha_0, \alpha_1, \ldots \alpha_p, \sigma^2 = E\varepsilon_t^2$ the maximum likelihood estimates of these parameters derived under the assumption of normality of the process, even when the process is not normal. If the process were normal, the probability density of $x_1, \ldots x_N$ would be given by

$$\frac{1}{(2\pi)^{N/2} \sigma^N} \exp\ -\frac{1}{2\sigma^2} \sum_{t=1}^N (x_t - \alpha_1 x_{t-1} - \cdots - \alpha_p x_{t-p} - \alpha_0)^2].$$

The maximum likelihood estimates maximize this expression. On differentiating the logarithm of the density with respect to the parameters, we obtain the following system of equations that the estimates $a_0, a_1, \ldots, a_p, s^2$ of $\alpha_0, \alpha_1, \ldots \alpha_p, \sigma^2$ satisfy

$$\sum_{t=1}^N x_t - \sum_{i=1}^p a_i \sum_{t=1}^N x_{t-i} - N a_0 = 0$$

$$\sum_{t=1}^N x_t x_{t-j} - \sum_{i=1}^p a_i \sum_{t=1}^N x_{t-i} x_{t-j} - a_0 \sum_{t=1}^N x_{t-j} = 0$$

$$(j = 1, \ldots, p)$$

3.7

$$s^2 = \frac{1}{N} \sum_{t=1}^{N} (x_t - a_1 x_{t-1} - \cdots - a_p x_{t-p} - a_0)^2.$$

We introduce the stochastic variables

$$y_0 = \frac{1}{\sqrt{N}} \sum_{t=1}^{N} (x_t - \alpha_1 x_{t-1} - \cdots - \dot{\alpha}_p x_{t-p} - \alpha_0) = \frac{1}{\sqrt{N}} \sum_{t=1}^{N} \varepsilon_t$$

$$y_i = \frac{1}{\sqrt{N}} \sum_{t=1}^{N} (x_t - \alpha_1 x_{t-1} - \cdots - \alpha_p x_{t-p} - \alpha_0) x_{t-i} = \frac{1}{\sqrt{N}} \sum_{t=1}^{N} \varepsilon_t x_{t-i}.$$

Note that

$$\left. \begin{aligned} y_i &= \sum_{j=1}^{p} \sqrt{N} \, (a_j - \alpha_j) \sum_{t=1}^{N} x_{t-i} x_{t-j}/N + \sqrt{N} \, (a_0 - \alpha_0) \sum_{t=1}^{N} x_{t-i}/N \\ &\qquad\qquad (i = 1, \ldots, p) \\ y_0 &= \sum_{j=1}^{p} \sqrt{N} \, (a_j - \alpha_j) \sum_{t-1}^{N} x_{t-j}/N + \sqrt{N} \, (a_0 - \alpha_0). \end{aligned} \right\} \qquad (2)$$

Assume that the variance of x_t is one. Let $E x_t = c$. Clearly

$$E \frac{1}{N} \sum_{t=1}^{N} x_{t-i} = c$$

$$E \frac{1}{N} \sum_{t=1}^{N} x_{t-i} x_{t-j} = \varrho_{i-j} + c^2.$$

Moreover

$$E \left(\frac{1}{N} \sum_{t=1}^{N} x_{t-i} - c \right)^2 = \frac{1}{N^2} \sum_{t,\, z=1}^{N} \varrho_{t-z} = \frac{1}{N} \sum_{s=-N+1}^{N-1} \left(1 - \frac{|s|}{N} \right) \varrho_s$$

and

$$E \left(\frac{1}{N} \sum_{t=1}^{N} x_{t-i} x_{t-j} - \varrho_{i-j} - c^2 \right)^2 \sim \frac{1}{N} \left\{ \sum_{\nu=-\infty}^{\infty} (\varrho_{i-j}^2 + \varrho_{\nu-i+j} \varrho_{\nu+i-j}) + e \, \varrho_{i-j}^2 \right\}$$

(see Bartlett [1], where $e = E \varepsilon_t^4/\sigma^4 - 3$. On the other hand

$$|\varrho_s| \leq K R^{|s|}$$

where K is a constant and $0 < R < 1$ since all the roots of (1) have modulus less than one. Thus

$$E \left(\frac{1}{N} \sum_{t=1}^{N} x_{t-i} - c \right)^2 \to 0$$

$$E \left(\frac{1}{N} \sum_{t=1}^{N} x_{t-i} x_{i-j} - \varrho_{i-j} - c^2 \right)^2 \to 0$$

112

and
$$\frac{1}{N} \sum_{t=1}^{N} x_{t-i}, \quad \frac{1}{N} \sum_{t=1}^{N} x_{t-i} x_{t-j}$$

are consistent estimates of c and $\varrho_{i-j} + c^2$ respectively. Set

$$\frac{1}{N} \sum_{t=1}^{N} x_{t-i} = D_{i0N} = D_{0iN}, \quad i \neq 0$$

$$\frac{1}{N} \sum_{t=1}^{N} x_{t-i} x_{t-j} = D_{ijN}, \quad i, j \neq 0$$

$$1 = D_{00N}.$$

The system of equations (2) can then be rewritten in the form

$$y_i = \sum_{j=0}^{p} \sqrt{N} (a_j - \alpha_j) D_{ijN}. \tag{3}$$

As we have seen

$$D_{ijN} \to D_{ij} = \begin{cases} \varrho_{i-j} + c^2 & i, j \neq 0 \\ 1 & i = j = 0 \\ c & \text{otherwise,} \end{cases}$$

in probability as $N \to \infty$. The limiting determinant in probability of the system of equations is after reduction

$$|D_{ij}| = \begin{vmatrix} 1 & 0 & 0 & \dots & 0 \\ 0 & \varrho_0 & \varrho_1 & \dots & \varrho_p \\ 0 & \varrho_{-1} & \varrho_0 & \dots & \varrho_{p-1} \\ \vdots & \vdots & \vdots & & \vdots \\ 0 & \varrho_{-p} & \varrho_{-p+1} & \dots & \varrho_0 \end{vmatrix} \neq 0.$$

On the other hand, the stochastic variables y_i, $i = 0, 1, \ldots, p$, are asymptotically normally distributed with mean zero (since the y_i's have mean zero) and covariance matrix (see Diananda [1])

$$\{E y_i y_j\} = \sigma^2 \begin{pmatrix} 1 & c & c & \dots \\ c & \varrho_0 + c^2 & \varrho_1 + c^2 & \dots \\ c & \varrho_{-1} + c^2 & \varrho_0 + c^2 & \dots \\ \vdots & \vdots & \vdots & \end{pmatrix}.$$

Solving equations (3) for $\sqrt{N} (a_i - \alpha_i)$ in terms of the y_i's we see that the stochastic variables $\sqrt{N} (a_i - \alpha_i)$ are asymptotically normally distributed with mean zero and covariance matrix

$$\sigma^2 \left\{ \begin{matrix} 1 & c & c & \cdots \\ c & \varrho_0 + c^2 & \varrho_1 + c^2 & \cdots \\ c & \varrho_{-1} + c^2 & \varrho_0 + c^2 & \cdots \\ \vdots & \vdots & \vdots & \end{matrix} \right\}^{-1}.$$

The estimates a_i are clearly consistent estimates of the parameters α_i and therefore

$$s^2 = \frac{1}{N} \sum_{t=1}^{N} (x_t - \alpha_1 x_{t-1} - \cdots - \alpha_p x_{t-p} - \alpha_0)^2$$

is a consistent estimate of σ^2. Mann and Wald prove this without assuming stationarity. However, the proof in their somewhat more general context is the same as that given above. A nonstationary process of the autoregressive type satisfying the other assumptions given above approaches the stationary case as $t \to \infty$. But the theorem proved above is an asymptotic theorem and so one would not expect anything different to arise in the nonstationary case.

In our discussion of the autoregressive scheme, we assumed that the roots of the equation (1) have modulus less than one. This assumption is necessary because without such a restriction the parameters α_i, σ^2 are in general not uniquely determined. When the parameters in a statistical context are not uniquely determined by the probability distributions and hence clearly not capable of being estimated, the parameters are called *nonidentifiable*. We consider a simple autoregressive scheme to illustrate the fact that one has nonidentifiability of the parameters α_i, σ^2 without the restriction that the roots of (1) have modulus less than one. Let x_t be a normal stationary process with mean zero and spectral density $(1/2\pi)(1/|e^{i\lambda} - \varrho|^2)$, where ϱ is a real number with modulus less than one. Then x_t satisfies the difference equation

$$x_t - \varrho x_{t-1} = \varepsilon_t$$

where the ε_t's are normal, independent stochastic variables with mean zero and variance one and also the difference equation

$$x_t - \frac{1}{\varrho} x_{t-1} = \eta_t,$$

where the η_t's are normal, independent with mean zero and variance $1/\varrho^2$.

We note that Mann and Wald have also discussed vector processes $(x_{1t}, \ldots x_{rt})$ satisfying a system of linear difference equations

$$\sum_{j=1}^{r} \sum_{k=0}^{p} \alpha_{ijk} x_{j,t-k} + \alpha_j = \varepsilon_{it} \quad (i = 1, \ldots, r)$$

with restrictions on the vectors $(\varepsilon_{1t}, \ldots, \varepsilon_{rt})$ and the parameters of the system paralleling those imposed on the difference equation in the 1-dimensional case. Under the assumption that $\{\alpha_{ij0}\}$ is the unit matrix, they obtain analogous results on estimation of the parameters of the system. The assumption that $\{\alpha_{ij0}\}$ is the unit matrix is natural and essential. Otherwise the parameters of the system are not uniquely determined, that is not identifiable.

T. W. Anderson has looked into the power aspects of certain tests mentioned in this chapter in one of his papers [1]. The interested reader will benefit by studying this paper and, further, R. L. Anderson and T. W. Anderson [1].

3.8. Discussion of the Methods described in this Chapter

The exposition given in this section is not complete in the sense of covering all the work that has been done on finite parameter models. References to other work can be found in Kendall [1]. However it gives a fairly representative picture of the work of the past few decades and the main ideas advanced to solve problems in this field.

All these methods deal with models that are of the finite parameter form: a finite moving average or an autoregressive process perhaps with a trigonometric regression component superimposed. This is certainly sensible since a wide class of stationary processes can be approximated by these schemes as closely as is required by choosing a model of sufficiently high order.

Of course in practice one very seldom has *a priori* information concerning the order of the scheme or even that it is a finite parameter scheme (except perhaps in a few special contexts). It is therefore not a very realistic procedure to test various assumptions of this type against each other, e.g. an autoregressive scheme of order two against one of order three. An exception should be made for schemes of order zero, i.e. pure white noise, as these have a more immediate interpretation in practical terms.

One difficulty in many of the applications of time series analysis is that there is very little theory built up from experience so that one is not led to very well specified schemes. In such fields it seems more promising to use empirical data to form confidence regions for the models than to test sharply defined models whose validity is questionable to say the least. These testing problems may have some theoretical interest, but they are seldom relevant to problems arising in practice.

In engineering and in the physical sciences there has been a strong demand for realistic methods to analyse stationary time series. We believe

115

that the approach taken by the research workers in these fields is more promising and in closer contact with reality than some of the earlier techniques developed by theoreticians. This belief is strengthened by the success of the methods in various applied fields; some of these methods will be discussed later on in this book. A discussion of related topics can be found in Grenander [5].

This approach consists in not specifying the model very much, and instead of dealing with a finite number of parameters one considers the spectral density or some similar nonparametric concept. Although we will develop some tests of hypotheses, our main concern will be to form confidence regions. Many statistical problems arise and we will discuss some of them in the following chapters. Very much remains to be done, especially in extending the scope of relevant techniques to wider classes of stochastic processes. However, we believe that the results obtained indicate that a statistical theory of stationary time series of great practical value can be constructed. The success of such a nonparametric approach in certain fields does not guarantee its success in other fields, e.g. in the social sciences and economics. This can be judged only after application of these techniques to relevant data arising in these fields, but one suspects that the stationary assumption may break down in such contexts.

CHAPTER 4

ESTIMATION OF THE SPECTRUM

4.0. Introduction

We now proceed to study one of the nonparametric problems mentioned in section 3.9, specifically the estimation of the spectral density when the class of admissible spectra is restricted only by mild regularity assumptions to be introduced later.

At first we consider a very wide family of estimates and derive some of their properties. This leads us to narrow down the family considered, especially when we see that the so-called *spectrograph estimates* (see section 4.2) are optimal in a certain sense.

After studying the spectrograph estimates and a closely related family, we examine some specific estimates in section 4.6. Other examples are to be found in the next chapter. Using the mean square error as an optimality criterion we try to choose good weight functions for these estimates in section 4.7. As only some of the simpler cases are considered, we cannot offer any final and unique solution of this problem; instead one has to make the choice of a good estimate from case to case. A good deal of work remains before this problem can be settled adequately.

4.1. A General Class of Estimates

Let $x_1, x_2, \ldots, x_N$ be a *sample time series drawn from the real stationary stochastic process* $\{x_n\}$, $E x_n \equiv 0$, $E x_n^4 < \infty$. We want to estimate the spectrum of the stochastic process $\{x_n\}$ from the time series $x_1, x_2, \ldots, x_N$. The discussion of section 1.7 indicates that if the spectrum has jumps, one cannot in general expect to estimate it consistently. Since the singular part of the spectrum is of little practical interest, *we restrict ourselves to an absolutely continuous spectrum with a continuous spectral density* $f(\lambda)$. The fact that the stochastic process is real implies that $f(\lambda)$ *is symmetrical about zero*. The problem of estimating the spectrum can be approached in several different ways. One might be interested in estimating the spectral mass $F(\lambda_2) - F(\lambda_1)$ in a fixed interval (λ_1, λ_2) or perhaps in estimating the spectral density at the point λ. It is clear that for this purpose it is necessary to use some nonlinear device, and as the most tractable analytically are the quadratic ones, *we restrict ourselves to estimates which are quadratic forms in the observations.*

Let the quadratic form be

$$\alpha_N^* = \frac{1}{2\pi N} \sum_{\nu,\,\mu=1}^{N} b_{\nu\mu}^{(N)} x_\nu x_\mu; \quad b_{\nu\mu}^{(N)} = b_{\mu\nu}^{(N)}. \tag{1}$$

Since the observations x_ν are real and we are trying to estimate a real quantity, it seems reasonable to *assume that $b_{\nu\mu}^{(N)}$ is real.* In fact, since α_N^* is real, the $b_{\nu\mu}^{(N)}$ can always be chosen real since the x's are real. We can always find a function $W_N(x,\,y)$ *defined in the square* $-\pi \le x,\ y < \pi$ *and of bounded variation,* that is $\int\!\!\int_{-\pi}^{\pi} |d\,W_N(x,y)| < \infty$, *such that*

$$b_{\nu\mu}^{(N)} = \int\!\!\int_{-\pi}^{\pi} e^{i\nu x - i\mu y} \, d\,W_N(x,\,y); \quad \nu,\,\mu = 1,\,2,\,\dots,\,N. \tag{2}$$

The condition $b_{\nu\mu}^{(N)} = b_{\mu\nu}^{(N)}$ *will be satisfied if* $d\,W_N(-y,\,-x) = d\,W_N(x,\,y)$. Note that the weight function $W_N(x,\,y)$ is not uniquely determined by $b_{\nu\mu}^{(N)}$, $\nu,\,\mu = 1,\,2,\,\dots,\,N$. The Fourier-Stieltjes coefficients of $W_N(x,\,y)$ with $\nu,\,\mu$ not both in the range 1 to N are at our disposal. If these coefficients are set equal to zero, $W_N(x,\,y) = \int_{-\pi}^{x} \int_{-\pi}^{y} w_N(u,\,v)\,d\,u\,d\,v$ is absolutely continuous with

$$w_N(x,\,y) = \frac{1}{(2\pi)^2} \sum_{\nu,\,\mu=1}^{N} b_{\nu\mu}^{(N)} e^{i\nu x + i\mu y}.$$

However, this will not always be the convenient choice for us. As the spectral mass is a nonnegative quantity, it may seem reasonable to require that α_N^* be a nonnegative form. One should then choose a nonnegative definite weight function $W_N(x,\,y)$, that is a weight function such that

$$\int_{-\pi}^{\pi} p(x)\,\overline{p(y)}\,d\,W_N(x,\,y) \ge 0$$

for any continuous function $p(x)$. *Note that $d W_N(x,x) \ge 0$ if $W_N(x,y)$ is nonnegative definite.* Nonetheless we will later discuss a few estimates whose weight functions are not nonnegative definite.

For the moment consider only the expected value of α_N^* for large values of N when the weight function $W_N(x,y) = W(x,y)$ is fixed. Suppose that $f(\lambda)$ has an absolutely convergent Fourier series so that

$$\sum_{\nu=0}^{\infty} |r_\nu| < \infty. \qquad (3)$$

Then
$$E\, \alpha_N^* = \frac{1}{2\pi} \sum_{p=-N+1}^{N-1} w_p^{(N)}\, r_p\, \frac{N-|p|}{N},$$

where

$$w_p^{(N)} = \begin{cases} \dfrac{1}{N-p} \sum\limits_{\nu=1+p}^{N} b_{\nu,\,\nu-p}, & p \geq 0 \\[2ex] \dfrac{1}{N+p} \sum\limits_{\nu=1}^{N+p} b_{\nu,\,\nu-p}, & p < 0. \end{cases}$$

For fixed $p \geq 0$ we have

$$w_p^{(N)} = \frac{1}{N-p} \int_{-\pi}^{\pi} e^{ipy}\, e^{i(1+p)(x-y)}\, \frac{1 - e^{i(N-p)(x-y)}}{1 - e^{i(x-y)}}\, d\,W(x,y),$$

Introducing the function

$$\Delta_\varepsilon(\mu) = \begin{cases} 1, & |\mu| < \varepsilon \\ 0, & |\mu| \geq \varepsilon, \ \varepsilon > 0, \end{cases}$$

we have

$$\left| w_p^{(N)} - \lim_{\varepsilon \to 0} \iint_{-\pi}^{\pi} e^{ipy}\, \Delta_\varepsilon(x-y)\, d\,W(x,y) \right|$$

$$\leq \lim_{\varepsilon \to 0} \iint_{-\pi}^{\pi} \left| \frac{1}{N-p}\, \frac{1 - e^{i(N-p)(x-y)}}{1 - e^{i(x-y)}} - \Delta_\varepsilon(x-y) \right| |d\,W(x,y)|.$$

Let ε first tend to zero. Since the integrand is bounded and tends to zero for all x, y as $N \to \infty$ we have

$$\lim_{N \to \infty} w_p^{(N)} = \int_{-\pi}^{\pi} e^{ipy}\, d\,m(y),$$

where
$$m(y) = \lim_{\varepsilon \to 0} \iint_{u,v \leq y} \Delta_\varepsilon(u-v)\, d\,W(u,v).$$

If one were to use the usual differential formalism, one would say that

$$d\,m(y) = d\,W(y,y).$$

The corresponding limiting relation holds for $p < 0$. Since the weights $w_p^{(N)}$ are bounded in absolute value by

$$\int_{-\pi}^{\pi} |d\,W\,(x,y)| < \infty$$

and (3) holds,

$$\lim_{N\to\infty} E\,\alpha_N^* = \int_{-\pi}^{\pi} f\,(\lambda)\,d\,m\,(\lambda).$$

Clearly $d\,m\,(\lambda) \equiv 0$ *if* $W\,(x,y)$ *is absolutely continuous.* If one were only interested in the expected value of the estimate for large samples, it would not matter how $dW\,(x,y)$ is chosen outside of the main diagonal. Of course one wants to reduce the variance as well as the bias of the estimate. There are many possibly good estimates. When estimating the spectral mass in a fixed interval (λ_1, λ_2), $0 \le \lambda_1 < \lambda_2 < \pi$, $W\,(x,y)$ could be chosen so as to have $dW\,(x,y)$ $\equiv 0$ when $x \neq y$, $d\,m\,(\lambda) \equiv \frac{1}{2}$ when $\lambda_1 < |\lambda| < \lambda_2$, and $d\,m\,(\lambda) \equiv 0$ outside $\lambda_1 < |\lambda| < \lambda_2$. In the important case of estimating the spectral density at λ the weight function must vary with N and it seems plausible that the weight function should in some way become more and more concentrated about the points (λ, λ) and $(-\lambda, -\lambda)$ as $N \to \infty$. The reason for the symmetry in the choice of the weight function is that $f(\lambda) = f(-\lambda)$ and $d\,W_N(x, y) = d\,W_N(-y, -x)$.

Now consider the variance of the estimate α_N^* *when the process sampled is a normal process.* Since

$$\alpha_N^* = \frac{1}{2\,\pi\,N} \sum_{\nu,\,\mu=1}^{N} b_{\nu\mu}^{(N)}\,x_\nu\,x_\mu$$

it is clear that

$$4\,\pi^2\,N^2\,D^2\,[\alpha_N^*] = \sum_{\nu_i,\,\mu_i=1}^{N} b_{\nu_1,\,\mu_1}^{(N)}\,b_{\nu_2,\,\mu_2}^{(N)}\,[r_{\nu_1-\nu_2}\,r_{\mu_1-\mu_2} + r_{\nu_1-\mu_2}\,r_{\nu_2-\mu_1}]$$

$$= \sum\,[\alpha_{pq} + \beta_{pq}]\,r_p\,r_q = S_1 + S_2$$

(see the discussion in section 4.2 on the moments of linear processes). We assume that $W_N(x, y)$ is absolutely continuous. It will be enough to consider only S_1 since

$$S_1 = S_2 = \int_{-\pi}^{\pi} \left| \sum_{\nu,\,\mu=1}^{N} b_{\nu\mu}^{(N)}\,e^{-i\nu u + i\mu v} \right|^2 f\,(u)\,f\,(v)\,d\,u\,d\,v.$$

This follows from the fact that $b_{\nu\mu}^{(N)} = b_{\mu\nu}^{(N)}$.
Note that if we set

$$w_N\,(x, y) = \frac{1}{(2\,\pi)^2} \sum_{\nu,\,\mu=1}^{N} b_{\nu\mu}^{(N)}\,e^{-i\nu x + i\mu y}$$

then
$$D^2\left[\alpha_N^*\right] = \frac{8\pi^2}{N^2} \int\limits_{-\pi}^{\pi}\int \left|w_N(u,v)\right|^2 f(u)\,f(v)\,du\,dv. \tag{4}$$

However $w_N(x,y)$ may be some other weight function corresponding to the coefficients $b_{\nu\mu}^{(N)}$, $\nu, \mu = 1, \ldots, N$ and we would like to know under what conditions relation (4) still holds asymptotically as $N \to \infty$.

Now S_1 is a monotone functional of the spectral density. *Let $f(\lambda)$ be positive and continuous.* Given any $\varepsilon > 0$, we can find two positive trigonometric polynomials

$$p_l(\lambda) = \sum_{j=-m}^{m} \gamma_{lj}\,e^{ij\lambda}, \quad l = 1, 2,$$

such that $p_1(\lambda) \le f(\lambda) \le p_2(\lambda)$ and $\left|p_1(\lambda) - p_2(\lambda)\right| < \varepsilon$. The inequality

$$S_1(p_1(\lambda)) < S_1(f(\lambda)) \le S_1(p_2(\lambda))$$

holds. The summation in the expression

$$S_1(p(\lambda)) = \sum_{p,q} \alpha_{pq}\,r_p\,r_q$$

is over a finite range which does not vary with N if $p(\lambda)$ is a trigonometric polynomial. Note that

$$\alpha_{pq} = \sum_{\substack{\nu = p+1 \\ \mu = q+1}}^{N} b_{\nu\mu}^{(N)}\,b_{\nu+p,\,\mu+q}^{(N)} \quad \text{if } p, q \ge 0$$

while analogous expressions hold when p, q have different sign. We shall obtain the desired asymptotic relation under appropriate conditions for $f(\lambda) = p(\lambda)$ a positive trigonometric polynomial. Since the summation in $S_1(p(\lambda))$ is over a fixed and finite range, one need only discuss what happens to a typical coefficient α_{pq}. Let the coefficients $b_{\nu\mu}^{(N)}$ be the Fourier coefficients of $w_N(x,y)$. Here the coefficients $b_{\nu\mu}^{(N)}$ are not necessarily zero if ν, μ are not both in the range 1 to N. We shall show that *if*

$$\frac{\sum\limits_{\nu,\,\mu=s}^{N-s} \left|b_{\nu\mu}^{(N)}\right|^2}{\sum\limits_{\nu,\,\mu=-\infty}^{\infty} \left|b_{\nu\mu}^{(N)}\right|^2} \to 1 \tag{5}$$

as $N \to \infty$ for every fixed $s \ge 0$, then

$$D^2\left[\alpha_N^*\right] \sim \frac{8\pi^2}{N^2} \int\limits_{-\pi}^{\pi}\int \left|w_N(x,y)\right|^2 f(x)\,f(y)\,dx\,dy \tag{6}$$

as $N \to \infty$. Now

$$[\max_{\lambda} f(\lambda)]^2 \sum_{\nu, \mu=1}^{N} |b_{\nu\mu}^{(N)}|^2 \geq \frac{S_1}{(2\pi)^2} \geq [\min_{\lambda} f(\lambda)]^2 \sum_{\nu, \mu=1}^{N} |b_{\nu\mu}^{(N)}|^2.$$

It will be enough to show that α_{pq} is asymptotically the same as

$$A_{pq} = \sum_{\nu, \mu=-\infty}^{\infty} b_{\nu\mu}^{(N)} b_{\nu+p, \mu+q}^{(N)}.$$

But

$$\frac{|\alpha_{pq} - A_{pq}|}{\sum\limits_{\nu, \mu=1}^{N} |b_{\nu\mu}^{(N)}|^2} \leq \sqrt{\frac{\sum\limits_{\nu, \mu=-\infty}^{\infty} |b_{\nu\mu}^{(N)}|^2 \left(\sum\limits_{\nu, \mu=-\infty}^{\infty} - \sum\limits_{\nu, \mu=\max(|p|, |q|)}^{N-\max(|p|, |q|)} \right) |b_{\nu\mu}^{(N)}|^2}{\left(\sum\limits_{\nu, \mu=1}^{N} |b_{\nu\mu}^{(N)}|^2 \right)^2}} \to 0$$

as $N \to \infty$ by the Schwarz inequality. Since there are only a finite number of coefficients α_{pq} it follows that

$$S_1(p(\lambda)) = \sum_{p, q} \alpha_{pq} r_p r_q \sim \sum_{p, q} \left(\sum_{\nu, \mu=-\infty}^{\infty} b_{\nu\mu}^{(N)} b_{\nu+p, \mu+q}^{(N)} \right) r_p r_q$$

$$= (2\pi)^4 \iint_{-\pi}^{\pi} |w_N(x, y)|^2 p(x) p(y) \, dx \, dy.$$

On letting the maximal difference ε between the two trigonometric polynomials $p_i(\lambda)$ approximating $f(\lambda)$ tend to zero, we see that

$$D^2[\alpha_N^*] \sim \frac{8\pi^2}{N^2} \iint_{-\pi}^{\pi} |w_N(x, y)|^2 f(x) f(y) \, dx \, dy$$

as $N \to \infty$. A condition similar to (5) is assumed in section 4.5 to establish the validity of the asymptotic relation (6).

In the case of a fixed weight function $w_N(x, y) = w(x, y)$ the variance goes down to zero as N^{-2}. However, as the expected value of α_N^* tends to zero, such an estimate would not be of any use in estimating the spectrum. In particular, in estimating the spectral density $f(\lambda)$ one could not use a fixed weight function $w(x, y) = w_N(x, y)$. A reasonable weight function $w_N(x, y)$ would concentrate more and more mass in the neighborhood of the points (λ, λ) and $(-\lambda, -\lambda)$ as $N \to \infty$ in order that the estimate α_N^* be asymptotically unbiased. On the other hand $w_N(x, y)$ must not concentrate the mass too rapidly since one could then not have $D^2[\alpha_N^*] \to 0$ as $N \to \infty$. This will be made more explicit later on in the discussion of the mean square error of various specific estimates in section 4.6.

If α_N^* is an asymptotically unbiased estimate of the spectral density $f(\lambda)$, result (6) *concerning the asymptotic variance of the estimate can be shown to hold in the more general context of a linear scheme* by using the method of section 4.2.

We discuss the problems of this chapter in the context of linear schemes for convenience and continuity. It should, however, by now be clear that one really only needs assumptions on moments up to the 4th order (see Parzen [1]).

4.2. An Optimum Property of Spectrograph estimates

Probably the most important estimates of the spectral density are of the form

$$f_N^*(\lambda) = \frac{1}{2\pi N} \sum_{\nu,\,\mu=1}^{N} x_\nu \, x_\mu \int_{-\pi}^{\pi} e^{i(\nu-\mu)y} \, w_N(y) \, dy, \tag{1}$$

that is, the weight function $w_N(x, y)$ of section 4.1 has all its variation on the main diagonal $x = y$. We shall call such an estimate a spectrograph estimate. On interchanging the order of summation and integration in (1), it can be rewritten as

$$f_N^*(\lambda) = \int_{-\pi}^{\pi} I_N(y) \, w_N(y) \, dy,$$

where $I_N(y) = \dfrac{1}{2\pi N} \left| \sum_{\nu=1}^{N} x_\nu \, e^{-i\nu y} \right|^2$ is the so-called *periodogram* that was introduced in section 3.1. We can also write

$$f_N^* = \frac{1}{2\pi N} \sum_{\nu,\,\mu=1}^{N} x_\nu \, x_\mu \, w_{\nu-\mu}^{(N)}$$

$$= \frac{1}{2\pi} \sum_{\nu=-n+1}^{n-1} \frac{C_\nu}{N} \, w_\nu^{(N)},$$

where the weights

$$w_\nu^{(N)} = \int_{-\pi}^{\pi} e^{i\nu y} \, w_N(y) \, dy$$

and C_ν is the product sum of lag ν

$$C_\nu = \sum_{t=1}^{N-|\nu|} x_t \, x_{t+|\nu|}.$$

123

4.2

The characteristic property of a spectrograph estimate is that the coefficients $b_{\nu\mu}^{(N)}$ depend only upon the difference $\nu - \mu$

$$b_{\nu\mu}^{(N)} = w_{\nu-\mu}^{(N)}$$

or equivalently the spectrograph estimate is an average of the periodogram. The assumption that $b_{\nu\mu}^{(N)} = b_{\mu\nu}^{(N)}$ implies that $w_p^{(N)} = w_{-p}^{(N)}$.

One might suspect that because of the stationary nature of the observed process it would be advantageous to choose the $b_{\nu\mu}^{(N)}$ in the way mentioned in the last paragraph. Such is the case, at least for large samples. To prove this a result on certain moments of a linear process will be needed.

A linear process can be written in the form

$$x_t = \sum_{\nu=-\infty}^{\infty} a_\nu \, \xi_{t-\nu}, \quad \sum_{\nu=-\infty}^{\infty} a_\nu^2 < \infty,$$

where ξ_t is pure white noise with

$$\left.\begin{array}{l} E \, \xi_t = 0 \\ E \, \xi_t^2 = 1 \end{array}\right\}.$$

Assuming that the fourth moment of ξ_t exists, we introduce the quantity

$$e = E \, \xi_t^4 - 3$$

which is the fourth cumulant of ξ_ν. Then

$$E \, x_\alpha \, x_\beta \, x_\gamma \, x_\delta$$

$$= \sum_{\nu i = \infty}^{\infty} a_{\alpha-\nu_1} a_{\beta-\nu_2} a_{\gamma-\nu_3} a_{\delta-\nu_4} E \, \xi_{\nu_1} \xi_{\nu_2} \xi_{\nu_3} \xi_{\nu_4}$$

$$= e \sum_{\nu=-}^{\infty} a_{\alpha-\nu} a_{\beta-\nu} a_{\gamma-\nu} a_{\delta-\nu} +$$

$$+ \sum_{\nu,\,\mu=-\infty}^{\infty} a_{\alpha-\nu} a_{\beta-\nu} a_{\gamma-\mu} a_{\delta-\mu} + \sum_{\nu,\,\mu=-\infty}^{\infty} a_{\alpha-\nu} a_{\beta-\mu} a_{\gamma-\mu} a_{\delta-\nu} +$$

$$+ \sum_{\nu,\,\mu=-\infty}^{\infty} a_{\alpha-\nu} a_{\beta-\mu} a_{\gamma-\nu} a_{\delta-\mu}.$$

Since the covariance of a linear process is given by

$$r_{\alpha-\beta} = \sum_{\nu=-\infty}^{\infty} a_{\alpha-\nu} a_{\beta-\nu},$$

124

it follows that

$$\operatorname{cov}\left(x_\alpha\, x_\beta,\; x_\gamma\, x_\delta\right) = e \sum_{\nu=-\infty}^{\infty} a_{\alpha-\nu}\, a_{\beta-\nu}\, a_{\gamma-\nu}\, a_{\delta-\nu} + r_{\alpha-\delta}\, r_{\beta-\gamma} + r_{\alpha-\gamma}\, r_{\beta-\delta}.$$

Now consider a general estimate

$$a_N^* = \frac{1}{2\,\pi\,N} \sum_{\nu,\,\mu=1}^{\infty} b_{\nu\mu}^{(N)}\, x_\nu\, x_\mu$$

with
$$b_{\nu\mu}^{(N)} = \iint\limits_{-\pi}^{\pi} e^{i\nu x - i\mu y}\, w_N\,(x,\,y)\, d\,x\, d\,y,$$

$$w_N\,(x,\,y) = \frac{1}{(2\pi)^2} \sum_{\nu,\,\mu=1}^{N} b_{\nu\mu}^{(N)}\, e^{-i\nu x + j\mu y}$$

with nonnegative definite weight functions $w_N\,(x,\,y)$ and such that the integrals

$$\iint\limits_{-\pi}^{\pi} |\, w_N\,(x,\,y)\, |\, d\,x\, d\,y \le K < \infty \qquad (2)$$

are uniformly bounded. Introduce

$$w_p^{(N)} = \frac{1}{N - |\,p\,|} \sum_{\nu-\mu=p} b_{\nu\mu}^{(N)},$$

where the summation with respect to ν is extended over the range $1 + p$, $2 + p$, ..., N if $p \ge 0$ and over $1,\, 2,\, ...,\, N + p$ if $p < 0$. *The estimate*

$$f_N^* = \frac{1}{2\,\pi\,N} \sum_{p=-N+1}^{N-1} w_p^{(N)}\, C_p$$

is a spectrograph estimate. Now f_N^* has the same mean value as α_N^* since

$$E\,f_N^* = \frac{1}{2\,\pi\,N} \sum_{p=-N+1}^{N-1} w_p^{(N)}\, (N - |\,p\,|)\, r_p$$

$$= \frac{1}{2\,\pi\,N} \sum_{\nu,\,\mu=1}^{N} b_{\nu\mu}^{(N)}\, r_{\nu-\mu} = E\,\alpha_N^*$$

so that with respect to bias they are equally good (or bad).

We assume that α_N^* is an asymptotically unbiased estimate of the spectral density $f\,(\lambda)$. It then follows that

$$E \, \alpha_N^* = \frac{1}{2\pi N} \int\limits_{-\pi}^{\pi} \sum_{\nu, \, \mu = 1}^{N} b_{\nu\mu}^{(N)} \, e^{-i(\nu-\mu)y} \, f(y) \, dy$$

$$= \frac{2\pi}{N} \int\limits_{-\pi}^{\pi} w_N(y, y) \, f(y) \, dy \to f(\lambda)$$

as $N \to \infty$ for any continuous nonnegative function $f(y)$ symmetric about zero. But $w_N(x, y)$ is nonnegative definite so that $w_N(y, y) \geq 0$. Thus for any fixed $\varepsilon > 0$

$$\frac{2\pi}{N} \int\limits_{|y \pm \lambda| \geq \varepsilon} w_N(y, y) \, dy \to 0, \quad \frac{2\pi}{N} \int\limits_{|y \pm \lambda| < \varepsilon} w_N(y, y) \, dy \to 1$$

as $N \to \infty$. On using the Schwarz inequality one can see that

$$1 - \varepsilon \leq 2 \, \varepsilon \int\limits_{-\pi}^{\pi} w_N^2(y, y) \, dy \, \frac{4\pi^2}{N^2}$$

as $N \to \infty$. It then follows that

$$\frac{(2\pi)^3}{N^2} \int\limits_{-\pi}^{\pi} w_N^2(y, y) \, dy = \frac{1}{N^2} \sum_{p=-N+1}^{N-1} \left| \sum_{\nu, -\mu = p} b_{\nu\mu}^{(N)} \right|^2 \to \infty$$

as $N \to \infty$. Now consider the variance of α_N^*. It is given by

$$4 \, \pi^2 \, N^2 \, D^2 [\alpha_N^*]$$

$$= \sum_{\nu_i, \, \mu_i = 1}^{N} b_{\nu_1 \mu_1}^{(N)} \, b_{\nu_2 \mu_2}^{(N)} [r_{\nu_1 - \nu_2} \, r_{\mu_1 - \mu_2} + r_{\nu_1 - \mu_2} \, r_{\nu_2 - \mu_1} + \tag{3}$$

$$+ e \sum_{\nu = -\infty}^{\infty} a_{\nu_1 - \nu} \, a_{\nu_2 - \nu} \, a_{\mu_1 - \nu} \, a_{\mu \, -\nu}].$$

But

$$\sum_{\nu_i, \, \mu_i = 1}^{N} b_{\nu_1 \mu_1}^{(N)} \, b_{\nu_2 \mu_2}^{(N)} \sum_{\nu = -\infty}^{\infty} a_{\nu_1 - \nu} \, a_{\nu_2 - \nu} \, a_{\mu_1 - \nu} \, a_{\mu_2 - \nu} = \sum_{\nu = -\infty}^{\infty} T_\nu,$$

where

$$|T_\nu| = \left| \iint\limits_{-\pi}^{\pi} \sum_{k=1}^{N} a_{k-\nu} \, e^{ikx} \sum_{j=1}^{N} a_{j-\nu} \, e^{-ijy} \, w_N(x, y) \, dx \, dy \right|^2$$

$$\leq K^2 \left(\sum_{k=1}^{N} |a_{k-\nu}| \right)^4 .$$

Under the assumption that $a_k = 0\,(1/|k|^2)$ as $|k| \to \infty$ we see that

$$
T_\nu = \begin{cases}
0\left(\dfrac{1}{\nu^4}\right) & \text{if } \nu < 0 \\[2ex]
0\,(1) & \text{if } 0 \le \nu \le N \\[2ex]
0\left(\dfrac{1}{(\nu - N)^4}\right) & \text{if } \nu > N.
\end{cases}
$$

Thus

$$
\sum_{\nu = -\infty}^{\infty} T_\nu = 0\,(N)
$$

as $N \to \infty$. But now

$$
S_1 = \sum b_{\nu_1 \mu_1}^{(N)} b_{\nu_2 \mu_2}^{(N)}\, r_{\nu_1 - \nu_2}\, r_{\mu_1 - \mu_2} \ge 4\,\pi^2 \min_\lambda f^2\,(\lambda) \sum_{\nu,\, \mu = 1}^{N} |b_{\nu\mu}^{(N)}|^2
$$

$$
\ge 4\,\pi^2 \min_\lambda f^2\,(\lambda)\, N\, \frac{1}{N^2} \sum_{p = -N+1}^{N-1} \left| \sum_{\nu - \mu = p} b_{\nu\mu}^{(N)} \right|^2
$$

using the Schwarz inequality. The asymptotic unbiasedness of the estimate implies that

$$
\lim_{N \to \infty} \frac{S_1}{N} = \infty.
$$

Thus for an asymptotically unbiased estimate of the spectral density, the variance component arising from the third term in (3) is negligible compared to the first two terms as $N \to \infty$. The same argument shows that this is also true of the corresponding spectrograph estimate.

Now set

$$
d_{\nu\mu}^{(N)} = b_{\nu\mu}^{(N)} - w_{\nu - \mu}^{(N)}.
$$

Note that

$$
\sum_{\nu - \mu = p} d_{\nu\mu}^{(N)} = 0.
$$

Then

$$
S_1 = \sum_{\nu_i,\, \mu_i = 1}^{N} \left[w_{\nu_1 - \mu_1}^{(N)}\, w_{\nu_2 - \mu_2}^{(N)} + d_{\nu_1 \mu_1}^{(N)}\, d_{\nu_2 \mu_2}^{(N)} + w_{\nu_1 - \mu_1}^{(N)}\, d_{\nu_2 \mu_2}^{(N)} + d_{\nu_1 \mu_1}^{(N)}\, w_{\nu_2 - \mu_2}^{(N)} \right] r_{\nu_1 - \mu_2}\, r_{\mu_1 - \mu_2}. \tag{4}
$$

The first term corresponds to the variance of the spectrograph estimate. The second term is nonnegative and is large when the deviation of α_N^* from a spectrograph estimate is large.

Let us now consider the third term. Sum $w_{\nu_1 - \mu_1}^{(N)}\, d_{\nu_2 \mu_2}^{(N)}\, r_{\nu_1 - \nu_2}\, r_{\mu_1 - \mu_2}$ over the range $\nu_1,\, \nu_2,\, \mu_1,\, \mu_2 = 1, 2, \ldots, N$. Consider first setting

$$\nu_1 - \nu_2 = p$$

$$\mu_1 - \mu_2 = q,$$

where let us say $p, q \geq 0$. Then let us set $\nu_2 - \mu_2 = s$ where $s \geq 0$ and sum the terms under these restraints.

We then obtain

$$w^{(N)}_{p-q+s} \, r_p \, r_q \sum_{\nu=1}^{N-\max(s+p,\,q)} d_{\nu+s,\,\nu}. \tag{5}$$

Now the coefficients $b^{(N)}_{\nu\mu}$, $w^{(N)}_p$, $d^{(N)}_{\nu\mu}$, are uniformly bounded in absolute value by some finite constant K since (2) holds. Using the fact that $\sum_{\nu-\mu=s} d^{(N)}_{\nu\mu} = 0$, it follows that (5) is bounded in absolute value by

$$K^2 \, |r_p r_q| \max(|p|, |q|).$$

Arguing in a completely analogous manner one can show that the sum under the restraint of fixed p, q, s, whatever sign they may have, is bounded in absolute value by

$$K^2 \, |r_p r_q| \max(|p|, |q|).$$

Now if $a_k = 0(1/|k|^{2+\delta})$, $\delta > 0$, then $r_p = 0(1/|p|^{2+\delta})$ since

$$|r_p| = \left| \sum a_k \, a_{k+p} \right|$$

$$\leq C \sum \frac{1}{|k|^{2+\delta} + 1} \frac{1}{|k+p|^{2+\delta} + 1}$$

$$\leq \frac{C}{\left|\dfrac{p}{2}\right|^{2+\delta}} \sum_{|k| > \frac{p}{2}} \frac{1}{|k|^{2+\delta} + 1}$$

so that on summing over p, q the bound

$$K^2 \sum |r_p| \, |r_p| \max(|p|, |q|) < \infty$$

is obtained. Now on summing over s, the third term is seen to be $0(N)$. The fourth term can be estimated in exactly the same manner. Since the first term of (4) diverges faster than N as $N \to \infty$ and the second is positive, it follows that nothing is gained when the sample is large by going outside the class of spectrograph estimates when considering asymptotically unbiased estimates of the spectral density. Clearly our criterion for a good estimate in this discussion has been a small mean square error.

We shall now formally restate what has been proved. *Let the observed process x_t be any linear process*

$$x_t = \sum_{\nu=-\infty}^{\infty} a_{t-\nu}\, \xi_\nu$$

$$\left.\begin{array}{l} E\,\xi_t = 0 \\ E\,\xi_t^2 = 1 \\ E\,\xi_t^4 < \infty \end{array}\right\} \tag{6}$$

$$a_k = 0\left(\frac{1}{|k|^{2+\delta}}\right), \quad \delta > 0,$$

with a positive spectral density. Let the estimate

$$\alpha_N^* = \frac{1}{2\,\pi\,N} \sum_{\nu,\,\mu=1}^{N} b_{\nu\mu}^{(N)}\, x_\nu\, x_\mu$$

be an asymptotically unbiased estimate of the spectral density of the observed process at the point λ, that is, an estimate of f(λ) with a nonnegative definite weight function

$$w_N(x, y) = \frac{1}{(2\,\pi)^2} \sum_{\nu,\,\mu=1}^{N} b_{\nu\mu}^{(N)}\, e^{-i\nu x + i\mu y}, \quad \int\!\!\int_{-\pi}^{\pi} |w_N(x, y)|\, dx\, dy \le K.$$

There is then a spectrograph estimate with the same bias as α_N^* and a mean square error that is asymptotically not larger than that of the estimate α_N^*.

In spite of this, there are estimates that are not spectrograph estimates but that are of considerable interest. We shall discuss such a class of estimates in section 4.5. This class is a natural one to use if one wishes to build an analogue computer to estimate the spectral density.

Note that an interesting result has been obtained as a by-product in the proof of this section. *Under the conditions specified above, the variance of an asymptotically unbiased estimator of the spectral density tends to zero slower than N^{-1} as $N \to \infty$, that is*

$$N^{-1} = o\left(D^2\left[f_N^*(\lambda)\right]\right).$$

4.3. A Remark on the Bias of Spectrograph Estimates

Consider a spectrograph estimate

$$f_N^*(\lambda) = \frac{1}{2\,\pi N} \sum_{\nu,\,\mu=1}^{N} x_\nu\, x_\mu\, w_{\nu-\mu}^{(N)} = \int_{-\pi}^{\pi} I_N(x)\, w_N(x)\, dx$$

$$= \frac{1}{2\,\pi N} \sum_{\nu=-N+1}^{N-1} C_\nu\, w_\nu^{(N)}, \text{ of } f(\lambda).$$

4.2

Since $w_p^{(N)} = w_{-p}^{(N)}$ the weight function $w_N(x)$ can be chosen so that $w_N(x) = w_N(-x)$. Note that the periodogram is an even function. The mean value of the estimate is

$$E f_N^*(\lambda) = \int\limits_{-\pi}^{\pi} E I_N(x)\, w_N(x)\, d\,x.$$

But
$$E I_N(y) = \frac{1}{2\pi N} E \left| \sum_{\nu=1}^{N} x_\nu\, e^{i\nu y} \right|^2$$

$$= \frac{1}{2\pi N} E \left| \int\limits_{-\pi}^{\pi} e^{i(u-y)} \frac{1 - e^{iN(u-y)}}{1 - e^{i(u-y)}}\, d\,z(u) \right|^2$$

$$= \frac{1}{2\pi N} \int\limits_{-\pi}^{\pi} \frac{\sin^2 \dfrac{N}{2}(y-u)}{\sin^2 \dfrac{y-u}{2}}\, f(u)\, d\,u.$$

Let $w_N(x) \geq 0$ and $\int\limits_{-\pi}^{\pi} w_N(x)\, d\,x = 1$. The bias is then given by

$$b_N(\lambda) = E f_N^*(\lambda) - f(\lambda)$$

$$= \frac{1}{2\pi N} \int\limits_{-\pi}^{\pi} w_N(x) \int\limits_{-\pi}^{\pi} \frac{\sin^2 \dfrac{N}{2}(y-x)}{\sin^2 \dfrac{y-x}{2}}\, [f(y) - f(\lambda)]\, d\,y\, d\,x.$$

Assuming that

$$f(x) - f(y) = 0\,(|\,x-y\,|),$$

it is seen that

$$b_N(\lambda) - \int\limits_{-\pi}^{\pi} w_N(x)\, [f(x) - f(\lambda)]\, d\,x$$

$$= \frac{1}{2\pi N} \int\limits_{-\pi}^{\pi} w_N(x) \int\limits_{-\pi}^{\pi} \frac{\sin^2 \dfrac{N}{2}(y-x)}{\sin^2 \dfrac{y-x}{2}}\, [f(y) - f(x)]\, d\,y\, d\,x$$

$$= 0\left(\frac{\log N}{N}\right)$$

(see Féjer [1]) so that the bias

130

$$b_N(\lambda) = \int\limits_{-\pi}^{\pi} w_N(x)\,[f(x) - f(\lambda)]\,dx + 0\left(\frac{\log N}{N}\right). \qquad (1)$$

Using the Schwarz inequality we find that

$$b_N(\lambda) = 0\,(\varepsilon_N) + 0\left(\frac{\log N}{N}\right), \qquad (2)$$

where

$$\varepsilon_N^2 = \int\limits_0^{\pi} (x - |\lambda|)^2\,w_N(x)\,dx$$

since $f(\lambda) = f(-\lambda)$ and $w_N(x) = w_N(-x)$. The quantity ε_N^2 describes the concentration of $w_N(x)$ about the points λ and $-\lambda$. ε_N might be called *the width* of the spectrograph. As we shall see later the second term of (1) is in most cases negligible compared to the first. For the periodogram the second term is the main one as the width ε_N is zero. However, in spite of its very low bias, the periodogram is not useful as an estimate of the spectral density since it is not even consistent (see section 4.6).

At best, (2) gives a crude estimate of the bias. In section 4.6 better estimates for the bias of specific spectrograph estimates will be obtained. *The relation (1) implies that $f_N^*(\lambda)$ will be an asymptotically unbiased estimate of $f(\lambda)$ if $w_N(x)$ concentrates all its mass at the points $\lambda, -\lambda$ as $N \to \infty$, that is, if for any $\varepsilon > 0$*

$$\int\limits_{|x \pm \lambda| < \varepsilon} w_N(x)\,dx \to 1$$

as $N \to \infty$.

4.4. The Asymptotic Variance of Spectrograph Estimates

There are two distinct situations that are considered in this section. We first discuss the case of an asymptotically unbiased estimate of the spectral density where the corresponding weight function

$$w_N(x) = \frac{1}{2\pi}\Sigma\,w_p^{(N)}\,e^{ipx}$$

varies with N. Then the case of a fixed weight function $w(x) = w_N(x)$ is considered. The second problem is of special interest when one wishes to estimate the spectral mass in a fixed interval.

Let the spectrograph estimate be

$$\alpha_N^* = \int\limits_{-\pi}^{\pi} I_N(x)\, w_N(x)\, dx = \frac{1}{2\pi N} \sum_{\nu,\,\mu=1}^{N} w_{\nu-\mu}^{(N)}\, x_\nu\, x_\mu.$$

We assume that $w_N(x) = w_N(-x)$ *and*

$$\int\limits_{-\pi}^{\pi} |w_N(x)|^2\, dx < \infty.$$

We shall also assume that

$$\frac{\displaystyle\sum_{r=-N}^{N} \frac{|r|}{N} |w_r^{(N)}|^2}{\displaystyle\sum_{r=-\infty}^{\infty} |w_r^{(N)}|^2} \to 0 \tag{1}$$

as $N \to \infty$. The variance of the estimate, when the observed process is a linear scheme, is given by (see 4.2)

$$N\, 4\pi^2 D^2[\alpha_N^*] =$$

$$\frac{1}{N} \sum_{\nu_i,\,\mu_i=1}^{N} w_{\nu_1-\mu_1}^{(N)}\, w_{\nu_2-\mu_2}^{(N)} [r_{\nu_1-\nu_2}\, r_{\mu_1-\mu_2} + r_{\nu_1-\mu_2}\, r_{\nu_2-\mu_1} + \tag{2}$$

$$+ e \sum_{\nu=-\infty}^{\infty} a_{\nu_1-\nu}\, a_{\nu_2-\nu}\, a_{\mu_1-\nu}\, a_{\mu_2-\nu}].$$

Let the spectral density $f(\lambda)$ be positive and continuous. One can then approximate $f(\lambda)$ above and below by a positive finite trigonometric form in treating the first two terms on the right of (2). It is enough to consider the first term. Let $\nu_1 - \nu_2 = p$, $\mu_1 - \mu_2 = q$ be fixed. Then we have to deal with the coefficient of $r_p r_q$, that is,

$$\frac{1}{N} \sum_{\nu,\,\mu=1,\,1}^{N-p,\,N-q} w_{\nu-\mu+p-q}^{(N)}\, w_{\nu-\mu}^{(N)}$$

$$= \frac{1}{N} \left\{ \sum_{r=0}^{q-p} w_{r+p-q}^{(N)}\, w_r^{(N)} (N-p) + \right.$$

$$+ \sum_{r=1}^{N-p-1} w_{r+p-q}^{(N)}\, w_r^{(N)} (N-p-r) + \sum_{r=q-p-1}^{-N+q+1} w_{r+p-q}^{(N)}\, w_r^{(N)} (N-q+r) \right\}$$

$$= a_{pq}$$

when say $p \geq q \geq 0$. Consider the difference between a_{pq} and

$$A_{pq} = \sum_{r=-\infty}^{\infty} w_{r+p-q}^{(N)} \, w_r^{(N)}.$$

Now

$$\frac{|a_{pq} - A_{pq}|}{\displaystyle\sum_{r=-\infty}^{\infty} |w_r^{(N)}|^2} \leq \frac{\displaystyle\sum_{|r| < N} |w_r^{(N)}|^2 \, \frac{(2\,|p| + 2\,|q| + |r|)}{N} + \sum_{|r| > N} |w_r^{(N)}|^2}{\displaystyle\sum_{r=-\infty}^{\infty} |w_r^{(N)}|^2}$$

by the Schwarz inequality. But

$$\frac{\displaystyle\sum_{r=-N}^{N} |w_r^{(N)}|^2 \left(1 - \frac{|r|}{N}\right)}{\displaystyle\sum_{r=-\infty}^{\infty} |w_r^{(N)}|^2} \to 1$$

as $N > \infty$ because of (1). Thus

$$\frac{|a_{pq} - A_{pq}|}{\displaystyle\sum_{r=-\infty}^{\infty} |w_r^{(N)}|^2} \to 0$$

as $N \to \infty$. If $f(\lambda)$ is approximated by the finite positive trigonometric form $p(\lambda)$, the first term

$$\frac{1}{N} \sum_{\nu_i,\,\mu_i = 1}^{N} w_{\nu_1 - \mu_1}^{(N)} \, w_{\nu_2 - \mu_2}^{(N)} \, r_{\nu_1 - \nu_2} \, r_{\mu_1 - \mu_2}$$

is asymptotically the same as

$$(2\pi)^3 \int_{-\pi}^{\pi} w_N^2(x) \, p^2(x) \, dx.$$

On letting the maximal difference between the two approximating trigonometric forms go to zero we see that the first two terms on the right of (2) are asymptotically the same as

$$2\,(2\pi)^3 \int_{-\pi}^{\pi} w_N^2(x) \, f^2(x) \, dx$$

as $N \to \infty$. For the moment the interest is in α_N^* as an asymptotically unbiased estimate of the spectral density at λ, that is $f(\lambda)$. If x_t is a linear process satisfying conditions (4.2.6), it seems appropriate to choose a weight function $w_N(x) \geq 0$ such that

$$\int\limits_{-\pi}^{\pi} w_N(x)\, dx = 1 \tag{3}$$

and for any $\varepsilon > 0$

$$w_N(x) \to 0 \tag{4}$$

uniformly for $|x \pm \lambda| > \varepsilon$ as $N \to \infty$. The estimate α_N^* is then asymptotically unbiased and just as in section 4.2 we can show that the third term on the right of (2) is negligible with respect to the first two terms as $N \to \infty$. Under these assumptions we see that

$$D^2[\alpha_N^*] \sim \frac{4\pi}{N} \int\limits_{-\pi}^{\pi} w_N^2(x)\, f^2(x)\, dx. \tag{5}$$

Note that the quantity e does not appear in this formula. *If x_t is a normal process, the third term on the right of (2) vanishes. The weight function $w_N(x)$ is now not assumed to be nonnegative. Condition (4) is replaced by*

$$|w_N(x)| \to 0$$

uniformly for $|x + \lambda| > \varepsilon$ as $N \to \infty$. If the weight function $w_N(x)$ satisfies this condition and (3) the asymptotic relation (5) holds. Since $w_N(x)$ concentrates all its mass in the neighborhood of the points $\lambda, -\lambda$ and $f(x)$ is continuous and even, we can rewrite (5) as

$$D^2[\alpha_N^*] \sim \frac{4\pi}{N} f^2(\lambda) \int\limits_{-\pi}^{\pi} w_N^2(x)\, dx.$$

At times it may be convenient to *introduce the auxiliary weight function*

$$\omega_N(x) = 2 w_N(x)$$

defined on $0 \le x < \pi$. Note that under our assumptions

$$\int\limits_{0}^{\pi} \omega_N(x)\, dx = 1$$

and for any $\varepsilon > 0$

$$|\omega_N(x)| \to 0$$

uniformly for $|x - \lambda| > \varepsilon$ as $N \to \infty$, $\lambda \ge 0$. It then follows that

$$D^2[\alpha_N^*] \sim \frac{2\pi}{N} f^2(\lambda) \int\limits_{0}^{\pi} \omega_N^2(x)\, dx.$$

Let us now *consider the variance of the spectrograph estimate* α_N^* *when the weight function* $w(x) = w_N(x)$ *does not depend on* N. *The observed process* x_t *is a assumed to be a linear process*

$$x_t = \sum a_{t-\nu}\, \xi_\nu$$

with

$$\left. \begin{array}{l} E\,\xi_\nu = 0 \\ E\,\xi_\nu^2 = 1 \\ E\,\xi_\nu^4 < \infty \end{array} \right\}.$$

The spectral density $f(y)$ *of the process is assumed to be positive and continuous. Let the weight function* $w(x)$ *be bounded, symmetric about zero and have at most a finite number of discontinuities. Note that the conditions on* $w(x)$ *imply that (1) is satisfied.* Just as in the early part of this section one can prove that the first two terms on the right of (2) tend to

$$2\,(2\,\pi)^3 \int\limits_{-\pi}^{\pi} w^2(x)\, f^2(x)\, dx$$

as $N \to \infty$. However the third term on the right is no longer of small order compared to the first two terms as $N \to \infty$ and we shall have to consider it in some detail. The third term is

$$\frac{e}{N} \sum_{\nu_i,\,\mu_i=1}^{N} w_{\nu_1-\mu_1} w_{\nu_2-\mu_2} \sum_{\nu=-\infty}^{\infty} a_{\nu_1-\nu}\, a_{\nu_2-\nu}\, a_{\mu_1-\nu}\, a_{\mu_2-\nu}$$

$$= \frac{e}{N} \int\limits_{-\pi}^{\pi}\int\limits_{-\pi}^{\pi} \sum_{\nu=-\infty}^{\infty} \left| \sum_{\alpha=1}^{N} a_{\alpha-\nu}\, e^{i\alpha x} \right|^2 \left| \sum_{\gamma=1}^{N} a_{\gamma-\nu}\, e^{i\gamma y} \right|^2 w(x)\, w(y)\, dx\, dy.$$ (6)

Consider the above integral with $w(x)$, $w(y)$ replaced by e^{-inx}, e^{-imy} respectively. Introduce the function

$$c_{n,\,m}(x) = \sum_{k=-\infty}^{\infty} a_k\, a_{k-n}\, e^{ikx} \sum_{l=-\infty}^{\infty} a_l\, a_{l-m}\, e^{-ilx}.$$

The function $c_{n,\,m}(x)$ is continuous. Now

$$\frac{1}{2\,\pi} \int\limits_{-\pi}^{\pi} c_{n,\,m}(x)\, e^{-i\,(\alpha-\gamma)\,x}\, dx = \sum_{\nu=-\infty}^{\infty} a_{\alpha-\nu}\, a_{\alpha-n-\nu}\, a_{\gamma-\nu}\, a_{\gamma-m-\nu}$$

so that

$$\frac{e}{N} \int\limits_{-\pi}^{\pi} \int\limits_{-\pi}^{\pi} \sum_{\nu=-\infty}^{\infty} \left| \sum_{\alpha=1}^{N} a_{\alpha-\nu} e^{i\alpha x} \right|^2 \left| \sum_{\gamma=1}^{N} a_{\gamma-\nu} e^{i\gamma y} \right|^2 e^{-inx} e^{-imy} \, dx \, dy$$

$$= \frac{e}{N} (2\pi)^2 \sum_{\alpha=\max(1,\,1+n)}^{\min(N,\,N+n)} \sum_{\gamma=\max(1,\,1+m)}^{\min(N,\,N+m)} \frac{1}{2\pi} \int\limits_{-\pi}^{\pi} c_{n,\,m}(x) \, e^{-i(\alpha-\gamma)x} \, dx.$$

But if $n, m \geq 0$ expression (6) can be written

$$4\pi^2 e \frac{1}{2\pi N} \int\limits_{-\pi}^{\pi} e^{\frac{i(n-m)}{2} x} c_{n,\,m}(x) \, \frac{\sin \frac{N-n}{2} x \, \sin \frac{N-m}{2} x}{\sin^2 \frac{x}{2}} \, dx \cdot$$

$$= 4\pi^2 e \frac{1}{2\pi N} \int\limits_{-\pi}^{\pi} e^{\frac{i(n-m)}{2} x} c_{n,\,m}(x)$$

$$\left[\frac{\sin^2 \frac{N-n}{2} x}{\sin^2 \frac{x}{2}} \cos \frac{n-m}{2} x + \frac{\sin \frac{(N-n)}{2} x \sin^2 \frac{n-m}{2} x}{\sin^2 \frac{x}{2}} \right] dx.$$

According to the Riemann-Lebesgue lemma the second term tends to zero as $N \to \infty$. The first term tends to $4\pi^2 e c_{n,\,m}(0) = 4\pi^2 \, e \, r_n r_m$. The argument is quite analogous for other values of n, m. Now consider a finite trigonometric polynomial

$$h(x, y) = \sum_{n,\,m=-p}^{p} h_{n,\,m} \, e^{-inx} \, e^{-imy}$$

replacing $w(x) w(y)$ in (6). The limit of the corresponding expression as $N \to \infty$ is then

$$4\pi^2 e \sum_{n,\,m=-p}^{p} h_{n,\,m} \, r_n r_m = 4\pi^2 e \int\limits_{-\pi}^{\pi} \int\limits_{-\pi}^{\pi} h(x, y) f(x) f(y) \, dx \, dy.$$

Given any function $w(x)$ satisfying the conditions specified above, two finite trigonometric polynomials $h_1(x,y)$, $h_2(x,y)$ can be chosen satisfying the conditions

$$h_1(x,y) \leq w(x) w(y) \leq h_2(x,y)$$

and

$$\int\limits_{-\pi}^{\pi} \int\limits_{-\pi}^{\pi} [h_2(x, y) - h_1(x, y)] \, dx \, dy < \varepsilon$$

for any $\varepsilon > 0$. Expression (6) lies between the corresponding expressions with $h_1(x,y)$, $h_2(x,y)$ respectively in place of $w(x)w(y)$. On letting $N \to \infty$, we see that the $\varvarlimsup\limits_{N \to \infty}$ and $\varliminf\limits_{\overline{N \to \infty}}$ of expression (6) lie between

$$4 \pi^2 e \iint\limits_{-\pi}^{\pi} h_1(x,\, y)\, f(x)\, f(y)\, dx\, dy$$

and

$$4 \pi^2 e \iint\limits_{-\pi}^{\pi} h_2(x,\, y)\, f(x)\, f(y)\, dx\, dy.$$

Now on letting $\varepsilon \to 0$ it is clear that the limit of (6) as $N \to \infty$ is

$$4 \pi^2 e \left[\int\limits_{-\pi}^{\pi} w(x)\, f(x)\, dx \right]^2 .$$

Thus

$$\lim\limits_{N \to \infty} N\, D^2\, [\alpha_N^*] = 4 \pi \int\limits_{-\pi}^{\pi} w^2(x)\, f^2(x)\, dx + e \left[\int\limits_{-\pi}^{\pi} w(x)\, f(x) \right]^2 .$$

If the limiting variance of the estimate is expressed in terms of

$$w(x) = 2\, \omega(x), \quad 0 \le x \le \pi,$$

making use of the fact that $w(x)$ and $f(x)$ are even functions,

$$\lim\limits_{N \to \infty} N\, D^2\, [\alpha_N^*] = e \left[\int\limits_{0}^{\pi} \omega(x)\, f(x)\, dx \right]^2 + 2 \pi \int\limits_{0}^{\pi} \omega^2(x)\, f^2(x)\, dx.$$

4.5. Another Class of Estimates

The estimates discussed in this section are a subclass of the family of estimates of the form (4.1.1) but they are not of the spectrograph type. However, they are of considerable interest because they seem to be well suited for use when building certain types of analogue computers to estimate the spectral density of a stationary process.

It is convenient to discuss these estimates in terms of an observed continuous parameter stationary normal stochastic process x_t, $-\infty < t < \infty$, $E x_t \equiv 0$, that is continuous in the mean. The spectrum is assumed to be absolutely continuous. One has observed x_t, $0 < t < T$, and one wishes to estimate the spectral density $f(\lambda)$ of the process. An estimate analogous to (4.1.1) would be

$$\alpha_T^* = \frac{1}{2\pi T} \int\limits_0^T \!\!\int x_u\, x_v\, b_T\,(u,\,v)\, d\,u\, d\,v$$

where $b_T\,(u,\,v) = b_T\,(v,\,u)$. Here

$$b_T\,(u,\,v) = \int\limits_{-\infty}^{\infty}\!\!\int e^{iux-ivy}\, d\,W_T\,(x,\,y)$$

where $W_T(x,y)$ is of bounded variation.

Let us first discuss this subclass of estimates in a heuristic manner. The basic idea is as follows. Pass the message x_t, $0 < t < T$, through a linear filter $\mathcal{F}$ with frequency response function $\varphi_T(y)$ highly concentrated about the point λ at which one wishes to estimate the spectral density. The average power of the output is then measured. The filtered process

$$z_t = \mathcal{F} x_t = \int\limits_0^t x_s g_T\,(t-s)\, ds, \quad 0 < t < T,$$

where the real function $g_T(t)$ is the transient response function of $\mathcal{F}$. We assume that $g(t) = 0$ for $t < 0$. The average power of the filtered process is

$$\frac{1}{T}\int\limits_0^T |z_t|^2\, d\,t = \frac{1}{T}\int\limits_0^T\!\!\int\!\!\int x_u\, x_v\, g_T\,(t-u)\, g_T\,(t-v)\, d\,u\, d\,v\, d\,t.$$

Here $\qquad b_T\,(u,\,v) = 2\pi\int\limits_0^T g_T\,(t-u)\, g_T\,(t-v)\, dt.$

A physical device using such an estimate has been suggested by Stoner and Bates [1]. Let $\mathcal{F}$ be a linear filter governed by the differential equation

$$A\,[\ddot z_t + \beta \dot z_t + \lambda^2 z_t] = x_t, \quad \beta > 0,$$

where z_t is the output of $\mathcal{F}$. Here $\dot z_t$ denotes the derivative of z_t with respect to t. Note that here

$$\varphi\,(y) = \frac{A^{-1}}{-y^2 + i\beta y + \lambda^2}$$

and that

$$g\,(t) = \begin{cases} \dfrac{e^{-\beta t/2}\, \sin\,(\sqrt{4\,\lambda^2 - \beta^2}\, t/2)}{A\sqrt{4\,\lambda^2 - \beta^2}} & \text{if } t > 0 \\[2ex] 0 & \text{if } t < 0. \end{cases}$$

The concentration of $\varphi(y)$ at the points $\lambda, -\lambda$ is increased by making β smaller as $T \to \infty$. The power would be a reasonable estimate for $f(\lambda) = f(-\lambda)$, the spectral density at λ.

The class of estimates that we shall discuss in some detail differs slightly from the estimate discussed above in that a shift of the centering at the point λ at which one wishes to estimate the spectral density is accomplished by multiplying the message x_t by $e^{it\lambda}$. This is convenient if the analogue computer is an electronic device since it can then be accomplished by mixing x_t with the wave $e^{it\lambda}$ from a local oscillator of frequency λ.

The spectral density $f(y)$ of the process x_t is assumed to be positive, continuous and bounded. We shall have to make various assumptions about the *transient response function* $g_T(t)$ and the *frequency characteristic* $\varphi_T(x) = \int_{-\infty}^{\infty} e^{-itx} g_T(t) dt$. The transient response function $g_T(t)$ *is assumed to be a real-valued function that is zero when $t < 0$. But then $\varphi_T(x) = \overline{\varphi_T(-x)}$. Let $|g_T(t)|$, $|g_T(t)|^2$, $|g_T(t)|^4$ and $|\varphi_T(x)|$, $|\varphi_T(x)|^2$, $|\varphi_T(x)|^4$ be integrable. The function $|\varphi_T(x)|^2$ is assumed to behave more and more like a δ-function at $x = 0$ when $T \to \infty$, that is,*

$$\int_{-\infty}^{\infty} |\varphi_T(x)|^2 dx = 1$$

$$\int_{|x| < \varepsilon} |\varphi_T(x)|^2 dx \to 1 \tag{1}$$

for any $\varepsilon > 0$ as $T \to \infty$ and

$$|\varphi_T(x)| \to 0 \tag{2}$$

uniformly when $|x| \geq \varepsilon$ as $T \to \infty$. Additional assumptions will be introduced in the development when required.

The signal x_t which is mixed with the local oscillator wave $e^{it\lambda}$ becomes

$$z_t = \mathcal{F} M x_t = \mathcal{F} x_t e^{it\lambda} = \int_0^t x_s e^{is\lambda} g_T(t-s) ds,$$

$0 < t < T$, after filtering. Here $M x_t = x_t e^{it\lambda}$. Our estimate of $f(\lambda)$ is the average power of this output and is given by

$$\alpha_T^* = \frac{1}{T} \int_0^T |z_t|^2 dt = \frac{1}{T} \int_0^T \int \int x_u x_v \cos(u-v)\lambda\, g_T(t-u) g_T(t-v)\, du\, dv\, dt.$$

4.5

Thus
$$b_T(u, v) = 2\pi \cos(u-v) \lambda \int_0^T g_T(t-u) g_T(t-v) dt,$$

$0 < u, v < T$.

The estimate of the bias that we get is very crude and is obtained by making a very restrictive assumption about $g_T(t)$. We *assume that* $g_T(t) = 0$ *when* $t > h(T) > 0$ *where* $h(T) = o(T^{1/2})$. The expected value of $|z_t|^2$ is

$$E\,|z_t|^2 = E \int\!\!\int_0^t x_u x_v e^{i(u-v)\lambda} g_T(t-u) g_T(t-v) \, du \, dv$$

$$= \int_{-\infty}^{\infty} \int\!\!\int_0^t e^{-i(u-v)(x-\lambda)} f(x) g_T(t-u) g_T(t-v) \, du \, dv \, dx$$

$$= \int_{-\infty}^{\infty} \left| \int_0^t e^{-iu(x-\lambda)} g_T(u) \, du \right|^2 f(x) \, dx.$$

But then

$$E\left\{ \frac{1}{T} \int_0^T |z_t|^2 \, dt \right\} = \int_{-\infty}^{\infty} \frac{1}{T} \int_0^T \left| \int_0^t e^{-iu(x-\lambda)} g_T(u) \, du \right|^2 dt f(x) \, dx.$$

On using the Schwarz inequality we see that

$$\left| \int_0^t e^{-iu(x-\lambda)} g_T(u) \, du \right|^2 \le t \int_0^t g_T^2(u) \, du \le t.$$

The bias

$$b_T(\lambda) = E\left\{ \frac{1}{T} \int_0^T |z_t|^2 \, dt \right\} - f(\lambda)$$

$$= \int_{-\infty}^{\infty} \frac{1}{T} \left\{ \int_{h(T)}^T + \int_0^{h(T)} \right\} \left| \int_0^t e^{-iu(x-\lambda)} g_T(u) \, du \right|^2 dt f(x) \, dx - f(\lambda)$$

$$= \int_{-\infty}^{\infty} \frac{1}{T} (T - h(T)) |\varphi_T(x-\lambda)|^2 f(x) \, dx - f(\lambda) + 0\left(\frac{h^2(T)}{T} \right)$$

$$= \int_{-\infty}^{\infty} |\varphi_T(x-\lambda)|^2 [f(x) - f(\lambda)] \, dx + 0\left(\frac{h^2(T)}{T} \right).$$

140

Since $|\varphi_T(x)|^2$ behaves like a δ-function at $x = 0$ as $T \to \infty$, the estimate is asymptotically unbiased. In section 4.6 we shall consider in some detail a specific estimate of the type discussed here with $g_T(t)$ nonzero for every $t > 0$.

Now let us consider the asymptotic variance of the estimate. Note that

$$b_T(u, v)$$

$$= 2\pi \cos(u - v)\,\lambda \cdot \int_0^T g_T(t - u)\,g_T(t - v)\,dt$$

$$= \frac{1}{4\pi} \int_0^T \int_{-\infty}^{\infty} \int [e^{i(t-u)(x-\lambda)}\,e^{-i(t-v)(y-\lambda)} + e^{i(t-u)(x+\lambda)}\,e^{-i(t-v)(y+\lambda)}]$$

$$\varphi_T(x)\,\overline{\varphi_T(y)}\,dx\,dy\,dt$$

$$= \frac{1}{4\pi} \int_0^T \int_{-\infty}^{\infty} \int e^{i(t-u)x}\,e^{-i(t-v)y}\,[\varphi_T(x+\lambda)\,\overline{\varphi_T(y+\lambda)} +$$

$$+ \varphi_T(x-y)\,\overline{\varphi_T(y-\lambda)}]\,dx\,dy\,dt$$

$$= \frac{1}{4\pi} \int_{-\infty}^{\infty} \int e^{-iux+ivy}\,\frac{e^{iT(x-y)} - 1}{i(x-y)}\,[\varphi_T(x+\lambda)\,\overline{\varphi_T(y+\lambda)} +$$

$$+ \varphi_T(x-\lambda)\,\overline{\varphi_T(y-\lambda)}]\,dx\,dy.$$

The weight function

$$w_T(x, y) = \frac{1}{4\pi}\,\frac{e^{iT(x-y)} - 1}{i(x-y)}\,[\varphi_T(x+\lambda)\,\overline{\varphi_T(y+\lambda)} + \varphi_T(x-\lambda)\,\overline{\varphi_T(y-\lambda)}]$$

is one of the weight functions that correspond to the given estimate. The function $w_T(x, y)$ is the Fourier transform of $b_T(u, v)$, $-\infty < u,\ v < \infty$, rather than the Fourier transform of $b_T(u, v)$ on the square $0 < u,\ v < T$. For this reason we cannot expect the analogue of (4.1.4) to hold for $w_T(x, y)$. However, it does hold for

$$\Omega_T(x, y) = \frac{1}{(2\pi)^2} \int_0^T \int b_T(u, v)\,e^{-iux+ivy}\,dx\,dy,$$

that is,

$$D^2[\alpha_T^*] = \frac{8\pi^2}{T^2} \int_{-\infty}^{\infty} \int |\Omega_T(x, y)|^2\,f(x)\,f(y)\,dx\,dy.$$

4.5

One would like to find a condition that would allow us to assume that the analogue of (4.1.6) holds, that is,

$$D^2[\alpha_T^*] \sim \frac{8\pi^2}{T^2} \int\int_{-\infty}^{\infty} |w_T(x, y)|^2 f(x) f(y)\, dx\, dy. \tag{3}$$

The inequality

$$\left| \left(\int\int_{-\infty}^{\infty} |w_T(x, y)|^2 f(x) f(y)\, dx\, dy \right)^{1/2} - \left(\int\int_{-\infty}^{\infty} |\Omega_T(x, y)|^2 f(x) f(y)\, dx\, dy \right)^{1/2} \right|$$

$$\leq \left(\int\int_{-\infty}^{\infty} |D_T(x, y)|^2 f(x) f(y)\, dx\, dy \right)^{1/2}$$

follows from the Minkowski inequality. Here $D_T(x, y) = w_T(x, y) - \Omega_T(x, y)$. But

$$\int\int_{-\infty}^{\infty} |D_T(x, y)|^2 f(x) f(y)\, dx\, dy$$

$$\leq C \int\int_{-\infty}^{\infty} |D_T(x, y)|^2\, dx\, dy$$

$$= \frac{C}{(2\pi)^2} \left(\int\int_{-\infty}^{\infty} - \int\int_{0}^{T} \right) |b_T(u, v)|^2\, du\, dv$$

$$\leq \frac{C}{2\pi^2} \int_{-\infty}^{T} \int_{-\infty}^{0} \left| \int_{0}^{T} g_T(t-u) g_T(t-v)\, dt \right|^2 du\, dv$$

by the Parseval relation, where C is a constant. *We assume that*

$$\int_{-\infty}^{T} \int_{-\infty}^{0} \left| \int_{0}^{T} g_T(t-u) g_T(t-v)\, dt \right|^2 du\, dv = o\left(\int\int_{-\infty}^{\infty} |w_T(x, y)|^2 f(x) f(y)\, dx\, dy \right)$$

since then relation (3) holds. *We also assume that*

$$\max_{|u| \leq \frac{A}{T}} \left| \frac{\int_{-\infty}^{\infty} |\varphi_T(x)|^2 |\varphi_T(x+u)|^2\, dx}{\int_{-\infty}^{\infty} |\varphi_T(x)|^4\, dx} - 1 \right| \to 0 \tag{4}$$

as $T \to \infty$ for any $A > 0$.

142

Now the variance

$$D^2 [\alpha_T^*] \sim \frac{8\,\pi^2}{T^2} \int\limits_{-\infty}^{\infty}\!\!\int |w_T (x, y)|^2 f (x) f (y) \, d x \, d y$$

$$= \frac{1}{2\,T^2} \int\limits_{-\infty}^{\infty}\!\!\int \frac{\sin^2 \dfrac{T}{2} (x-y)}{\left(\dfrac{x-y}{2}\right)^2} \, | \varphi_T (x+\lambda) \, \overline{\varphi_T (y+\lambda)} +$$

$$+ \varphi_T (x-\lambda) \, \overline{\varphi_T (x-\lambda)}|^2 f (x) f (y) \, d x \, d y$$

$$= \frac{1}{2\,T^2} \int\limits_{-\infty}^{\infty}\!\!\int \frac{\sin^2 \dfrac{T}{2} (x-y)}{\left(\dfrac{x-y}{2}\right)^2} \, \{| \varphi_T (x+\lambda) \, \varphi_T (y-\lambda) |^2 +$$

$$+ 2\,R\,[\varphi_T (x+\lambda) \, \overline{\varphi_T (y+\lambda)} \, \overline{\varphi_T (x-\lambda)} \, \varphi_T (y-\lambda)] +$$

$$+ | \varphi_T (x-\lambda) \, \varphi_T (y-\lambda) |^2\} f (x) f (y) \, d x \, d y$$

$$= H_1 + H_2 + H_3.$$

We shall show the second term H_2 to be of smaller order than H_1 and H_3 as $T \to \infty$. The spectral density $f(\lambda)$ is bounded by some finite constant K. Thus

$$\left| \int\limits_{-\infty}^{\infty} R e\,[\varphi_T (y+u+\lambda) \overline{\varphi_T (y+\lambda)} \; \overline{\varphi_T (y+u-\lambda)} \, \varphi_T (y-\lambda)] f (y+u) f (y) \, d y \right|$$

$$\leq K^2 \int\limits_{-\infty}^{\infty} | \varphi_T (y+u+\lambda) \, \varphi_T (y+\lambda) \, \varphi_T (y+u-\lambda) \, \varphi_T (y-\lambda) | \, d y$$

$$\leq K^2 \int\limits_{-\infty}^{\infty} | \varphi_T (y+\lambda) \, \varphi_T (y-\lambda) |^2 \, d y$$

by the Schwarz inequality. Let us assume $\lambda \neq 0$. Then given any $\varepsilon > 0$, condition (2) implies that

$$\int\limits_{-\infty}^{\infty} | \varphi_T (y+\lambda) \, \varphi_T (y-\lambda) |^2 \, d y < \varepsilon$$

for T sufficiently large. But then

$$|H_2| \leq \frac{K^2 \varepsilon}{2\,T^2} \int\limits_{-\infty}^{\infty} \frac{\sin^2 \dfrac{T u}{2}}{\left(\dfrac{u}{2}\right)^2} \, d u \leq \frac{\pi\,K^2\,\varepsilon}{T}.$$

Therefore
$$H_2 = o\left(\frac{1}{T}\right)$$

as $T \to \infty$. Since expressions H_1 and H_3 can be treated in exactly the same manner, we need only consider H_1. Now

$$H_1 = \frac{1}{2\,T^2} \int\limits_{-\infty}^{\infty} \frac{\sin^2 \dfrac{T\,u}{2}}{\left(\dfrac{u}{2}\right)^2} \int\limits_{-\infty}^{\infty} |\varphi_T(y+u+\lambda)\,\varphi_T(y+\lambda)|^2 \, f(y+u)\,f(y)\,dy\,du.$$

We divide H_1 into two parts and estimate each part separately. The first part

$$\frac{1}{2\,T^2} \int\limits_{|u|>\frac{A}{T}} \frac{\sin^2 \dfrac{T\,u}{2}}{\left(\dfrac{u}{2}\right)^2} \int\limits_{-\infty}^{\infty} |\varphi_T(y+u+\lambda)|^2 \, |\varphi_T(y+\lambda)|^2 \, f(y+u)\,f(y)\,dy\,du$$

$$\leq \frac{2\,K^2}{T^2} \int\limits_{|u|>\frac{A}{T}} \frac{1}{u^2}\,du \int\limits_{-\infty}^{\infty} |\varphi_T(y)|^4 \, dy$$

$$= \frac{4\,K^2}{T\,A} \int\limits_{-\infty}^{\infty} |\varphi_T(y)|^4 \, dy = o\left(\frac{1}{T} \int\limits_{-\infty}^{\infty} |\varphi_T(y)|^4 \, dy\right)$$

since A can be chosen arbitrarily large. On the other hand

$$\frac{1}{2\,T^2} \int\limits_{|u|<\frac{A}{T}} \frac{\sin^2 \dfrac{T\,u}{2}}{\left(\dfrac{u}{2}\right)^2} \int\limits_{-\infty}^{\infty} |\varphi_T(y+u+\lambda)\,\varphi_T(y+\lambda)|^2 \, f(y+u)\,f(y)\,dy\,du$$

$$= \frac{1}{2\,T^2} \int\limits_{|u|<\frac{A}{T}} \frac{\sin^2 \dfrac{T\,u}{2}}{\left(\dfrac{u}{2}\right)^2}\,du \int\limits_{-\infty}^{\infty} |\varphi_T(y+\lambda)|^4 \, f^2(y)\,dy \; +$$

$$+ \; o\left(\frac{1}{T} \int\limits_{-\infty}^{\infty} |\varphi_T(y)|^4 \, dy\right)$$

$$= \frac{\pi\,f^2(\lambda)}{T} \int\limits_{-\infty}^{\infty} |\varphi_T(y)|^4 \, dy + o\left(\frac{1}{T} \int\limits_{-\infty}^{\infty} |\varphi_T(y)|^4 \, dy\right)$$

because of conditions (1), (2) and (4) imposed on $\varphi_T(y)$. Note that

$\int\limits_{-\infty}^{\infty} |\varphi_T(y)|^4\,dy \to \infty$ as $T \to \infty$. Thus

$$H_1 \sim \frac{\pi f^2(\lambda)}{T} \int\limits_{-\infty}^{\infty} |\varphi_T(y)|^4\,dy$$

as $T \to \infty$ so that

$$D^2[\alpha_T^*] \sim \frac{2\,\pi\,f^2(\lambda)}{T} \int\limits_{-\infty}^{\infty} |\varphi_T(y)|^4\,dy \tag{5}$$

as $T \to \infty$, if $\lambda \neq 0$. It is easily seen that

$$D^2[\alpha_T^*] \sim \frac{4\,\pi\,f^2(0)}{T} \int\limits_{-\infty}^{\infty} |\varphi_T(y)|^4\,dy$$

if $\lambda = 0$.

4.6. Special Estimates of the Spectral Density

We discuss some specific estimates that have been proposed for the estimation of the spectral density in this section. Let us first consider the periodogram. This estimate was introduced in section 3.1. It was originally designed to isolate "periods" of a time series as described in Chapter 3, and not for the estimation of the spectral density. In section 4.3 its bias as an estimate of the spectral density $f(\lambda)$ was seen to be very small, at most of the order $(\log N)/N$ as $N \to \infty$. If the observed process is normal, the variance of the periodogram

$$D^2[I_N(\lambda)] \sim \begin{cases} f^2(\lambda) & \text{if } \lambda \neq 0 \\ 2\,f^2(0) & \text{if } \lambda = 0 \end{cases}$$

as $N \to \infty$. The estimate does not converge in the mean square to $f(\lambda)$. One can even show that it does not converge to any stochastic variable (see Grenander [2]). Thus $I_N(\lambda)$ is not a consistent estimate of $f(\lambda)$ and for this and other reasons it is useless as an estimate of $f(\lambda)$.

The other estimates discussed in this section are all consistent estimates of $f(\lambda)$. All, except for the last, are spectrograph estimates. The last one is a specific example out of the class of estimates discussed in section 4.5. In the following discussion $f(\lambda)$ is assumed to be sufficiently regular, that is, it has a sufficient number of derivatives for the arguments to be carried out. The spectral density $f(\lambda)$ should be thought of as a function defined and regular on a circle, that is, the point $\lambda = -\pi$ is identified with the point $\lambda = \pi$. Formulas (4.4.5) and (4.5.4) will be used in the derivation of the asymptotic variance of the estimates.

Bartlett [2] has introduced an estimate

$$f_N^*(\lambda) = \frac{1}{2\pi} \sum_{\nu=-m+1}^{m-1} \left(1 - \frac{|\nu|}{m}\right) \frac{C_\nu}{N-|\nu|} \cos \nu \lambda$$

of $f(\lambda)$ where $m = o(N)$ but tends to infinity with N. For convenience consider a slightly modified estimate

$$f_N^*(\lambda) = \frac{1}{2\pi} \sum_{\nu=-m+1}^{m-1} \left(1 - \frac{|\nu|}{m}\right) \frac{C_\nu}{N} \cos \nu \lambda. \tag{1}$$

The weights are

$$w_\nu^{(N)} = \begin{cases} \left(1 - \dfrac{|\nu|}{m}\right) \cos \nu \lambda & |\nu| \le m \\ 0 & |\nu| > m \end{cases}$$

and the corresponding weight function is

$$w_N(x) = \frac{1}{4\pi m} \left\{ \frac{\sin^2 \dfrac{m}{2}(\lambda - x)}{\sin^2 \dfrac{1}{2}(\lambda - x)} + \frac{\sin^2 \dfrac{m}{2}(\lambda + x)}{\sin^2 \dfrac{1}{2}(\lambda + x)} \right\}.$$

The asymptotic variance

$$D^2[f_N^*(\lambda)] \sim \frac{4\pi}{N} f^2(\lambda) \int_{-\pi}^{\pi} w_N^2(x)\, dx = \frac{4\pi}{N} f^2(\lambda) \frac{1}{2\pi} \sum |w_\nu^{(N)}|^2$$

$$= \frac{2 f^2(\lambda)}{N} \sum_{\nu=-m}^{m} \left(1 - \frac{|\nu|}{m}\right)^2 \cos^2 \nu \lambda$$

$$\sim \begin{cases} \dfrac{2}{3} \dfrac{m}{N} f^2(\lambda) & \text{if } \lambda \ne 0 \\ \dfrac{4}{3} \dfrac{m}{N} f^2(0) & \text{if } \lambda = 0. \end{cases}$$

The bias

$$b_N(\lambda) = E f_N^*(\lambda) - f(\lambda)$$

$$= \frac{1}{2\pi} \sum_{\nu=-m+1}^{m-1} \left(1 - \frac{|\nu|}{m}\right)\left(1 - \frac{|\nu|}{N}\right) r_\nu \cos \nu\lambda - \frac{1}{2\pi} \sum_{\nu=-\infty}^{\infty} r_\nu \cos \nu\lambda$$

$$\sim -\frac{1}{2\pi} \sum_{\nu=-m+1}^{m-1} \frac{|\nu|}{m} r_\nu \cos \nu\lambda = -\frac{1}{\pi} \sum_{\nu=0}^{m-1} \frac{|\nu|}{m} r_\nu \cos \nu\lambda$$

$$= \frac{1}{\pi m} \sum_{\nu=0}^{m-1} \cos \nu\lambda \int_{-\pi}^{\pi} \sin \nu x \, f'(x) \, dx$$

$$= \frac{1}{\pi m} \sum_{\nu=0}^{m-1} \int_{-\pi}^{\pi} \frac{\sin \nu(x-\lambda) + \sin \nu(x+\lambda)}{2} f'(x) \, dx$$

$$= \frac{1}{\pi m} \int_{-\pi}^{\pi} \frac{1}{2} Im \left\{ \frac{1 - e^{im(x-\lambda)}}{1 - e^{i(x-\lambda)}} + \frac{1 - e^{im(x+\lambda)}}{1 - e^{i(x+\lambda)}} \right\} f'(x) \, dx$$

$$= \frac{1}{\pi m} \int_{-\pi}^{\pi} \left\{ \frac{\sin(x-\lambda) - \sin m(x-\lambda) + \sin(m-1)(x-\lambda)}{4(1 - \cos(x-\lambda))} \right.$$

$$\left. + \frac{\sin(x+\lambda) - \sin m(x+\lambda) + \sin(m-1)(x+\lambda)}{4(1 - \cos(x+\lambda))} \right\} f'(x) \, dx$$

$$\sim \frac{1}{2\pi m} P \int_{-\pi}^{\pi} \frac{\sin(x-\lambda)}{1 - \cos(x-\lambda)} f'(x) \, dx,$$

where the principal value of the last integral is to be taken. Note that the weight function of this estimate is positive. This implies that the estimate is positive with probability one and this is certainly a desirable property in many contexts.

Another estimate of the spectral density that might be called the *rectangular estimate* is given by

$$f_N^*(\lambda) = \frac{1}{2\pi} \sum_{\nu=-N}^{N} \frac{C_\nu}{N} \frac{\sin \nu h}{\nu h} \cos \nu\lambda \tag{2}$$

where $h = \pi/m$ and $m = o(N)$ tends to infinity with N. The weight function of this spectrograph estimate is

$$w_N(x) = \begin{cases} \dfrac{1}{4h} & \text{if } |x \pm \lambda| < h \\ 0 & \text{otherwise} \end{cases}$$

and this is what suggests the name rectangular estimate. The variance

$$D^2\left[f_N^*(\lambda)\right] \sim \frac{4\pi}{N} \int\limits_{-\pi}^{\pi} w_N^2(x) f^2(\lambda)\, dx$$

$$\sim \begin{cases} \dfrac{m}{N} f^2(\lambda) & \text{if } \lambda \neq 0 \\[2ex] \dfrac{2\,m}{N} f^2(0) & \text{if } \lambda = 0. \end{cases}$$

The bias

$$b_N(\lambda) \sim \int\limits_{\lambda-h}^{\lambda+h} \frac{1}{2h}[f(x)-f(\lambda)]\, dx \sim \frac{f''(\lambda)}{2h} \int\limits_{\lambda-h}^{\lambda+h} \frac{(x-\lambda)^2}{2}\, dx$$

$$= f''(\lambda)\, h^2/6 = f''(\lambda)\, \pi^2/6\, m^2.$$

This estimate also has a positive weight function.

A third estimate is easily obtained by truncating the expansion of the periodogram in terms of the product lag moments C_ν. This estimate is

$$f_N^*(\lambda) = \frac{1}{2\pi} \sum_{\nu=-m}^{m} \frac{C_\nu}{N} \cos \nu\lambda \tag{3}$$

where $m = o(N)$ but tends to infinity with N. The weight function corresponding to the estimate is

$$w_N(x) = \frac{1}{4\pi} \left\{ \frac{\sin (m+\frac{1}{2})(x-\lambda)}{\sin \frac{1}{2}(x-\lambda)} + \frac{\sin (m+\frac{1}{2})(x+\lambda)}{\sin \frac{1}{2}(x+\lambda)} \right\}.$$

This estimate has rather small bias and variance. However, this estimate may be negative for some values of λ since the weight function $w_N(x)$ is not positive for all values of x. Under some circumstances it may be rather unpleasant to have a negative estimate of a positive quantity, e.g. when one is interested in $\log f(\lambda)$. The variance of the estimate

$$D^2\left[f_N^*(\lambda)\right] \sim \frac{2\,f^2(\lambda)}{N} \sum_{\nu=-m}^{m} \cos^2 \nu\lambda$$

$$\sim \begin{cases} \dfrac{2\,m}{N} f^2(\lambda) & \text{if } \lambda \neq 0 \\[2ex] \dfrac{4\,m}{N} f^2(0) & \text{if } \lambda = 0. \end{cases}$$

The bias

$$b_N(\lambda) = \frac{1}{2\pi} \sum_{\nu=-m}^{m} \left(1 - \frac{|\nu|}{N}\right) r_\nu \cos \nu\lambda - \frac{1}{2\pi} \sum_{\nu=-\infty}^{\infty} r_\nu \cos \nu\lambda$$

$$\sim \frac{1}{2\pi N} P \int_{-\pi}^{\pi} \frac{\sin(x-\lambda)}{1 - \cos(x-\lambda)} f'(x)\, dx.$$

Tukey [1] has used the following expression

$$\frac{1}{2m}\left[\frac{C_0}{N} + 2\sum_{\nu=1}^{m-1} \frac{C_\nu}{N-\nu} \cos \nu\lambda \left(.46 \cos \frac{\pi\nu}{m} + .54\right) + \right.$$

$$\left. + \frac{C_m}{N-m} \cos m\lambda (.46 \cos \pi + .54)\right],$$

$$\lambda = \frac{\pi p}{m},\ p = 1.\ 2,\ \dots,\ m-1,$$

as an estimate of the spectral mass in the interval $(\lambda - \frac{1}{2}(\pi/m), \lambda + \frac{1}{2}(\pi/m))$. It is again understood that $m = o(N)$ and that m tends to infinity with N. On dividing by π/m we get an estimate of the spectral mass at λ. For convenience we modify this estimate of the spectral density slightly and consider

$$f_N^*(\lambda) = \frac{1}{2\pi} \frac{C_0}{N} + \frac{1}{\pi} \sum_{\nu=1}^{m} \frac{C_\nu}{N} \cos \nu\lambda \left(.46 \cos \frac{\pi\nu}{m} + .54\right). \qquad (4)$$

This estimate is a linear combination of estimates of the form (3). The corresponding weight function is

$$w_N(x) = \frac{1}{4\pi}\left\{ .54 \frac{\sin(m+\frac{1}{2})(x-\lambda)}{\sin\frac{1}{2}(x-\lambda)} + .54 \frac{\sin(m+\frac{1}{2})(x+\lambda)}{\sin\frac{1}{2}(x+\lambda)} + \right.$$

$$+ .23 \frac{\sin(m+\frac{1}{2})\left(x-\lambda-\frac{\pi}{m}\right)}{\sin\frac{1}{2}\left(x-\lambda-\frac{\pi}{m}\right)} + .23 \frac{\sin(m+\frac{1}{2})\left(x+\lambda-\frac{\pi}{m}\right)}{\sin\frac{1}{2}\left(x+\lambda-\frac{\pi}{m}\right)} +$$

$$\left. + .23 \frac{\sin(m+\frac{1}{2})\left(x-\lambda+\frac{\pi}{m}\right)}{\sin\frac{1}{2}\left(x-\lambda+\frac{\pi}{m}\right)} + .23 \frac{\sin(m+\frac{1}{2})\left(x+\lambda+\frac{\pi}{m}\right)}{\sin\frac{1}{2}\left(x+\lambda+\frac{\pi}{m}\right)}\right\}.$$

4.6

The variance of the estimate

$$D^2[f_N^*(\lambda)] \sim \frac{2}{N} f^2(\lambda) \sum_{\nu=-m}^{m} \left(.46 \cos \frac{\pi \nu}{m} + .54 \right)^2 \cos^2 \nu \lambda$$

$$\sim \begin{cases} \dfrac{m}{N} f^2(\lambda) \left((.46)^2 + 2(.54)^2 \right) & \lambda \neq 0 \\[2ex] \dfrac{2m}{N} f^2(0) \left((.46)^2 + 2(.54)^2 \right) & \lambda = 0. \end{cases}$$

The bias

$$b_N(\lambda) = \frac{1}{2\pi} \sum_{\nu=-m}^{m} r_\nu \left(1 - \frac{|\nu|}{N} \right) \left(.46 \cos \frac{\pi \nu}{m} + .54 \right) \cos \nu \lambda - f(\lambda)$$

$$\sim \frac{1}{2\pi} (.46) \sum_{\nu=-m}^{m} r_\nu \left(\cos \frac{\pi \nu}{m} - 1 \right) \cos \nu \lambda$$

$$\sim .46 \left[\tfrac{1}{2} f \left(\lambda + \frac{\pi}{m} \right) + \tfrac{1}{2} f \left(\lambda - \frac{\pi}{m} \right) - f(\lambda) \right]$$

$$\sim .23 f''(\lambda) \left(\frac{\pi}{m} \right)^2 \quad \text{if} \quad m^2 = o(N).$$

This estimate also may be negative for some values of λ since the corresponding weight function is not positive for all values of x.

Still another spectrograph estimate of interest is the one whose weights are the products of the weights of Bartlett's estimate and the rectangular estimate respectively. This estimate is

$$f_N^*(\lambda) = \frac{1}{2\pi} \sum_{\nu=-m}^{m} \frac{C_\nu}{N} \left(1 - \frac{|\nu|}{m} \right) \frac{\sin \nu h}{\nu h} \cos \nu \lambda \qquad (5)$$

where $h = \pi/m$. The weight function of the estimate is

$$w_N(x) = \frac{1}{4\pi m} \left\{ \frac{1}{2h} \int_{\lambda-h}^{\lambda+h} \frac{\sin^2 \frac{m}{2}(x-\mu)}{\sin^2 \frac{1}{2}(x-\mu)} \, d\mu + \frac{1}{2h} \int_{\lambda-h}^{\lambda+h} \frac{\sin^2 \frac{m}{2}(x+\mu)}{\sin^2 \frac{1}{2}(x+\mu)} \, d\mu \right\}.$$

The estimate is positive with probability one since the weight function is positive. The asymptotic variance

$$D^2[f_N^*(\lambda)] \sim \frac{2}{N} f^2(\lambda) \sum_{\nu=-m}^{m} \left(1 - \frac{|\nu|}{m}\right)^2 \left(\frac{\sin \nu h}{\nu h}\right)^2 \cos^2 \nu \lambda$$

$$\sim \begin{cases} \dfrac{2m}{N} f^2(\lambda) \displaystyle\int_0^1 (1-x)^2 \left(\frac{\sin \pi x}{\pi x}\right)^2 dx & \text{if } \lambda \neq 0 \\[4mm] \dfrac{4m}{N} f^2(0) \displaystyle\int_0^1 (1-x)^2 \left(\frac{\sin \pi x}{\pi x}\right)^2 dx & \text{if } \lambda = 0. \end{cases}$$

The asymptotic bias is the same as in the case of Bartlett's estimate.

It is worthwhile contrasting the inconsistent periodogram with the spectrograph estimates described here that are consistent estimates of the spectral density. Anyone looking at the problem of estimating the spectral density might have thought the periodogram a good estimate. The statistics C_ν/N are good estimates of the covariances r_ν, $\nu = 0, 1, \ldots, N$, even though they are biased. Since the spectral density is given by

$$f(\lambda) = \frac{1}{2\pi} \sum_{\nu=-\infty}^{\infty} r_\nu \cos \nu \lambda$$

it might seem reasonable to replace r_ν by its estimate C_ν/N when $|\nu| < N$ and by zero when $|\nu| \geq N$. But we then get

$$I_N(\lambda) = \frac{1}{2\pi} \sum_{\nu=-N}^{N} \frac{C_\nu}{N} \cos \nu \lambda = \frac{1}{2\pi N} \left| \sum_{\nu=1}^{N} x_\nu e^{i\nu\lambda} \right|^2,$$

i.e., the periodogram. The inconsistency of $I_N(\lambda)$ arises from the fact that for large $|\nu|$, the statistics C_ν/N are relatively unstable estimates of r_ν. In order to obtain consistency, one should delete the contribution from them as was done in the case of the truncated estimate (3), or give them a very small weight as compared with the contribution from the C_ν/N with small $|\nu|$ as was done in the case of the rectangular estimate (2).

Let us now consider a special estimate of the type considered in section 4.1. Note that all those estimates are positive with probability one. Let

$$g_\beta(t) = \begin{cases} \sqrt{\dfrac{\beta}{\pi}} e^{-\beta t} & \text{when } t \geq 0 \\[3mm] 0 & \text{when } t < 0 \end{cases}$$

so that

$$\varphi_\beta(x) = \sqrt{\frac{\beta}{\pi}} \int_0^\infty e^{-ixt} e^{-\beta t} dt = \sqrt{\frac{\beta}{\pi}} \frac{1}{\beta + ix}.$$

Here $\beta = \beta(T)$ is a function of T which approaches zero as $T \to \infty$. Clearly

$$\int_{-\infty}^{\infty} |\varphi_\beta(x)|^2 \, dx = \frac{\beta}{\pi} \int_{-\infty}^{\infty} \frac{1}{|\beta + ix|^2} \, dx \equiv 1.$$

Moreover

$$\int_{-\infty}^{\infty} |\varphi_\beta(x)|^4 \, dx = \frac{\beta^2}{\pi^2} \int_{-\infty}^{\infty} \frac{1}{|\beta + ix|^4} \, dx = \frac{1}{2\pi\beta}.$$

Let us now consider the asymptotic bias of the estimate

$$f_T^*(\lambda) = \frac{1}{T} \int_0^T |z_t|^2 \, dt,$$

where

$$z_t = \int_0^t x_s \, e^{is\lambda} \, g_\beta(t-s) \, ds.$$

Now

$$\int_0^t e^{-ixu} \, g_\beta(u) \, du = \sqrt{\frac{\beta}{\pi}} \, [1 - e^{-(ix+\beta)t}] \frac{1}{\beta + ix}$$

so that

$$\frac{1}{T} \int_0^T \left| \int_0^t e^{-iu(x-\lambda)} \, g_\beta(u) \, du \right|^2 \, dt$$

$$= \frac{\beta}{\pi |\beta + i(x-\lambda)|^2} \frac{1}{T} \int_0^T |1 - e^{-(i(x-\lambda)+\beta)t}|^2 \, dt$$

$$= \frac{\beta}{\pi |\beta + i(x-\lambda)|^2} \frac{1}{T} \int_0^T [1 - 2e^{-\beta t} \cos (x-\lambda)t + e^{-2\beta t}] \, dt$$

$$= \frac{\beta}{\pi |\beta + i(x-\lambda)|^2} \left\{ 1 - \frac{2\beta}{T |\beta + i(x-\lambda)|^2} + \frac{1}{2\beta T} + 0(e^{-\beta T}) \right\}.$$

The bias

$$b_T(\lambda) = E f_T^*(\lambda) - f(\lambda)$$

$$= \frac{\beta}{\pi} \int_{-\infty}^{\infty} \frac{f(x) - f(\lambda)}{\beta^2 + (x-\lambda)^2} \, dx - \frac{2\beta^2}{\pi T} \int_{-\infty}^{\infty} \frac{f(x)}{(\beta^2 + (x-\lambda)^2)^2} \, dx$$

$$+ \frac{1}{2\pi T} \int_{-\infty}^{\infty} \frac{f(x)}{\beta^2 + (x-\lambda)^2} \, dx + 0(e^{-\beta T}).$$

Note that

$$\int\limits_{-\infty}^{T}\int\limits_{-\infty}^{0}\left|\int\limits_{0}^{T} g_\beta(t-u)\,g_\beta(t-v)\,dt\right|^2 du\,dv\leq\frac{1}{\beta^2}=o\left(\frac{T}{\beta}\right)$$

if $1/T=0\,(\beta)$. Clearly condition (4.5.4) is satisfied if $1/T=o\,(\beta)$.

On using (4.5.5) we see that the asymptotic variance of the estimate

$$D^2\,[f_T^*(\lambda)]\sim\frac{2\,\pi\,f^2\,(\lambda)}{T}\int\limits_{-\infty}^{\infty}|\varphi_\beta(x)|^4\,dx=\frac{f^2\,(\lambda)}{\beta\,T}$$

if $\lambda\neq0$ and that

$$D^2\,[f_T^*(0)]\sim\frac{2\,f^2\,(0)}{\beta\,T}.$$

Before closing this section it is worthwhile looking at the consistency of the spectrograph estimates that we have considered. As we mentioned, this was due to the attenuation of the influence of the product lag moments C_ν/N with $|\nu|$ large. However, this can be looked at from a different point of view. All these consistent spectrograph estimates were smoothings of the periodogram. The weight function approached a δ-function in behavior as $N\to\infty$ at λ and $-\lambda$ but slowly enough so that the estimate was consistent.

4.7. The Mean Square Error of Estimates

It is clear from the general discussion of estimates of the spectral density, as well as from the discussion of special estimates, that *one cannot improve the asymptotic behavior of the bias and variance of the estimate simultaneously.* If the estimate is modified so as to improve the asymptotic behavior of the bias, the variance will behave worse and vice versa. One is therefore led to consider some function of both the bias and the variance of the estimate. A reasonable choice of such a function is the mean square error of the estimate, that is

$$E\,|f_N^*(\lambda)-f(\lambda)|^2=[b_N(\lambda)]^2+D^2[f_N^*(\lambda)].$$

Of course, a small mean square error may not be the only property required of an estimate. If one were to make use of an estimate of the spectral density in a prediction problem, it would seem reasonable to require also that the estimate be positive with probability one as we then have to deal with the logarithm of the spectral density.

Consider the mean square error of the estimates discussed in section 4.6. It should be noted that the discussion concerns itself with the asymptotic behavior of the mean square error. Assuming that m is of form $m = KN^\alpha$ where K is a constant, we ask for the α which ensures that the mean square error is of smallest order as $N \to \infty$. Only in a few cases will the optimal choice of K be discussed.

In the case of Bartlett's estimate

$$E\,|\,f_N^*(\lambda) - f(\lambda)\,| \sim \frac{2}{3}\frac{m}{N}f^2(\lambda) + \left[\frac{1}{2\pi m}\,P\int_{-\pi}^{\pi}\frac{\sin{(x-\lambda)}}{1-\cos{(x-\lambda)}}f'(x)\,dx\right]^2,$$

$\lambda \neq 0$, as $m, N \to \infty$, $m = o(N)$. The optimal choice of α if $m = KN^\alpha$ is $\alpha = \frac{1}{3}$ for then

$$E\,|\,f_N^*(\lambda) - f(\lambda)\,|^2 = 0\,(N^{-\frac{2}{3}}).$$

The rectangular estimate (4.6.2) has mean square error

$$E\,|\,f_N^*(\lambda) - f(\lambda)\,|^2 \sim \frac{m}{N}f^2(\lambda) + \left[\frac{f''(\lambda)\,\pi^2}{6\,m^2}\right]^2, \quad \lambda \neq 0,$$

as $m, N \to \infty$, $m = o(N)$. If $m = KN^\alpha$, the optimal choice of α is $\alpha = \frac{1}{5}$ and then

$$E\,|\,f_N^*(\lambda) - f(\lambda)\,|^2 \sim (\gamma K + \delta/K^4)\,N^{-4/s},$$

where $\gamma = f^2(\lambda)$ and $\delta = [f''(\lambda)\,\pi^2/6]^2$. The coefficient $\gamma k + \delta/K^4$ is minimized by taking

$$K = \left(\frac{4\,\delta}{\gamma}\right)^{1/s} = \left(\frac{|\,f''(\lambda)\,|}{f(\lambda)}\right)^{2/s}\left(\frac{\pi^2}{3}\right)^{2/s}.$$

Then

$$E\,|\,f_N^*(\lambda) - f(\lambda)\,|^2 \sim 5 \cdot 4^{-4/s}\,\gamma^{4/s}\,\delta^{1/s}$$

$$= 5 \cdot 4^{-4/s}\,(f(\lambda))^{8/s}\,(|\,f''(\lambda)\,|)^{2/s}\left(\frac{\pi^4}{36}\right)^{1/s}N^{-4/s}.$$

The truncated estimate (4.6.3) has a mean square error

$$E\,|\,f_N^*(\lambda) - f(\lambda)\,|^2 \sim \frac{2m}{N}f^2(\lambda) + \left[\frac{1}{2\pi N}\,P\int_{-\pi}^{\pi}\frac{\sin{(x-\lambda)}}{1-\cos{(x-\lambda)}}f'(x)\,dx\right]^2.$$

Here there is no optimal choice of α. Clearly the mean square error is asymptotically the same as

$$2\,K\,N^{\alpha-1}\,f^2(\lambda)$$

if $m = KN^{\alpha}$. However, by choosing α smaller we implicitly assume $f(\lambda)$ more regular.

The mean square error of the estimate suggested by Tukey (4.6.4) is given by

$$E\,|f_N^*(\lambda) - f(\lambda)|^2 \sim \frac{m}{N}\, f^2(\lambda)\,(\,.7748) + \left(\,.23\, f''(\lambda)\frac{\pi^2}{m^2}\right)^2.$$

If $m = KN^{\alpha}$, the optimal choice of α is $1/5$. A discussion analogous to that on the rectangular estimate indicates that the best choice of K is

$$K = \left[\frac{|f''(\lambda)|}{f(\lambda)}\right]^{2/5} \left(\frac{2116}{7748}\,\pi^4\right)^{1/5}$$

and then

$$E\,|f_N^*(\lambda) - f(\lambda)|^2 \sim 5\cdot 4^{-4/5}\,(f(\lambda))^{8/5}\,|f''(\lambda)|^{2/5}$$
$$(\,.7748)^{4/5}\,(\,.23\,\pi^2)^{2/5}\,N^{-4/5}.$$

Note that the asymptotic mean square error is of the same order as that of the rectangular estimate but with a coefficient smaller by about a fifth.

The mean square errors of the last two estimates considered in section 4.6 are $0(N^{-2/3})$ and $0(T^{-2/3})$ respectively if one chooses $m = KN^{1/3}$ and $\beta = KT^{-1/3}$. Note that all of the spectrograph estimates except for the rectangular estimate are well suited for computation since one only needs to compute m of the product lag moments C_r/N.

4.8. An Example from Statistical Optics

Consider the following model of light that has been suggested by Parke [1]. At a given point (x, y, z) at time t the electric field vector e_t is given by

$$e_t = \int\limits_{-\pi}^{\pi} \exp\left[i\left(t - \frac{x}{c}\right)\lambda\right]\,dz(\lambda),$$

where $z(\lambda)$ is an orthogonal stochastic process taking as values vectors in the (y, z)-plane. The components of $e_t = (e_t^{(1)},\, e_t^{(2)})$ in the y and z directions form the *Maxwell vector*. It is assumed to be stationary with spectrum determined by the matrix of the spectral distribution functions

$$F_{ij}(\lambda),\ i, j = 1, 2.$$

This might be called the *coherency matrix* and it describes the *polarization* of the light. If $F_{11}(\lambda) = F_{22}(\lambda)$, $F_{12}(\lambda) = F_{21}(\lambda) = 0$ the light is circularly polarized. If $F_{22} = F_{12} = F_{21} = 0$ the light is *linearly polarized* and we shall deal with this case.

The two following examples are highly idealized versions of methods used in practice to estimate the spectrum. Consider a grating spectroscope with a grating width Δ and a large number of lines n. Huyghen's principle tells us that at the point (x_0, d) the electric field is the sum of the contributions from the various grating intervals

$$\sum_{\nu=1}^{n} x(t_\nu).$$

Here we have set

$$t_\nu = t + \frac{1}{c} \sqrt{x_0^2 + (d + \nu \Delta)^2}$$

where c stands for the velocity of light. Using the approximation

$$t_\nu \sim t + \frac{x_0}{c} \left(1 + \frac{(d + \nu \Delta)^2}{2 x_0^2} \right)$$

$$= t + \frac{1}{c} \left(x_0 + \frac{d^2}{2 x_0} \right) + \frac{d \nu \Delta}{c x_0} = a + b \, d \nu$$

the intensity at the point of observation is seen to be proportional to

$$\frac{1}{n} \left[\sum_{\nu=1}^{n} x(a + b \, d \nu) \right]^2.$$

The mean value of the intensity at d is then proportional to

$$\frac{1}{2 \pi n} \int_{-\infty}^{\infty} \frac{\sin^2 (n + \frac{1}{2}) b \, d \lambda}{\sin^2 \frac{1}{2} b \, d \lambda} f(\lambda) \, d \lambda$$

which for large values of n tends to

$$f(0) + 2 \sum_{N=1}^{\infty} f(2 \pi N / b d). \tag{1}$$

If the spectrum is essentially confined to an interval (α, β),

$$0 < \alpha < \beta < \infty,$$

expression (1) is given by

$$2 f \left(\frac{2 \pi c x_0}{d \Delta} \right)$$

if $d < 4\pi c x_0/\Delta\beta$, so that we estimate the spectral density at the frequency $2\pi c x_0/d\Delta$. By varying d we can estimate the spectral density in a certain range. The limiting variance of this estimate is positive. However, this should not be taken too seriously as what one actually observes in practice is not the intensity at an isolated point but rather the average in a small but finite interval $d_1 < d < d_2$. This "smoothing" is carried out when the light is received on a photographic plate. In analogy to what has been said in section 4.6 about the periodogram one might expect that in this case too, the smoothing produces a consistent estimate. It would be interesting to find whether this can be shown rigorously.

Let us now consider another method using a prism. The prism separates the harmonic components of the incident ray of light, and the resolved light is projected on a plate. Smoothing the intensity over a small range of frequencies (λ_1, λ_2) another estimate of the spectral energy in (λ_1, λ_2) is obtained. Note that both estimates of this section are of the general form introduced in 4.1.

CHAPTER 5

APPLICATIONS

5.0. Introduction

In this chapter three fields in which stationary models have proved to be useful are considered. We look at some problems that arise in the study of random noise, turbulence and storm-generated ocean waves. The rational behind the choice of a statistical model that is stationary is discussed.

Knowledge of the spectrum of the process gives one information about the structure of the phenomenon of interest. In some cases one can obtain a partial determination of the spectrum of the process by deductive methods, e.g. from the equations of motion in turbulence. Such a procedure has to be supplemented by an empirical approach. Some of the methods of estimating the spectrum from data in these different contexts are discussed.

The reader should consult Goldman [1], Rice [1], James-Nichols-Phillips [1], Lawson-Uhlenbeck [1] and Woodward [1] for an extended study of noise and related topics.

5.1. Derivation of Spectra of Random Noise

There are several types of electronic random noise. We are going to discuss two types only in this section. *Shot noise* was mentioned already in section 1.6 where its spectrum was derived. In the case of shot noise, the observed current is due to the arrival of electrons at the anode of an electron tube and as this happens in a random manner the current will fluctuate around a mean value, the direct current or d.c. component. The model used in section 1.6 is based on the assumption that the time points for these arrivals are governed by a Poisson process with parameter β. As β tends to infinity it is easy to prove that the normed process tends to a normal process distribution wise.

Another very important type of random noise is commonly referred to as *thermal noise*. Between the endpoints of any conductor there will be a fluctuating voltage due to the random motion of the electrons in the conductor. In order to derive the spectrum of this voltage we shall carry out a thought experiment following C. W. McCombie [1]. Consider a resistance R and the random voltage x_t due to thermal noise. We connect the resistance in

158

series with an inductance L and a capacitance C. The resonant frequency of this circuit is $\lambda_0 = 1/2\pi\sqrt{LC}$. Let the random current produced by x_t be y_t. We know that y_t is the result of a filter operating on x_t with frequency response function

$$\varphi(\lambda) = \frac{1}{R + 2\pi i\,\lambda L - \dfrac{i}{2\pi C\lambda}}.$$

Introduce the spectral densities $f_x(\lambda)$ and $f_y(\lambda)$ corresponding to the processes x_t and y_t respectively. The spectral density (see section 1.9)

$$f_y(\lambda) = |\varphi(\lambda)|^2 f_x(\lambda) = \frac{f_x(\lambda)\,\lambda^2}{\lambda^2 R^2 + 4\pi^2 L^2(\lambda^2 - \lambda_0^2)^2}.$$

If R is very small compared to L/C, the filter will allow only frequencies in the neighborhood of λ_0 to pass through it. But then $f_x(\lambda)$ can be regarded as a constant $f_x(\lambda_0)$ for all these frequencies, and hence

$$E\,y_t^2 = \int_{-\infty}^{\infty} f_y(\lambda)\,d\lambda \sim f_x(\lambda_0) \int_{-\infty}^{\infty} |\varphi(\lambda)|^2\,d\lambda = \frac{f_x(\lambda_0)}{4\,LR} \tag{1}$$

Now we consider this situation from the point of view of statistical mechanics. The total energy is the sum of the electric energy and the magnetic energy. The latter is $\frac{1}{2} L y_t^2$. According to the equipartition theorem (see Tolman [1], p. 93)

$$E\,\tfrac{1}{2}\,L\,y_t^2 = \tfrac{1}{2}\,k\,T, \tag{2}$$

where T is the absolute temperature and k is Boltzmann's constant. On using (1) and (2) it is seen that

$$f_x(\lambda_0) \sim 4\,R\,k\,T.$$

This is called *Nyquist's law*. The spectral density $f_x(\lambda_0)$ is independent of λ_0 so that we have white noise. It is clear that the spectral density cannot be constant on the whole real axis as we would then have infinite power. However the result holds up to very high frequencies. A detailed discussion of the upper limit of the thermal noise spectrum can be found in Lawson and Uhlenbeck [1], p. 77.

One can also prove that the thermal noise voltage is a normal process. We shall not carry out the proof but refer to Lawson and Uhlenbeck [1], p. 67.

5.2. Measuring Noise Spectra

In the last section we saw that sometimes the spectrum of the noise can be computed if we have sufficient knowledge of the mechanism that generates the noise. When studying the noise output of an electronic device that is not too complicated, one usually considers the output as generated by the various noise sources in the device and external noise fed into the device. If the statistical structure of these noise components is known, we can at least theoretically compute the spectrum of the output noise. This procedure will break down, either if the device is too complex or if some of the sources produce noise of unknown spectra. If the device has some nonlinear elements it will not be sufficient in general to know the spectra of the noise sources and the external noise. The whole probability structure of the noise sources then has to be specified.

In such a case it will be necessary to actually measure the spectrum of the output noise. It may also be of interest to study the probability distribution of the output noise, e.g., to find out whether the output noise is normal or not. This last problem is briefly discussed in Chapter 8. The first problem can be treated in various ways.

One very natural procedure is to feed the noise into a linear device with the frequency response function $\varphi_\alpha(\lambda)$, where α is a parameter that can be varied. Measuring the average power of the output we have

$$P_\alpha = \int\limits_{-\infty}^{\infty} |\varphi_\alpha(\lambda)|^2 f(\lambda) \, d\lambda.$$

Now if the device acts as a selective circuit, allowing only frequencies very close to α to pass through, it is clear that we can use P_α to estimate $f(\alpha)$, and as α is varied we will estimate the spectral density over the range of variation. Note that this estimate is a generalization of the one dealt with in section 4.5 and is of the general form introduced in Section 4.1. It has been suggested (see Davenport, Johnson, Middleton [1]) that one could choose the device as a tuned circuit (we would then estimate the spectral density at the resonant frequency, see section 4.5) or use a feedback amplifier in which the feedback loop has a variable characteristic attenuating frequencies which are not close to α.

A disadvantage of these methods is that as the elements in the tuned circuit vary the function $|\varphi_\alpha(\lambda)|^2$ varies not only with respect to location on the frequency axis but also in shape. A method that avoids this has been suggested by J. S. Cobine and J. R. Curry [1].

160

Mix x_t with the wave $A\,\cos(t\lambda+\varphi)$ from a local oscillator of frequency λ with amplitude A and a random phase $-\pi<\varphi<\pi$. Then the modulated wave

$$y_t=\mathcal{M}x_t=A\,\cos\,(t\lambda+\varphi)x_t$$

has the covariances

$$\varrho_{s-t}=E\,y_s\,y_t=\frac{A^2}{2}\,\cos\,(s-t)\,\lambda\,E\,x_s\,x_t=\frac{A^2}{2}\,\cos\,(s-t)\,\lambda\,r_{s-t}.$$

Assuming the spectral density of the original process to be $f(\mu)$ the spectral density of y_t is

$$f_y\,(\mu)=\frac{A^2\,(f\,(\mu+\lambda)+f\,(\mu-\lambda))}{4}\,,$$

as is easily verified. Let y_t pass through a filter $\mathcal{F}$ with a frequency response function $\varphi(\lambda)$. The average power of the output gives us an estimate of

$$\int\limits_{-\infty}^{\infty}\frac{f\,(\mu+\lambda)+f\,(\mu-\lambda)}{4}\,|\varphi\,(\mu)|^2\,d\mu=\int\limits_{-\infty}^{\infty}f\,(x)\,\frac{|\varphi\,(x+\lambda)|^2+|\varphi\,(x-\lambda)|^2}{4}\,d\,x.$$

If $|\varphi(\mu)|^2$ is concentrated around $\mu=0$ this is close to $f(\lambda)/2$. Now the filter is kept fixed but the frequency λ of the local oscillator is varied. We then see that varying λ means translating the weight functions $|\varphi\,(x+\lambda)|^2$ and $|\varphi\,(x-\lambda)|^2$ that belong to the two sidebands, and in this way the difficulty of change in shape of weight functions mentioned above is avoided.

It might be of interest to consider the estimates obtained by applying the *heterodyne principle* (i.e., the procedure described above using a local oscillator). We have already discussed these estimates in section 4.5. For convenience the complex representation of the process was used so that

$$z_t=\mathcal{F}\,\mathcal{M}\,x_t=\mathcal{F}\,x_t\,e^{it\lambda}=\int\limits_0^t x_s\,e^{is\lambda}\,g\,(t-s)\,d\,s,$$

where $g(u)$ is the transient response function of $\mathcal{F}$ and the observation interval is $(0,T)$. The average power is then

$$\frac{1}{T}\int\limits_0^T|z_t|^2\,dt=\frac{1}{T}\int\limits_0^T\int\limits_0^T\int\limits_0^T x_u\,x_v\,e^{i(u-v)\lambda}\,g\,(t-u)\,g\,(t-v)\,d\,u\,d\,v\,dt,$$

since $g(u)=0$ for $u<0$. Our estimate of $f(\lambda)$ is

$$\alpha_T^* = \frac{1}{T} \int_0^\infty \int_0^\infty x_u\, x_v\, b_T(u,v)\, du\, dv, \tag{1}$$

where
$$b_T(u,v) = \cos(u-v)\,\lambda \int_0^T g(t-u)\, g(t-v)\, dt,$$

and as this function is zero for $u > T$ or $v > T$ the integrals in (1) are extended over the square with sides $(0, T)$.

The bias and variance of estimates of this family have been discussed in some detail in section 4.5. Let $g(u) = 0$ for $u > h(T)$ where $h(T) = o(T^{\frac{1}{2}})$. The bias is then

$$E\left\{ \frac{1}{T} \int_0^T |z_t|^2\, dt - f(\lambda) \right\}$$

$$= \int_{-\infty}^\infty |\varphi(x)|^2 [f(x) - f(\lambda)]\, dx + o\left(\frac{h^2(T)}{T} \right).$$

On the other hand, it is clear from section 4.5 that the variance of

$$\frac{1}{T} \int_0^T |z_t|^2\, dt$$

is given by

$$2\pi \int_{-\infty}^\infty \int_{-\infty}^\infty \frac{\sin^2 \frac{T}{2}(x-y)}{\left(\frac{T(x-y)}{2} \right)^2} |\varphi(x)|^2 |\varphi(y)|^2 f(x)\, f(y)\, dx\, dy$$

asymptotically. This suggests that under reasonable conditions on the rate at which $|\varphi(x)|^2$ becomes a delta function at λ, the variance is asymptotically the same as

$$f^2(\lambda) \frac{2\pi}{T} \int_{-\infty}^\infty |\varphi(x)|^4\, dx.$$

The reader may be interested by another estimation method proposed by Grützmacher [1].

One could also estimate the covariance function and then use the Fourier inversion formula to get an estimate of the spectral density. It has been noted in the engineering literature that one should use only the parts of the covariance function corresponding to moderate lags, as the rest of it has a large relative error due to sampling variability (see McCombie [1]). One would then be led to the continuous parameter analogues of the spectrograph estimates that were analyzed in some detail in Chapter 4. Although we were concerned with discrete parameter processes in our discussion of spectrograph estimates in Chapter 4, it is clear that the results could be extended to continuous time parameter processes. Such an extension would be more natural in this context.

If one wants greater precision in the computation, a digital computer will be preferred to an anlogue computer. In such a case the data will be discretized so that it can be fed into the digital computer. If the original time series is x_t, $0 < t < T$, the result of discretizing the data will be $x_{Tk/n}$, $k = 0, \ldots, n$.

When we have a sample of n observations and want to obtain the spectrum of the underlying process, there are two types of limitations that occur. The first one is due to the finite sample size and implies that one cannot get much information about the very fine structure, i.e., one cannot distinguish between frequencies very close to each other because of the finite resolvability of the estimate. The other limitation is on detection of high frequencies because of the discrete nature of the sampling. This was discussed in section 1.9.D. One should point out that if one is sampling continuously, the inertia of the recording instruments will introduce errors (usually of high frequency) which will mask the spectral density in the high frequency range.

The reader will find a treatment of similar questions in Davenport-Johnson-Middleton [1] and Spetner [1].

5.3. Turbulence

The interest in problems of turbulence has grown in the past few decades. In the study of turbulence the model of a stationary process has been fruitful. Because of this we append this section in which a few selected and simple topics in the theory of turbulence are discussed. The first question that arises is the nature of turbulence. We do not claim to give any definitive answer. In fact there still is some disagreement among research workers as to what they would call turbulence. Nonetheless, we will discuss a few characteristics of turbulence that would be agreed upon as basic by most research workers.

Perhaps the best way in which to describe turbulence is to discuss a simple physical context in which it arises. Consider a regular grid of bars with the spacing between bars M centimeters. Suppose that there is a uniform flow of a fluid with speed U centimeters per second perpendicular to the grid and

163

through it. Assume that the kinematic viscosity ν of the fluid is small. The Reynold's number of the grid UM/ν then is large. If the velocity field of the flow, after it has passed through the grid, is measured repeatedly under the same macroscopic conditions (the boundary conditions are held fixed), it is noted that the measurements do not coincide but vary substantially in what seems to be a random manner about the mean velocity. This is what happens in a wind tunnel when one generates turbulence. The random variation cannot be explained by errors in measurement. It has been suggested that the random character of the velocity field is due to the instability of the flow. As a deterministic model seems inadequate in such a context, it is reasonable to look for an appropriate statistical approach.

Let us see how a statistical approach is suggested by deterministic considerations. If a deterministic approach were appropriate, the fluid flow would be specified by the equations of motion and the boundary conditions. Once the boundary conditions are fixed it is physically plausible that the course of the flow would be completely determined by the equations of motion. Turbulence may be due to the solutions of the equations being unstable so that a small perturbation (which one cannot detect and over which one has no control) changes the solution radically. It then seems reasonable to consider a probability distribution of velocity fields each of which satisfies the equations of motion. This is in fact the statistical approach used in the theory of turbulence.

Assume that the fluid is incompressible. Let $u(x,t)$ be the velocity at point x at time t. The incompressibility is a reasonable assumption if the root mean square velocity $\sqrt{Eu^2}$ of the fluid is small compared to the average velocity of sound in the fluid. The velocity field $u(x,t)$ then satisfies the continuity equation

$$\nabla \cdot u = \sum_{i=1}^{3} \frac{\partial u_i}{\partial x_i} = 0.$$

Here u_i and x_i are the ith components of u and x respectively. Let ϱ be the density of the fluid and $p(x,t)$ the pressure at x at time t. The velocity field satisfies

$$\frac{\partial u}{\partial t} + u \cdot \nabla u = -\frac{1}{\varrho} \nabla \varrho + \nu \triangle^2 u,$$

the Navier-Stockes equation. Here ∇u is the gradient of u and $\nabla^2 u$ is the Laplacian of u. The term $u \cdot \nabla u$ is often referred to as the inertial term. The term $\nu \nabla^2 u$ is due to the viscous forces.

164

The general problem of turbulence is very complicated. For this reason symmetry conditions that simplify the problem are introduced. These symmetry conditions lead to idealized models of turbulence. Nonetheless even these idealized models are sometimes approached in experimental situations. Homogeneous turbulence is such a model. In homogeneous turbulence all space is considered turbulent and the statistical structure of the turbulence is assumed invariant under space translation. This means that the velocity $u(x,t)$ is a stochastic process in (x,t) that is stationary in x, that is, $\{u(x_j + y, t_j); \ j = 1, \ldots, n\}$ has the same probability distribution as $\{u(x_j, t_j); \ j = 1, \ldots, n\}$. Though homogenous turbulence is an idealization, it can be realized approximately in practice. In the case of turbulence generated by a flow passing through a grid, the turbulence dies off slowly with the distance from the grid. Locally this turbulence can be considered a homogeneous turbulence. This is probably the case in measurements of atmospheric wind velocities if one restricts oneself to a sufficiently small volume. Homogeneous turbulence is at times further qualified by the assumption that the probability distribution is invariant under rotation and reflection. By this we mean the following. Let $x_1, \ldots, x_n$ be any n points and $a_1, \ldots, a_n$ any fixed directions at these points. Consider the joint probability distribution of the components of the velocities at $x_1, \ldots, x_n$ in the directions $a_1, \ldots, a_n$ respectively. The distribution is assumed to be invariant under any rigid rotation or reflection in any plane of the configuration formed by the n points and the associated directional vectors. The homogeneous turbulence generated by flow through a grid seems to be locally isotropic a small distance from the grid. This is certainly not true of atmospheric wind velocities close to the earth's surface. One would not expect isotropic turbulence close to the boundary of the region of fluid flow. Isotropic turbulence might develop at some height above the earth's surface.

Intuitively one feels that a turbulent velocity field is a superposition of different modes of motion and one way to study turbulence is to decompose it into these different modes of motion. A convenient way of doing this is to carry out a Fourier analysis of homogeneous turbulence with respect to x. Some people feel that this particular decomposition is not the natural one but at present they have not suggested a concrete alternative. For convenience we subtract the mean velocity field from the turbulent velocity field so that $Eu(x,t) = 0$. Since $u(x,t)$ is a process stationary in the space variable x, it has the representation

$$u(x, t) = \int_K e^{ik \cdot x} d_k z(k, t),$$

where $z(k,t)$ is a vector-valued stochastic process that is an orthogonal set function in wave number space K. The dependence of functions on t will sometimes be omitted. The covariance matrix

$$R(r) = \{R_{ij}(r)\} = \int_K e^{ik \cdot r} f(k) \, dk,$$

where $f(k) = \{f_{ij}(k)\}$ is the spectral matrix. Here

$$E \, dz_i(k) \, \overline{dz_j(k')} = f_{ij}(k) \, dk \, \delta_{k, k'}.$$

It seems appropriate to call $f(k)$ the energy spectrum matrix since

$$R_{ij}(r) = Eu_i(x)u_j(x+r).$$

Note that absolute continuity of the spectrum has been assumed. However, we will see that this is proper since the nonlinear or inertial term in the equations of motion acts as a transfer term and would immediately spread the energy of a line or jump in the spectrum over a continuous range of wave numbers. The velocity field $u(x,t)$ is now expressed as a linear superposition of Fourier components $e^{ik \cdot x} dz(k,t)$ and we identify these with the different modes of motion. These Fourier components are sometimes referred to as "eddies". Note that the term eddy as used here does not agree with common usage as it is in fact a plane wave. The study of turbulence is now the study of these Fourier components. Since k has the dimension [length]$^{-1}$, when we speak of small eddies we mean Fourier components corresponding to large $|k|$; large eddies correspond to small $|k|$.

Average $f_{ij}(k)$ over all directions of the vector argument k so as to obtain

$$\psi_{ij}(\mathbf{k}) = \int_{|k|=\mathbf{k}} f_{ij}(k) \, dk.$$

Now $\psi_{ij}(\mathbf{k})d\mathbf{k}$ is the contribution to Eu_iu_j from wave numbers k with $\mathbf{k} \leq |k| \leq \mathbf{k} + d\mathbf{k}$. The functions $\psi_{ik}(\mathbf{k})$ are important in the study of isotropic turbulence because the dependence on k is determined by spherical symmetry. The function

$$E(\mathbf{k}) = \tfrac{1}{2} \sum_{i=1}^{3} \psi_{ii}(\mathbf{k})$$

is called the spectral energy function because it is the contribution to the kinetic energy from Fourier components with wave numbers $|k| = \mathbf{k}$. The mean kinetic energy per unit of fluid is

166

$$\tfrac{1}{2}\,E\,|\,u\,|^2 = \int\limits_0^\infty E\,(\mathbf{k})\,d\,\mathbf{k}.$$

Let us see what we can infer from the equations of motion about homogeneous turbulence. The equation of continuity

$$\nabla \cdot u = \int\limits_K e^{ik\cdot x}\,i\,k\cdot d\,z\,(k) = 0,$$

implies that

$$k \cdot d\,z\,(k) = 0.$$

Thus $dz(k)$ is orthogonal to k. By $dz(k)$ we mean the value of the spectral stochastic set function z on a small interval in wave number space centered at the point k. The Navier-Stokes equation can be written in the form

$$\frac{\partial u}{\partial t} + u \cdot \nabla u + \frac{1}{\varrho}\,\nabla \varrho - \nu\,\nabla^2 u$$

$$= \int e^{ik\cdot x}\,\frac{\partial}{\partial t}\,d\,z\,(k) + i \int\int e^{ik\cdot x}\,d\,z\,(k)\cdot k'\,e^{ik'\cdot x}\,d\,z\,(k') +$$

$$+ \frac{1}{\varrho}\int e^{ik\cdot x}\,d\,w\,(k) + \nu \int k^2\,e^{ik\cdot x}\,d\,z\,(k)$$

$$= 0,$$

where $p\,(x)/\varrho = \int e^{ik\cdot x}\,d\,w\,(k)$. But this can hold if and only if

$$\frac{\partial}{\partial t}\,d\,z\,(k) + i \int\limits_{K'} k'\cdot d\,z\,(k - k')\,d\,z\,(k') + i\,k\,d\,w\,(k) + \nu\,k^2\,d\,z\,(k) = 0. \qquad (1)$$

Note that $z(k)$, $w(k)$ are the integrated Fourier transforms of $u(x)$ and $p(x)/\varrho$ (the integrated Fourier transform exists but the Fourier transform does not). If the divergence of the Navier-Stokes equation is taken, the following equation is obtained relating the pressure and the velocity field

$$\frac{1}{\varrho}\,\nabla^2 p = -\sum_{i,j}\frac{\partial^2 u_i\,u_j}{\partial x_i\,\partial x_j}.$$

On taking the Fourier transform of this equation we obtain

$$d\,w\,(k) = -\frac{1}{k^2}\int\limits_{K'} k\cdot d\,z\,(k - k')\,k\cdot d\,z\,(k').$$

5.3

An integral of this form has not been defined previously. However, integrals of such a form can be defined in a way analogous to that used in chapter 1 if higher order moments of u are assumed to exist. The continuity equation can be rewritten in the form

$$k \cdot dz(k - k') = k' \cdot dz(k - k').$$

Using this and the representation of $dw(k)$ we find that (1) can be rewritten as

$$\frac{\partial \, dz(k)}{\partial t} = i \int_K k \cdot dz(k - k') \left[- dz(k') + \frac{k}{k^2} k \cdot dz(k') \right] - \nu k^2 dz(k).$$

It follows from this equation that the rate of change of energy associated with $dz(k)$ is given by

$$\frac{\partial \, \overline{dz_i(k) \, dz_j(k)}}{\partial t}$$

$$= i \int_{K'} [k \cdot dz(k - k') \, \overline{dz_i(k')} \, dz_j(k) - k \cdot dz(k - k') \, \overline{dz_i(k)} \, dz_j(k') +$$

$$+ i \int_{K'} \frac{1}{k^2} [k \cdot dz(k - k') \, k \cdot dz(k') \, k_j \overline{dz_i(k)} -$$

$$- k \cdot dz(k - k') \, k \cdot dz(k') \, k_i \, dz_j(k)] - 2 \nu k^2 \overline{dz_i(k)} \, dz_j(k).$$

The three terms on the right give the effects of inertial, pressure and viscous forces respectively. The term due to the viscous forces is linear and if no other forces were present $dz(k)$ would decrease with time as $e^{-\nu k^2 t}$. This term is the one that causes the dissipation of energy in turbulence. Note that $\overline{dz(k)} = dz(-k)$ since $u(x)$ is real. It follows from this that

$$\frac{\partial}{\partial t} \int_K \overline{dz_i(k) \, dz_j(k)}$$

is not affected by inertial forces. The effect of the inertial forces is to transfer energy from one part of wave number space to another without changing the total amount of energy associated with any directional component of the energy. On using the fact that $k \cdot dz(k) = 0$, the contribution to $\partial/\partial t$ $(dz(k) \cdot dz(k))$ from the pressure forces is seen to be zero so that the effect of pressure forces is to transfer energy from one directional component of $dz(k)$ to another.

168

The exchange of energy between the different modes of motion (the different Fourier components) and the dissipation of energy are basic aspects of turbulence. Much of the study of turbulence today is centered on these two important aspects that are not understood completely. Experimental results have shown that $u(x,t)$, the velocity at a point, is normally distributed but that $u(x,t)$ and $u(x',t)$, the velocities at two distinct points, are not jointly normally distributed. Thus $u(x,t)$ is not a normal process. This is not surprising since, as we have seen, turbulence is a nonlinear phenomenon.

One can see from equation (1) that

$$\frac{d}{dt}\frac{1}{2}\,E\,u^2(x,t) = \frac{d}{dt}\int_0^\infty E(\mathbf{k})\,d\,\mathbf{k}$$

$$= \frac{d}{dt}\int \frac{1}{2}\sum f_{ii}(k)\,d\,k = \frac{\partial}{\partial t}\frac{1}{2}\,E\,\overline{d\,z(k)\cdot d\,z(k)}$$

$$= -\nu\int k^2\,E\,\overline{d\,z(k)\cdot d\,z(k)} = -2\,\nu\int_0^\infty \mathbf{k}^2\,E(\mathbf{k})\,d\,\mathbf{k}.$$

The change of energy per unit mass is given by $2\nu\int_0^\infty \mathbf{k}^2\,E(\mathbf{k})\,d\,\mathbf{k}$. But this implies that the small eddies lose energy by viscous dissipation more rapidly than the large eddies. Since the effect of inertial forces is to spread energy over the range of wave numbers it is plausible that the net transfer of energy is to regions of low energy density in wave number space. Since viscous dissipation is more rapid at large wave numbers, the inertial transfer of energy is from small wave numbers to large wave numbers, that is, from large eddies to small eddies. A similar physical argument implies that the transfer of energy by pressure forces will equalize the mean squares of the directional components. But then it distributes energy associated with the volume element $d\,k$ of wave number space uniformly over directions normal to k. This implies that there would be a tendency towards isotropy. If we now think in terms of a box in which turbulence is set up, this tendency towards isotropy would manifest itself only for wave numbers appreciably larger than $1/L$ where L is the dimension of the box.

It would be of great interest to find out something about the form of the spectral energy function $E(\mathbf{k})$. Consider the range of $\mathbf{k}$

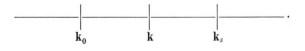

5.3

Let $1/\mathbf{k}_0$ be of the same magnitude as the box in which turbulence has been set up. Beyond $\mathbf{k}_s$ are the small eddies where only viscosity is important and we should like to get some idea about the form of $E(\mathbf{k})$ in the range $\mathbf{k}_0 < \mathbf{k} < \mathbf{k}_s$. Assume that the turbulence is stationary in time. This is a reasonable assumption if energy is fed in at the boundaries of the box at a rate adequate to replace the energy dissipated in the box. Let

$$\varepsilon_{\mathbf{k}} = \frac{\partial}{\partial t} \int_0^{\mathbf{k}} E(\mathbf{k}) \, d\mathbf{k}.$$

The term $\varepsilon_{\mathbf{k}}$ is the rate of transfer of energy from wave numbers less than $\mathbf{k}$ to wave numbers greater than $\mathbf{k}$. This is a constant since the turbulence is stationary in time. We now give a dimensional argument used by Kolmogorov to obtain information about the form of $E(\mathbf{k})$. Kolmogorov makes two basic assumptions. There are two parameters ε, the constant rate of dissipation of energy, and the viscosity ν. The first assumption is that statistical considerations in the range $\mathbf{k}_s > \mathbf{k} > \mathbf{k}_0$ depend only on these two parameters. His second assumption is that $E(\mathbf{k})$ is independent of ν when $\nu \to 0$ (the Reynold's number then approaches infinity). The dimensional argument is as follows. First note that

$$\left(\frac{\nu^3}{\varepsilon}\right)^{\frac{1}{4}} = [\text{length}]$$

$$(\nu \varepsilon)^{\frac{1}{4}} = [\text{velocity}]$$

$$E(\mathbf{k}) = [\text{velocity}]^2 \times [\text{length}].$$

But then

$$E(\mathbf{k}) = (\nu^5 \varepsilon)^{\frac{1}{4}} \, \Phi\left(\mathbf{k} \left(\frac{\nu^3}{\varepsilon}\right)^{\frac{1}{4}}\right)$$

where Φ is a universal function. Using the second assumption one sees that one must have

$$\Phi(x) = C x^{-\frac{5}{3}}$$

so that $\qquad E(\mathbf{k}) = C \varepsilon^{\frac{2}{3}} \mathbf{k}^{-\frac{5}{3}}.$

This form is confirmed by experimental data.

An extended discussion of turbulence is to be found in G. K. Batchelor's book, *The Theory of Homogeneous Turbulence* [1].

5.4. Measuring Turbulence Spectra

In the last section we discussed homogeneous turbulence carefully avoiding all difficult or technical aspects. It should be clear from that section that the spectrum is one of the most important concepts for describing turbulence, although it does not furnish a complete description due to the nonnormality of the velocity field.

We will now discuss briefly some methods of actually measuring spectra. One of the most important devices for this purpose is the *hot wire anemometer*. Denote the velocity at time t at the point of measurement by $u(t)$. If the scale of the turbulence is large compared to the length of the wire then

$$M \frac{d\,v(t)}{d\,t} + v(t) = c\,u(t),$$

where $v(t)$ is the voltage with which the anemometer responds to $u(t)$. Here M is the time constant and c the sensitivity of the anemometer. (See H. Liepmann, [1].) By sending $v(t)$ through a linear circuit with the frequency response function $\varphi(\lambda)$, on measuring the mean power we clearly estimate the quantity

$$c^2 \int_0^\infty \frac{|\varphi(\lambda)|^2}{1 + M^2\,\lambda^2} f(\lambda)\,d\lambda.$$

If $\varphi(\lambda)$ is concentrated around a frequency λ_0, we estimate approximately

$$c^2 f(\lambda_0) \int_0^\infty \frac{|\varphi(\lambda)|^2}{1 + M^2\,\lambda^2}\,d\lambda.$$

There are several things that should be observed at this point. We have been measuring time averages instead of the spatial averages that were used to define the spectrum of the turbulence. However, according to *Taylor's hypothesis* the velocity field of the turbulent motion is carried past a fixed point without any material change, i.e., we have a frozen pattern of turbulence moving with the mean velocity U of the fluid. If we are willing to accept this hypothesis, observed time averages can be converted into space averages if we know U.

Another complication is caused by the fact that the length of the wire is finite so that what we measure is an average over this length. We shall briefly study how this affects the observed spectrum separately. We may want to measure the one dimensional spectral density

171

$$f_{11}(k_1) = \iint f_{11}(k)\, dk_2\, dk_3$$

(see section 5.3) corresponding to the stationary process $u_1(x,0,0)$. A hot wire of length $2l$ is set up parallel to the x_3-axis. Assume that its output is proportional to the integral of the velocity over the wire

$$V(x_1, x_2, x_3) = \alpha \int_{x_3-l}^{x_3+l} u_1(x_1, x_2, y_3)\, dy_3.$$

Then we can consider the measured quantity V as the output of a filter $\mathfrak{F}$ with the frequency response function

$$\alpha \int_{-l}^{l} e^{ik_3 y}\, dy = 2\alpha \frac{\sin k_3 l}{k_3}$$

so that (see section 1.9.A) the spectral density of the V process is

$$g_{11}(k) = 4\alpha^2 \frac{\sin^2 k_3 l}{k_3^2} f_{11}(k).$$

While we are interested in the spectral density $\iint f_{11}(k_1, k_2, k_3)\, dk_2\, dk_3$, we actually estimate instead the density $\iint 4\alpha^2 [(\sin^2 k_3 l)/k_3^2] f_{11}(k_1, k_2, k_3)\, dk_2\, dk_3$. It is clear that an estimate can be obtained just as in section 5.2. For a detailed discussion of how the first density can be recovered approximately from the second see M. S. Uberoi and Leslie G. Kovasznay [1]. These authors also discuss the following method of measuring turbulence.

Consider a fluid with a fluctuating density $\varrho(x_1, x_2, x_3)$ which can be thought of as a stationary process. We study the density fluctuations in the volume bounded by two planes perpendicular to the x_3-axis at the points $x_3 - l$ and $x_3 + l$ respectively. Light is sent through this volume and is received on a photographic plate. The relative fluctuations of the intensity of the incident light are described by a function $h(x_1, x_2, x_3)$ given by (see Uberoi and Kovasznay [1], p. 387)

$$h(x_1, x_2, x_3) = \int_{x_3-l}^{x_3+l} \left(\frac{\partial^2 \varrho}{\partial x_1^2} + \frac{\partial^2 \varrho}{\partial x_2^2} \right) dx_3$$

so that it is the result of ϱ put through a filter with the frequency response function

$$\varphi(\lambda) = -2(k_1^2 + k_2^2) \frac{\sin l k_3}{k_3}.$$

If the spectral density of $\varrho(x)$ is called $f(k_1, k_2, k_3)$ and that of $h(x)$ $g(k_1, k_2, k_3)$ (see section 1.9.A),

$$g(k_1, k_2, k_3) = 4(k_1^2 + k_2^2)^2 \frac{\sin^2 l\, k_3}{k_3^2} f(k_1, k_2, k_3).$$

Let us now assume that $\varrho(x)$ is an isotropic process and introduce the surface spectral density on the sphere $|k| = \mathbf{k}$, $\psi(\mathbf{k}) = 4\mathbf{k}^2 f(k_1, k_2, k_3)$. Then the correlation function of the $h(x)$ process is

$$\beta(\xi) = E\,h(x)\,h(x+\xi)$$

$$= \frac{1}{\pi} \int \int \int (k_1^2 + k_2^2)^2 \frac{\sin^2 k_3\, l}{k_3^2} \frac{\psi(\mathbf{k})}{\mathbf{k}^2} e^{-ik\cdot\xi} \, dk_1\, dk_2\, dk_3.$$

But if l is large compared to the scale of turbulence, using a known property of the Féjer kernel we see that the above expression is approximately equal to

$$l \int\int (k_1^2 + k_2^2)\, \psi\,[(k_1^2 + k_2^2)^{\frac{1}{2}}]\, e^{-i(k_1\xi_1 + k_2\xi_2)} \, dk_1\, dk_2,$$

Set

$$\begin{aligned} \xi_1 &= a\cos\varphi \\ \xi_2 &= a\sin\varphi \end{aligned} \right\} \qquad \begin{aligned} k_1 &= \nu\cos\theta \\ k_2 &= \nu\sin\theta. \end{aligned}$$

Then

$$\beta(a) = 2l \int_0^\infty \nu^3\, \psi(\nu)\, J_0(\nu a)\, d\nu.$$

The quantity we want is $\psi(\nu)$. However we can estimate $\beta(a)$ in a convenient way. The transparency of the photographic plate is

$$t(x) = d + c\,h(x),$$

where d is the average transparency, so that if two identical photographic plates are prepared and placed parallel to each other with a translation $\xi = (\xi_1, \xi_2)$, the combined transparency

$$t_2(x) = [d + c\,h(x)][d + c\,h(x + \xi)]$$

and hence

$$E\,t_2(x) = d^2 + c^2\beta(\xi).$$

After estimating the left member in the usual way, one could use the Fourier-Bessel inversion formula to estimate the quantity we desire, $\psi(\nu)$. However, it should be remembered that the periodogram was obtained in this way from the Fourier inversion formula and was not a very good estimate.

5.5. Basic Ideas in a Statistical Theory of Ocean Waves

Very recently Willard J. Pierson, Jr., G. Birkhoff, and J. Kotik have proposed a model for storm generated ocean surface waves (see Pierson [1] and Birkhoff-Kotik [1]). In this section we give a very brief outline of some of the basic ideas and assumptions on which this model is based.

Let the (x,y)-plane coincide with the free ocean surface when it is calm. The disturbed ocean is described by the height of its free surface, which is a function $\eta(x,y,t)$ of position and time. Consider the velocity potential Φ and the pressure p. The density ϱ of the water is considered constant. Under certain assumptions and of which we mention one, viz. that the waves be small, the motion is governed by the linear equations (see Pierson [1] or Lamb [1])

$$\Delta\Phi = 0$$

$$\frac{p}{\varrho} = \Phi_t - g z$$

together with the appropriate boundary conditions at the ocean surface. One should note that this is a linear model. At the free surface the pressure is zero so that the second equation becomes

$$\eta = \frac{1}{g}\,\Phi_t.$$

One possible solution for the surface is the wave

$$\eta(x, y, t) = \cos\left[\frac{\mu^2}{g}(x\cos\theta + y\sin\theta) - \mu t + \psi\right] \tag{1}$$

$$= h(x, y, t\,|\,\mu, \theta)$$

of amplitude 1, phase ψ with wave crests infinitely long forming an angle θ with the positive x-axis. The waves propagate in the direction perpendicular to the wave crests with a speed g/μ. The frequency μ is the frequency of the oscillation at a fixed point on the ocean surface. The corresponding potential then is

$$\Phi = -\frac{g}{\mu}\,e^{\frac{\mu^2 z}{g}}\sin\left[\frac{\mu^2}{g}(x\cos\theta + y\sin\theta) - \mu t + \psi\right]$$

and the pressure a distance z below the surface

$$p = \varrho g\,e^{\frac{\mu^2 z}{g}}\cos\left[\frac{\mu^2}{g}(x\cos\theta + y\sin\theta) - \mu t + \psi\right] - g\varrho z.$$

To get a realistic description of the sea surface Pierson proposes a super-position of waves of the type (1) with random phases, i.e.,

$$\eta\,(x,\,y,\,t) = \int\limits_{0}^{\infty} \int\limits_{-\frac{\pi}{2}}^{\frac{\pi}{2}} \cos\left[\frac{\mu^2}{g}\,(x\,\cos\,\theta + y\,\sin\,\theta) - \mu\,t + \psi\,(\mu,\,\theta)\right] \cdot$$

$$\cdot f\,(\mu,\,\theta)\,\sqrt{d\mu\,d\,\theta}, \qquad (2)$$

where $\psi\,(\mu,\theta)$ is uniformly distributed on $-\pi < \psi < \pi$ and $\psi(\mu,\theta)$, $\psi(\mu',\theta')$ are independent if $(\mu,\theta) \neq (\mu',\theta')$. This integral should be interpreted in the same way as the integral with random phases in section 1.5. Note that (2) can be considered as the usual sort of spectral representation over a two dimensional spectrum, where the wave number $\lambda = (\lambda_1, \lambda_2)$ has been transformed to polar coordinates

$$\lambda_1 = \mu\,\cos\,\theta$$

$$\lambda_2 = \mu\,\sin\,\theta.$$

The angle θ is allowed to take only the values between $-\pi/2$ and $\pi/2$ since it seems rather natural for a storm generated wave system which has the main direction $\theta = 0$.

It might be worthwhile to point out a few differences from the model usually used in the theory of turbulence. The random phase representation used in this model of the sea surface implies that the process $\eta\,(x,y,t)$ is a normal process. The random integrals used in the model of turbulence need not be normal. In fact, it has already been noted that actual measurements indicate that turbulence is not a normal process (see Batchelor [1]). It is clear that one could modify this model of the sea surface and use the same representation as is used in the theory of turbulence so as to avoid the assumption of normality. Another difference is that while in turbulence a considerable interest is devoted to the isotropic case this is not so in the present context as is seen from the restriction $-\pi/2 < \theta < \pi/2$.

The expression for the velocity potential is

$$\Phi = - \int\limits_{0}^{\infty} \int\limits_{-\frac{\pi}{2}}^{\frac{\pi}{2}} \sin\left[\frac{\mu^2}{g}\,(x\,\cos\,\theta + y\,\sin\,\theta) - \mu\,t + \psi\,(\mu,\,\theta)\right] \cdot$$

$$\cdot \frac{g\,e^{\frac{\mu^2\,z}{g}}}{\mu}\,f\,(\mu,\,\theta)\,\sqrt{d\,\mu\,d\,\theta}\,,$$

and we get the pressure in a similar form.

5.5

Consider the average potential energy

$$\frac{\varrho\, g}{2\, T} \int\limits_{t=0}^{T} \eta^2\,(x, y, t)\, d\,t$$

at some point (x,y) over the time period $0 < t < T$. As the process is ergodic (see section 1.7, it is normal with a continuous spectrum) it follows that when $T \to \infty$ the average potential energy converges (say in the mean) to

$$\frac{\varrho\, g}{2}\, E\, \eta^2\,(x, y, t) = \frac{\varrho\, g}{4} \int\limits_{0}^{\infty} \int\limits_{-\frac{\pi}{2}}^{\frac{\pi}{2}} f\,(\mu, \theta)\, d\,\mu\, d\,\theta.$$

The integral of $f\,(\mu, \theta)$ over the half plane is then proportional to the average potential energy at any point in the plane. The form of *the spectral density* $f\,(\mu, \theta)$ *describes how the potential energy is distributed over various frequencies* μ *and directions* θ. Let most of the spectral energy be in the neighborhood of μ_0, θ_0. The waves will have fairly long crests in the θ_0 direction and the surface will look fairly smooth if μ_0 is small. The situation will resemble that of *swell*. On the other hand high frequency components will make the surface rougher. If θ has a greater range of variation the crests will be shorter and we have a situation typical of *sea*.

As $\eta\,(x,y,t)$ is normally distributed with mean zero and variance

$$\int\limits_{0}^{\infty} \int\limits_{-\frac{\pi}{2}}^{\frac{\pi}{2}} f(\mu, \theta)\; d\mu d\,\theta,$$

we know its distribution completely and can predict wave heights, consider ship motions and make other analyses of similar nature.

This model can be used in the study of *propagation of storm generated ocean waves*. We will briefly outline how this is done in Pierson's theory. Suppose that a storm has been blowing over a time interval $T = \{0 < t < T\}$ and a region D of the (x,y)-plane. Let us assume that initially there are no disturbances of the ocean surface outside the region $T \times D$. In other words we consider η as locally stationary (over $T \times D$) and want to find out what happens outside this region. Consider the elemental wave $h\,(x,y \mid \mu, \theta)$ and modify it by multiplying it by the characteristic function $c\,(t,x,y)$ of the set $T \times D$

176

$$g(x,y,t\,|\,\mu,\theta) = c(t,x,y)\,h(x,y,t\,|\,\mu,\theta).$$

We want to know what happens at some point $p_0 = (x_0, y_0)$ at some future time point t_0. By making a Fourier analysis of $g(x,y,t\,|\,\mu,\theta)$ one finds that as a first approximation the contribution of this wave to the point p_0 at time t_0 has died out (at least approximately) unless (μ, θ) is in some set $S(p_0, t_0)$. For $(\mu, \theta) \in S(p_0, t_0)$ the corresponding amplitude of the wave is not changed very much. One can get more precise results. However, we are only sketching the idea and so refer to Pierson, Neumann and James [1] for a thorough treatment. One can then consider the waves travelling to the point p_0 from D as being passed through a filter with the frequency response function

$$\varphi(\mu, \theta) = \begin{cases} 1 & \text{if } (\mu, \theta) \,\varepsilon\, S(p_0, t_0) \\ 0 & \text{otherwise.} \end{cases}$$

Hence the variable $\eta(x_0, y_0, t_0)$ is normally distributed with mean zero and variance

$$\iint\limits_{S(p_0, t_0)} f(\mu, \theta)\, d\mu\, d\theta.$$

If the spectral density is known we can predict the average properties of the waves at p_0, t_0.

If $S(p_0, t_0)$ is computed in a few simple but typical cases, it is seen that when we go further away from the region D of wave generation a more and more narrow band of frequencies is singled out. This means that the waves behave more and more like swell. The amplitudes will clearly decrease as p_0 moves away. The "periods" of the swell will tend to decrease from high values to low values as time passes. All these characteristics have been observed (see Pierson [1]).

5.6. Other Applications

It is clear that as soon as the fluctuating phenomena we study are of a random character and locally homogeneous the stationary processes form an adequate class of models. Except for comparably few cases in which one knows the whole structure of the process *a priori* except for a small number of parameters, it will be necessary to use a nonparametric approach like that outlined in the previous chapter.

There are many other applications. We shall make only a few more remarks on such applications. For example when we have a filter $\mathcal{F}$ and want to find its response function it is possible to put pure sine waves or unit impulses into it and measure the output. This is not always the best procedure however. Instead one might use some sort of noise of known spectrum as the input and measure the spectrum of the output. A slightly modified procedure of this sort has been suggested for finding the acoustic properties of a hall (see H. Thiede [1]), and it is easy to think of other cases suited to this sort of analysis.

Concerning econometrics and the social sciences it should be pointed out that the stationarity assumption will often be valid only for short time intervals in general, and we would hesitate to apply any of the statistical techniques of this book in such a context, as it is questionable whether they would give more or as much as the common sense methods of the practical economist or social scientist. However, in a context where there is more quantitative theory there would be some hope of finding appropriate statistical tools for the analyses of such time series.

CHAPTER 6

DISTRIBUTION OF SPECTRAL ESTIMATES

6.0. Introduction

In Chapter 4 we studied the problem of estimating the spectrum, say the spectral distribution function, the density function or the spectral mass in an interval. In Chapter 5 such estimates were applied to problems arising in various fields of application. Although large sample expressions for the bias and variance of such estimates have been obtained, it is clear that they describe only crudely the random variability of the estimates. For a more detailed study it is necessary to find the distributions of these statistics or at least get approximations for these distributions. In this chapter, on the basis of such results, we proceed to set up statistical tests of hypotheses or confidence regions.

6.1. Preliminary Remarks

Many statisticians working with applications will agree that in practice one is more often interested in confidence statements than in the yes–no answer of a test. We shall therefore concentrate our attention on the construction of confidence regions and only in passing mention some tests. The confidence regions of greatest interest are those forming intervals in "parameter" space, i.e., bands of functions, of the type say

$$F_1(\lambda) \leq F(\lambda) \leq F_2(\lambda), \quad -\pi \leq \lambda \leq \pi,$$

where $F_1(\lambda)$, $F_2(\lambda)$ depend upon the observed sample and $F(\lambda)$ is the true spectral distribution function.

The results obtained in this chapter are all of the large sample variety, so that one wonders at what sample size the errors involved in using these results become negligible for practical purposes. No error terms are derived and at present it does not seem likely that one can obtain error terms sharp enough to be of any practical use. The only reasonable alternative seems to be to consider empirical verification by an artificial sampling procedure. So far only a small scale computational program has been carried out and we will present some spectral analyses of artificially generated time series

179

in a later section. They are intended as a numerical illustration rather than as a confirmation of the validity of the large sample approximation at a certain sample size.

Certain conditions restrict the validity of the results. Some conditions concern the regularity of the spectrum, so that the spectral density is not allowed to fluctuate too much but has to have a sufficiently smooth appearance. More serious than these are the restrictions on the distribution of the observed process. We deal only with linear processes (see section 1.6) and although this is a general class of processes and includes for example the usual models employed in time series analysis, it is still very far from the whole class of stationary processes. It should also be remarked that while the regularity assumptions concerning the spectrum can probably be weakened considerably, the same is likely not to be true with respect to the distribution type of the process. In fact, the crucial point in the derivations that follow is where we use the independence of the ξ_ν generating the linear scheme to establish joint asymptotic normality of certain statistics. For this purpose we employ the central limit theorem for independent variables. In the case of a general stationary process with absolutely continuous spectrum the ξ_ν's are still uncorrelated (see section 1.6) but not necessarily independent. Then the central limit theorem will in general not hold from the formal mathematical point of view. Countless examples of this could be given and we choose the following simple one as an illustration. Let

$$\xi_\nu = \cos \nu x 2\pi, \tag{1}$$

where x is a rectangular stochastic variable in the interval $(0,1)$. Consider the sum

$$\sum_{\nu=0}^{n} \xi_\nu = \tfrac{1}{2} + \tfrac{1}{2} \, \frac{\sin\,(n+\tfrac{1}{2})\,x\,2\,\pi}{\sin\,\tfrac{1}{2}\,x\,2\,\pi}.$$

Note that though the ξ's are uncorrelated so that the sum has a standard derivation of the order $N^{\frac{1}{2}}$, we have not normed the sum. The limiting distribution is that of the stochastic variable

$$\tfrac{1}{2} + \tfrac{1}{2} \, \frac{\sin\,\pi\,y}{\sin\,\pi\,x},$$

where y is another rectangular stochastic variable in the interval $(0,1)$ independent of x. This distribution is far from normal.

The reader may object that the process considered above is not strictly stationary. We now give an example of a strictly stationary process with orthogonal random variables that is not in the domain of the central limit theorem. Let the joint probability density of $\xi_j,\ \xi_{j+1}, \ldots,\ \xi_{j+n}$ be given by

$$p(\xi_j,\ \xi_{j+1},\ \ldots,\ \xi_{j+n}) = \tfrac{1}{2}\frac{1}{(2\pi)^{n/2}}\left[\frac{1}{\sigma_1^n}\,e^{-\sum\limits_{k=0}^{n}\xi_{j+k}^2/2\sigma_1^2}+\frac{1}{\sigma_2^n}\,e^{-\sum\limits_{k=0}^{n}\xi_{j+k}^2/2\sigma_2^2}\right],$$

where $j = \cdots,\ -1,\ 0,\ 1, \ldots,\ n = 0,\ 1, \ldots,\ \sigma_1 \neq \sigma_2$ and $\sigma_1,\ \sigma_2 > 0$. The limiting distribution of $\sum\limits_{k=1}^{n}\xi_k/\sqrt{n}$ is

$$\lim_{n\to\infty}P\left\{\frac{\sum\limits_{k=1}^{n}\xi_k}{\sqrt{n}}\leq\alpha\right\}=\tfrac{1}{2}\left[\Phi(\sigma_1\alpha)+\Phi(\sigma_2\alpha)\right],$$

a mixture of two normal distributions. The process $\{\xi_t\}$ could be called a symmetric process since $p(\xi_j,\ \xi_{j+1}, \ldots,\ \xi_{j+n})$ is a symmetric function of $\xi_j, \ldots,\ \xi_{j+n}$. An interesting discussion of such symmetric processes is to be found in de Finetti's article [1].

However, the experimentalist would argue that *in most physically realizable situations where a stationary process has been observed during a time interval long compared to time lags for which correlation is appreciable, the average of the sample would be asymptotically normally distributed.* Intuitively it seems likely that a strong mixing condition (see Hopf [1] and Rosenblatt [3]) would insure the validity of the central limit theorem. Unfortunately none of the extensions of the central limit theorem to dependent variables seems to answer this problem in terms well adapted for practical interpretation.

Let us return for a moment to the uncorrelated stochastic variables (1). For these variables the central limit theorem is not valid. However if one considers a subsequence ξ_n, $k = 1, 2, \ldots$, where gaps $n_{k+1} - n_k$ are sufficiently large, the central limit theorem will hold. In particular, it is enough to require that a Hadamard gap condition be satisfied, i.e.,

$$\frac{n_{k+1}}{n_k} > q > 1$$

from some value of k on (for an elegant survey of this and related results see M. Kac [1]). As the gaps become larger with increasing k the variables behave more and more like independent stochastic variables and this is the reason why the central limit theorem holds.

Summing up we feel that the results of this chapter ought to be valid if

(a) the spectrum is not too peaked, (b) the process is in the domain of the central limit theorem. Sampling experiments should be of great help in deciding the sample size and type of process for which the results have practical value.

Unfortunately the proofs are carried out only for a discrete parameter process which may seem a serious limitation as in most of the applications in Chapter 5 the process has a continuous parameter. However, it seems likely that the analogous results hold for continuous time although the proofs might require a more intricate apparatus. One should also note that in situations where great accuracy in determining the structure of the spectrum is required, it is necessary to use a digital computer. In that case the process has to be discretized. The analog computers could utilize all the information in a continuous time series but are likely to have larger computational errors. Which procedure one should choose will depend upon the required accuracy and the amount of time one is willing to spend on numerical computations.

6.2. A Heuristic Derivation of a Limit Theorem

Consider the estimate

$$F_N^*(\lambda) = \int_0^\lambda I_N(x)\,dx = \frac{1}{2\pi}\frac{C_0}{N}\lambda + \frac{1}{\pi}\sum_{\nu=1}^N \frac{C_\nu}{N}\frac{\sin\nu\lambda}{\nu}$$

of the spectral distribution function $F(\lambda)$, where

$$C_\nu = \sum_{k=1}^{N-\nu} x_k\,x_{k+\nu}.$$

In sections 6.3 to 6.5 we shall obtain the asymptotic distribution of expressions like

$$\sqrt{N}\max_{0<\lambda<\pi}\left|F_N^*(\lambda) - F(\lambda)\right|,$$

$$N\int_0^\pi \left|F_N^*(x) - F(x)\right|^2 dx$$

and the estimated spectral mass in several nonoverlapping λ-intervals. These derivations will be carried out rigorously and are valid under the assumption that the *stationary process* x_t *is a linear scheme*. The rigorous derivations will be lengthy and it may be difficult at times to see the basic ideas under the formal apparatus used to push the proofs through. For

this reason we preface these sections with a *heuristic derivation* of the
asymptotic distribution of

$$\sqrt{N} \max_{0 < \lambda < \pi} \left| F_N^*(\lambda) - F(\lambda) \right|.$$

These preliminary comments will emphasize the basic ideas of all these
derivations.

A first step in such a heuristic derivation (another heuristic derivation
is to be found in Grenander and Rosenblatt [4]) is to note that

$$\sqrt{N} \int_0^\lambda I_N(x) = \sqrt{N} \int_0^\lambda 2\pi f(x) I_{N,\xi}(x)\, dx + o(1) \tag{1}$$

where $o(1)$ is uniform in λ and $I_{N,\xi}(x)$ is the periodogram computed
for the process ξ_ν which generates the observed stochastic process
$x_t = \sum a_{t-\nu} \xi_\nu$. This can be made convincing by noting that

$$\sqrt{N} \int_0^\lambda [I_N(x) - 2\pi f(x) I_{N,\xi}(x)]\, dx = \frac{1}{\sqrt{N}} \sum_{r,s=-\infty}^{\infty} a_r a_s d_{rs}$$

where

$$d_{rs} = \sum_{n,m=1}^{N} \xi_{n-r}\, \xi_{m-s}\, \frac{e^{i(n-m)\lambda} - 1}{2\pi i (n-m)} -$$
$$- \sum_{\substack{n=1+r,\, N+r \\ m=1+s,\, N+s}} \xi_{n-r}\, \xi_{m-s}\, \frac{e^{i(n-m)\lambda} - 1}{2\pi i (n-m)}.$$

The terms d_{rs} will be negligible unless $|r|, |s|$ are large and then the coeffi-
cients $a_r a_s$ will be small since $\sum |a_r|^2 < \infty$. But one then expects the differ-
ence to be negligible and (1) to hold. We can then instead consider the process

$$\sqrt{N} \left[\int_0^\lambda 2\pi f(x) I_{N,\xi}(x)\, dx - F(\lambda) \right] = \sqrt{N} \int_0^\lambda 2\pi f(x) \left[I_{N,\xi}(x) - \frac{1}{2\pi} \right] dx$$

$$= \frac{c_0 - N}{\sqrt{N}} \int_0^\lambda f(x)\, dx + 2 \sum_1^N \frac{c_\nu}{\sqrt{N}} \int_0^\lambda f(x) \cos \nu x\, dx, \tag{2}$$

where

$$c_\nu = \sum_{k=1}^{N-\nu} \xi_k\, \xi_{k+\nu}.$$

If the spectral density is well behaved, the coefficients $\int_0^\lambda f(x) \cos \nu x\, dx$ will

decrease to zero as $\nu \to \infty$ at the rate $0(1/\nu)$. We can then get a good approximation to the distribution of the process (1) by considering a fixed but large number k of the initial terms of the expansion (2) since the remainder contributes little, that is, we should consider

$$\frac{c_0 - N}{\sqrt{N}} \int_0^\lambda f(x)\, dx + 2 \sum_1^k \frac{c_\nu}{\sqrt{N}} \int_0^\lambda f(x)\, \cos \nu x\, dx. \qquad (3)$$

But the stochastic variables $(c_0 - N)/\sqrt{N}, \ldots, c_k/\sqrt{N}$ are the normed sums of a k-step dependent stationary vector process (that is, stochastic variables more than k steps apart are independent) with mean zero, orthogonal components, and variances $e + 2, 1, 1, \ldots, 1$. But the central limit theorem holds for k-step dependent stationary processes so that the stochastic variables $(c_0 - N)/\sqrt{N}, \ldots, c_k/\sqrt{N}$ are asymptotically normal and independent with mean zero and variances $e + 2, 1, \ldots, 1$, as $N \to \infty$. The truncated process (3) should asymptotically have the same distribution as

$$\sqrt{e + 2}\, y_0 \int_0^\lambda f(x)\, dx + 2 \sum_1^k y_\nu \int_0^\lambda f(x)\, \cos \nu x\, dx$$

and on letting $k \to \infty$ we see that the process should asymptotically have the same distribution as

$$\sqrt{e + 2}\, y_0 \int_0^\lambda f(x)\, dx + 2 \sum_1^\infty y_\nu \int_0^\lambda f(x)\, \cos \nu x\, dx, \qquad (4)$$

where $y_0, y_1, \ldots$ are normal, independent variables with mean zero and variance one. On the other hand the stochastic model of linear Brownian motion can be written as

$$B(\lambda) = y_0 \lambda + \sqrt{2} \sum_{\nu=1}^\infty y_\nu \frac{\sin \nu \lambda}{\nu}, \qquad 0 < \lambda < \pi$$

(see section 1.1 of Chapter 1). The process (1) can then formally be written as

$$\sqrt{e}\, y \int_0^\lambda f(x)\, dx + \sqrt{2\pi} \int_0^\lambda f(x)\, dB(x) \qquad (5)$$

if $e > 0$, where $B(x)$ is the linear Brownian motion and y is a normal variable of mean zero and variance one independent of $B(x)$. The term on the right in formula (5) is not well-defined sample-functionwise but we really mean by it the stochastic process obtained from it by integrating by parts. The resultant expression will then be well-defined sample-functionwise. Intuitively it is clear that the limiting probability

$$\lim_{N\to\infty} P\left\{\sqrt{N}\max_{0<\lambda<\pi}\left|F_N^*(\lambda)-F(\lambda)\right|\le\alpha\right\}$$

$$=P\left\{\max_{0<\lambda<\pi}\left|y_0\sqrt{e+2}\int_0^\lambda f(x)\,dx+2\sum_1^\infty y_\nu\int_0^\lambda f(x)\cos\nu x\,dx\right|\le\alpha\right\}$$

and that it is equal to

$$P\left\{\max_{0<\lambda<\pi}\left|\sqrt{e}\,y\int_0^\lambda f(x)\,dx+\sqrt{2\pi}\int_0^\lambda f(x)\,dB(x)\right|\le\alpha\right\}$$

when $e\ge 0$. Note that (4) is a normal process with mean zero and covariance

$$e\,F(\lambda)\,F(\mu)+2\pi\int_0^{\min(\lambda,\mu)}f^2(x)\,dx.$$

The case $e=0$ is of particular practical interest because the limiting distribution can then be computed with ease. In particular, $e=0$ when x_t is a normal process.

The heuristic derivation given above is an abbreviated version of the rigorous proof to be given in the following sections. There are several places where the argument is accompanied by a rather convincing waving of the hands. These are the gaps that are filled in and reasoned out in detail in a strict proof. A few of these gaps are worth noting. One of these occurred when $\sqrt{N}[F_N^*(\lambda)-F(\lambda)]$ was approximated by a finite number of terms in its expansion in terms of the product lag moments of the ξ process. Another gap is to be found in the assertion that the limiting probability distribution of the maximum of $\sqrt{N}\left|F_N^*(\lambda)-F(\lambda)\right|$ is the same as the probability distribution of the maximum of the absolute value of the process which is the limit of $\sqrt{N}[F_N^*(\lambda)-F(\lambda)]$ distributionwise.

6.3. Preliminary Considerations

As remarked before, one of the primary objects of the following sections is to investigate the asymptotic distribution of

$$\max_{0 \leq \lambda \leq \pi} \sqrt{N} \, |[F_N^*(\lambda) - F(\lambda)]|$$

when the observed process x_t is a linear scheme, that is,

$$x_t = \sum a_{t-\nu} \, \xi_\nu, \quad \sum a_\nu^2 < \infty,$$

where the ξ_ν are independent, identically distributed stochastic variables with mean zero and variance one. The basic idea of the derivation is to first treat the special case of the process $x_t = \xi_t$ and then to reduce the general case of a linear scheme to this special case. Various auxiliary assumptions will be introduced occasionally and they will be carefully indicated when they appear. However, one does feel that some of these auxiliary assumptions are not really necessary.

In this section, a few results required in the main body of the proof will be demonstrated. It is assumed that $E|\xi_\nu|^8 < \infty$ throughout the proof.

LEMMA 1. Consider the covariances $c_\nu = \sum\limits_{n=1}^{N-|\nu|} \xi_n \, \xi_{n+|\nu|}$. If $\nu, \mu \neq 0$

$$|E \, c_\nu \, c_{\nu+j} \, c_\mu \, c_{\mu+j}| \leq \begin{cases} A_1 N & \text{if } \mu \neq \nu \\ A_2 N^2 & \text{if } \mu = \nu. \end{cases} \tag{1}$$

Proof. It is clear that (1) is made up of terms $E \prod\limits_{i=1}^{8} \xi_{n_i}$. If one of the indices n_i is different from the rest this term vanishes. Since each of the terms is bounded by $E|\xi_\nu|^8$, it is enough to enumerate the nonvanishing terms. But we have restraints, say

$$n_2 = n_1 + a$$
$$n_4 = n_3 + b$$
$$n_6 = n_5 + c$$
$$n_8 = n_7 + d,$$

where the integers a, b, c, d are all different from zero. In particular one can set $a = \nu$, $b = \nu + j$, $c = \mu$, $d = \mu + j$. The eight variables can then be treated in a completely symmetric way. Let us fix n_1. As $n_2 \neq n_1, n_2$ has to be equal to some other n_i, say n_3.

Now we separate two cases. Since $n_5 \neq n_6$, it has to be equal to either one of n_1, n_2, n_3, n_4 or to one of n_7, n_8. Consider the first alternative. Then n_7 has to be equal to one of n_1, n_2, n_3, n_4, n_5, n_6 and whichever is chosen, we have

$$n_i = n_1 + a_i, \ \ i = 2,3,\ldots, \ 8. \tag{2}$$

As $1 \le n_i \le N$ this gives us at most N possibilities.

In treating the second alternative, assume that $n_5 = n_7$. If any of the indices n_1, n_2, n_3, n_4 is equal to any of the indices n_5, n_6, n_7, n_8 we have again a set of restrictions of the type (2) and hence at most N possibilities again so we can exclude this case. But then $n_2 = n_3 \neq n_1$ and $n_6 \neq n_7 = n_5$ so that the only way of getting a nonvanishing term is by setting $n_2 = n_4$, $n_6 = n_8$ which implies that $a = b$, $c = d$. If that is the case we have at most N^2 possibilities. The result clearly follows.

Note that *the distribution of the stochastic variables $(c_0 - N)/\sqrt{N}$, $c_1/\sqrt{N}$, $\ldots, c_k/\sqrt{N}$ tends to the distribution of $k + 1$ normal and independent variables with mean zero and variances $e + 2, 1, 1, \ldots, 1$ respectively.* This can easily be seen in the following way. Introduce

$$Z_j = t_0(\xi_j^2 - 1) + t_1 \xi_j \xi_{j+1} + \cdots + t_k \xi_j \xi_{j+k}$$

so that $\quad U_N = \dfrac{1}{\sqrt{N}} \sum\limits_{j=1}^{N} Z_j = \dfrac{1}{\sqrt{N}} [t_0(c_0 - N) + t_1 c_1' + \cdots + t_k c_k']$

where $\quad c_\nu' = c_\nu + \sum\limits_{j=N-\nu+1}^{N} \xi_j \xi_{j+\nu}, \quad \nu > 0.$

It is clear that $(c_\nu' - c_\nu)/\sqrt{N} \to 0$ in probability as $N \to \infty$. But Z_j is a stationary $(k + 1)$-dependent sequence of stochastic variables. Applying a theorem of Hoeffding and Robins [1] we see that U_N is asymptotically normal with mean zero and variance

$$t_0^2(e + 2) + \sum_1^k t_\nu^2.$$

Thus

$$E \, e^{i U_N} = E \exp\left\{i t_0 \frac{c_0 - N}{\sqrt{N}} + i \sum_1^k t_\nu \frac{c_\nu'}{\sqrt{N}}\right\} \to \exp\left\{-\tfrac{1}{2}[t_0^2(e + 2) + \sum_1^k t_\nu^2]\right\}$$

and the statement concerning the asymptotic behavior of

$$\frac{c_0 - N}{\sqrt{N}}, \ \frac{c_1}{\sqrt{N}}, \ldots, \ \frac{c_k}{\sqrt{N}}$$

is demonstrated.

6.4. Treatment of Pure White Noise

We now discuss the limiting probability distribution of

$$\sqrt{N} \max_{0 \le \lambda \le \pi} \left| \left[F_{N,\xi}^*(\lambda) - \frac{\lambda}{2\pi} \right] \right|,$$

that is, we discuss the probability distribution of the statistic of interest when the observed process $x_t = \xi_t$ is pure white noise.

THEOREM 1. *Consider the empirical spectral distribution function*

$$F_{N,\xi}^*(\lambda) = \int_0^\lambda I_{N,\xi}(l)\, dl,$$

where
$$I_{N,\xi}(\lambda) = \frac{1}{2\pi N} \left| \sum_{\nu=1}^N \xi_\nu\, e^{-i\nu\lambda} \right|^2.$$

The limiting probability distribution of

$$\max_{0 \le \lambda \le \pi} \sqrt{N} \left| F_{N,\xi}^*(\lambda) - \frac{\lambda}{2\pi} \right|$$

as $N \to \infty$ is the same as that of

$$\max_{0 \le \lambda \le \pi} |\zeta(\lambda)|$$

where $\zeta(\lambda)$ is a normally distributed process with mean zero and covariance

$$E\, \zeta(\lambda)\, \zeta(\mu) = \frac{e\,\lambda\,\mu}{4\,\pi^2} + \frac{1}{2\,\pi} \min(\lambda, \mu).$$

Proof. Now

$$\sqrt{N} \left[F_{N,\xi}^*(\lambda) - \frac{\lambda}{2\pi} \right] = \frac{\lambda}{2\pi} \left(\frac{c_0}{\sqrt{N}} - \sqrt{N} \right) + \sum_1^{N-1} \frac{c_\nu}{\sqrt{N}} \frac{\sin \nu\lambda}{\pi\nu} = s_{N,k}(\lambda) + r_{N,k}(\lambda),$$

where $s_{N,k}(\lambda)$ consists of the first term and the $k-1$ first summands of the sum. We shall show that $s_{N,k}(\lambda)$ is a good approximation to $\sqrt{N}\,[F_{N,\xi}^*(\lambda) - \lambda/2\pi]$ uniformly in λ when k is fixed but large, or more formally that with probability close to one, for sufficiently large k, $|r_{N,k}(\lambda)|$ is small uniformly in N, λ.

We now carry on a detailed estimation of the remainder term to prove the validity of this approximation. Consider

$$\left| \sum_{\nu=m}^{l} \frac{c_\nu}{\sqrt{N}} \frac{\sin \nu \lambda}{\nu} \right| \leq \left| \sum_{\nu=m}^{l} \frac{c_\nu}{\sqrt{N}} \frac{e^{i\nu\lambda}}{\nu} \right|,$$

where $0 < m < l \leq N$. But

$$\left| \sum_{\nu=m}^{l} \frac{c_\nu}{\sqrt{N}} \frac{e^{i\nu\lambda}}{\nu} \right|^2 \leq 2 \sum_{j=0}^{l-m} \left| \sum_{\nu=m}^{l-j} \frac{c_\nu c_{\nu+j}}{N \nu (\nu+j)} \right|.$$

To get a bound for this sum consider

$$E \left| \sum_{\nu=m}^{l-j} \frac{c_\nu c_{\nu+j}}{N \nu (\nu+j)} \right|^2 = \sum_{\nu,\mu=m}^{l-j} \frac{E c_\nu c_{\nu+j} c_\mu c_{\mu+j}}{N^2 \nu (\nu+j) \mu (\mu+j)}. \tag{1}$$

We know by Lemma 1 that

$$\left| E c_\nu c_{\nu+j} c_\mu c_{\mu+j} \right| \leq \begin{cases} A_1 N^2 & \text{if } \nu = \mu \\ A_2 N & \text{if } \nu \neq \mu \end{cases}$$

so that expression (1) is bounded by

$$A_1 \sum_{\nu=m}^{l-j} \frac{1}{\nu^2 (\nu+j)^2} + \frac{A_2}{N} \sum_{\nu,\mu=m}^{l-j} \frac{1}{\nu (\nu+j) \mu (\mu+j)} \leq \sum_{\nu=m}^{l-j} \frac{A_3}{\nu^2 (\nu+j)^2}$$

using the Schwarz inequality. Now choose $m = 2^p$ and $l = 2^{p+1}$. Again using the Schwarz inequality we have

$$E \max_{0 \leq \lambda \leq \pi} \left| \sum_{\nu=2^p}^{2^{p+1}} \frac{c_\nu}{\sqrt{N}} \frac{\sin \nu \lambda}{\nu} \right| \leq A_4 \sum_{j=0}^{2^p} \left| \sum_{\nu=2^p}^{2^{p+1}-j} \frac{1}{\nu^2 (\nu+j)^2} \right|^{\frac{1}{2}}$$

$$\leq A_5 \sum_{j=0}^{2^p} \frac{1}{2^{3p/2}} = A_5 / 2^{p/2}.$$

Let $k = 2^n$. Then with probability greater than $1 - A_5 / 2^{p/4}$

$$T_p = \max_{0 \leq \lambda \leq \pi} \left| \sum_{\nu=2^p}^{2^{p+1}} \frac{c_\nu}{\sqrt{N}} \frac{\sin \nu \lambda}{\nu} \right| < \frac{1}{2^{p/4}}.$$

Therefore

$$\left| r_{N,k} (\lambda) \right| \leq \sum_{p=n}^{[\log N]+1} T_p \leq A_6 \frac{1}{2^{n/4}}$$

with probability greater than $1 - A_6 / 2^{n/4}$. By choosing n sufficiently large, $\left| r_{N,k} (\lambda) \right|$ is made uniformly small.

We want to find the limiting value of

$$P \left(\max_{0 \leq \lambda \leq \pi} \sqrt{N} \left| F_{N,\xi}^* (\lambda) - \frac{\lambda}{2\pi} \right| \leq \alpha \right).$$

From what has just been shown, we see that for any ε, $\delta > 0$

$$P\left(\max_{0 \leq \lambda \leq \pi} \left| s_{N,k}(\lambda) \right| < \alpha - \varepsilon \right) - \delta \leq P\left(\max_{0 \leq \lambda \leq \pi} \sqrt{N} \left| F_{N,\xi}^*(\lambda) - \frac{\lambda}{2\pi} \right| \leq \alpha \right)$$

$$\leq P\left(\max_{0 \leq \lambda \leq \pi} \left| s_{N,k}(\lambda) \right| < \alpha + \varepsilon \right) + \delta$$

for k sufficiently large, uniformly in $N > N(\varepsilon, \delta)$. But

$$s_{N,k}(\lambda) = \frac{c_0 - N}{2\sqrt{N}} \lambda + \frac{1}{\pi} \sum_1^k \frac{c_\nu}{\sqrt{N}} \frac{\sin \nu \lambda}{\nu}$$

and the joint distribution of $(c_0 - N)/\sqrt{N}$, $c_1/\sqrt{N}$, ..., $c_k/\sqrt{N}$ (k fixed) converges to the distribution of $k + 1$ independent normal variables with common mean zero and variances $e + 2, 1, 1, \ldots, 1$. Consider the related process

$$s_k(\lambda) = \frac{\gamma_0}{2} \sqrt{e + 2} \, \lambda + \sum_1^k \frac{\gamma_\nu}{\pi} \frac{\sin \nu \lambda}{\nu},$$

where the γ's are $N(0, 1)$ and independent. It is easily seen that

$$\lim_{N \to \infty} P\left(\max_{0 \leq \lambda \leq \pi} \left| s_{N,k}(\lambda) \right| \leq \alpha \right) \doteq P\left(\max_{0 \leq \lambda \leq \pi} \left| s_k(\lambda) \right| \leq \alpha \right)$$

as the relevant point set in $(k+1)$-space is closed. On letting k tend to infinity, $s_k(\lambda)$ converges uniformly to

$$\zeta(\lambda) = \frac{\gamma_0}{2\pi} \sqrt{e + 2} \, \lambda + \sum_1^\infty \frac{\gamma_\nu}{\pi} \frac{\sin \nu \lambda}{\nu}$$

(see Paley-Wiener [1], p. 148–151). Then

$$P\left(\max_{0 \leq \lambda \leq \pi} \left| \zeta(\lambda) \right| < \alpha - \varepsilon \right) - \delta < P\left(\max_{0 \leq \lambda \leq \pi} \sqrt{N} \left| F_{N,\xi}^*(\lambda) - \frac{\lambda}{2\pi} \right| \leq \alpha \right)$$

$$< P\left(\max_{0 \leq \lambda \leq \pi} \left| \zeta(\lambda) \right| < \alpha + \varepsilon \right) + \delta$$

and if $N \to \infty$ we can let $\delta, \varepsilon \to 0$. Since the distribution function of $\max_{0 \leq \lambda \leq \pi} \left| \zeta(\lambda) \right|$ is continuous (see section 6.7), this completes the proof.

6.5. The General Theorem

The object is now to reduce the discussion of a general linear process x_t to the case of pure white noise discussed in the previous section. This reduction is carried out in two steps. The first step is to note that

$$\sqrt{N} \max_{0 \leq \lambda \leq \pi} \left| \int_0^\lambda [I_N(l) - 2\pi f(l) I_{N,\xi}(l)] \, dl \right| = o(1)$$

under certain conditions. Then the distribution of

$$\max_{0 \leq \lambda \leq \pi} \sqrt{N} \left| \int_0^\lambda f(l) [2\pi I_{N,\xi}(l) - 1] \, dl \right|$$

is discussed and the asymptotic distribution of

$$\sqrt{N} \max_{0 \leq \lambda \leq \pi} |F_N^*(\lambda) - F(\lambda)|$$

is finally obtained.

THEOREM 2. *Let* $\qquad a_\nu = 0 (\nu^\beta),$

where $\beta < -3/2$. *Then given any* $\varepsilon > 0$

$$\sqrt{N} \max_{0 \leq \lambda \leq \pi} \left| \int_0^\lambda [I_N(l) - 2\pi f(l) I_{N,\xi}(l)] \, dl \right| < \varepsilon$$

with probability $1 - \varepsilon$ *for* $N > N(\varepsilon)$.

Proof. Using the representation of x_t as a linear scheme

$$x_t = \sum a_{t-\nu} \xi_\nu$$

and expanding we find that

$$2\pi \sqrt{N} \int_0^\lambda [I_N(l) - 2\pi f(\lambda) I_{N,\xi}(l)] \, dl = \frac{1}{\sqrt{N}} \sum_{r,s=-\infty}^{\infty} a_r a_s d_{rs}, \qquad (1)$$

where

$$d_{r,s} = \sum_{n,m=1}^{N}{}' \xi_{n-r} \xi_{m-s} \frac{e^{i(n-m)\lambda} - 1}{i(n-m)} - \sum_{\substack{n=1+r, N+r \\ m=1+s, N+s}}{}' \xi_{n-r} \xi_{m-s} \frac{e^{i(n-m)\lambda} - 1}{i(n-m)}.$$

The summation signs are primed to indicate that the coefficients of the terms with $n = m$ should be interpreted as λ. There may be a lattice rectangle $R_{r,s}^{(N)}$ of points (n,m) common to the two sums that add up to $d_{r,s}$. Call the complement of $R_{r,s}^{(N)}$ with respect to the set consisting of all the lattice points in both summations $C_{r,s}^{(N)}$. We then have

$$E \max_{0 \leq \lambda \leq \pi} |d_{rs}| \leq \sum_{n,m \in C_{r,s}^{(N)}} g(n-m),$$

6.5

where
$$g(x) = \begin{cases} \dfrac{2}{|x|} & \text{if } x \neq 0 \\ \pi & \text{if } x = 0. \end{cases}$$

One can verify that

$$\sum_{n,\,m \in C_{rs}^{(N)}} g(n-m) \leq \begin{cases} 2N \log N & \text{if } |r| > N \text{ or } |s| > N \\ 4(|s|+|r|) \log N & \text{otherwise.} \end{cases}$$

The expectation of the absolute value of expression (1) is then bounded by the following expression

$$\frac{2}{\sqrt{N}} \sum_{s=-\infty}^{\infty} \sum_{|r|>N} |a_r a_s| \, 2N \log N + \frac{8}{\sqrt{N}} \sum_{s=-\infty}^{\infty} \sum_{|r| \leq N} |a_r a_s r| \log N$$

$$\leq \left(\sum_{s=-\infty}^{\infty} |a_s| \right) \left(4\sqrt{N} \log N \sum_{|r|>N} |a_r| + \frac{8 \log N}{\sqrt{N}} \sum_{|r| \leq N} |r a_r| \right).$$

Under the assumptions made, this expression tends to zero as $N \to \infty$ which proves the theorem.

THEOREM 3. *Let $F(\lambda)$ be a nonnegative absolutely continuous function. Then*

$$\lim_{N \to \infty} P \left\{ \max_{0 \leq \lambda \leq \pi} \sqrt{N} \left| \int_0^\lambda f(l) \{ 2\pi I_{N,\xi}(l) - 1 \} \, dl \right| \leq \alpha \right\} = P \left(\max_{0 \leq \lambda \leq \pi} |\eta(\lambda)| < \alpha \right),$$

where $\eta(\lambda)$ is the normal process with

$$E \, \eta(\lambda) = 0$$

$$E \, \eta(\lambda) \eta(\mu) = e \, F(\lambda) \, F(\mu) + 2\pi G(\min(\lambda, \mu)).$$

Here
$$G(\lambda) = \int_0^\lambda f^2(l) \, dl.$$

Proof. On integrating by parts we find that

$$\int_0^\lambda f(l) \{ 2\pi I_{N,\xi}(l) - 1 \} \, dl = 2\pi f(\lambda) \left[F_{N,\xi}^*(\lambda) - \frac{\lambda}{2\pi} \right] -$$

$$- \int_0^\lambda 2\pi f'(l) \left[F_{N,\xi}^*(l) - \frac{l}{2\pi} \right] dl.$$

Theorem 1 tell us that for any $\varepsilon > 0$

$$\max_{0 \le \lambda \le \pi} \left| \sqrt{N} \left(F^*_{N,\xi}(\lambda) - \frac{\lambda}{2\pi} \right) - s_{N,k}(\lambda) \right| < \varepsilon$$

with probability $1 - \varepsilon$ uniformly in $N > N(\varepsilon)$ for k sufficiently large. But then

$$\max_{0 \le \lambda \le \pi} \left| f(\lambda) \left[\sqrt{N} \left(F^*_{N,\xi}(\lambda) - \frac{\lambda}{2\pi} \right) - s_{N,k}(\lambda) \right] - \right.$$
$$\left. - \int_0^\lambda f'(l) \left[\sqrt{N} \left(F^*_{N,\xi}(l) - \frac{l}{2\pi} \right) - s_{N,k}(l) \right] dl \right| < B_1 \varepsilon$$

with probability $1 - \varepsilon$. However

$$P \left\{ \max_{0 \le \lambda \le \pi} \left| f(\lambda) s_{N,k}(\lambda) - \int_0^\lambda f'(l) s_{N,k}(l) \, dl \right| \le \alpha \right\}$$
$$\to P \left\{ \max_{0 \le \lambda \le \pi} \left| f(\lambda) s_k(\lambda) - \int_0^\lambda f'(l) s_k(l) \, dl \right| \le \alpha \right\}$$

as $N \to \infty$ since the relevant point set in $(k+1)$-space is again closed. We know that for any $\varepsilon > 0$

$$\max_{0 \le \lambda \le \pi} |s_k(\lambda) - \zeta(\lambda)| < \varepsilon$$

with probability $1 - \varepsilon$ for sufficiently large k. Let

$$\eta(\lambda) = f(\lambda) \zeta(\lambda) - \int_0^\lambda f'(l) \zeta(l) \, dl.$$

Then

$$P \left\{ \max_{0 \le \lambda \le \pi} |\eta(\lambda)| < \alpha - \varepsilon \right\} - \delta$$
$$< P \left\{ \max_{0 \le \lambda \le \pi} \sqrt{N} \left| \int_0^\lambda f(l) \{2\pi I_{N,\xi}(l) - 1\} \, dl \right| \le \alpha \right\}$$
$$< P \left\{ \max_{0 \le \lambda \le \pi} |\eta(\lambda)| < \alpha + \varepsilon \right\} + \delta$$

193

an on letting $N \to \infty$ so that $\varepsilon, \delta \to 0$ we obtain the desired result. Note that the event $\max_{0 \le \lambda \le \pi} |\eta(\lambda)| \le \alpha$ has a well defined probability since $\eta(\lambda)$ is a process with continuous sample functions with probability one.

We now put the pieces together and state the following general theorem:

THEOREM 4. *Let*

1. $f(\lambda)$ *be absolutely continuous.*

2. $a_\nu = 0 \, (\nu^\beta)$, $\beta < -3/2$.

Then

$$\lim_{N \to \infty} P\left\{ \max_{0 \le \lambda \le \pi} \sqrt{N} \, |F_N^*(\lambda) - F(\lambda)| \le \alpha \right\} = P\left\{ \max_{0 \le \lambda \le \pi} |\eta(\lambda)| \le \alpha \right\}. \quad (2)$$

This general theorem follows immediately from theorems 3 and 4. Condition 2 of this theorem is a little disquieting. We know that $a(\lambda) = \sum a_j e^{-ij\lambda}$ is some square root of $2\pi f(\lambda)$, that is, $|a(\lambda)|^2 = 2\pi f(\lambda)$. It is most reasonable to take $a(\lambda)$ as $a(\lambda) = \sqrt{2\pi f(\lambda)}$ since one could then relate the asymptotic behavior of the a_j's to the regularity properties of $f(\lambda)$. This can be done in the case of a normal process since it makes no difference there which square root of $2\pi f(\lambda)$ is taken. However, in the case of a general linear process it will make a difference. In general there will be only one square root of $2\pi f(\lambda)$ which corresponds to the representation of x_t as a linear process. However, as noted in the section 6.1, it seems intuitively plausible that *this result ought to be valid* if the spectrum is regular (condition 1 of theorem 4) and if *the observed process x_t satisfies the central limit theorem*. Since essentially any moving average of a stationary process satisfying the central limit theorem will also satisfy the central limit theorem, it seems likely that for such processes it will not make any difference which square root of $2\pi f(\lambda)$ is chosen. In particular one would expect to be able to take $a(\lambda) = \sqrt{2\pi f(\lambda)}$ and have one condition specifying the regularity of the spectrum.

It is of interest to note that e is identifiable. The mean value

$$E \, x_t^2 \, x_{t+\mu}^2 = e \sum_{\nu = -\infty}^{\infty} a_{t-\nu}^2 a_{t+\mu-\nu}^2 + 2 \, r_\mu^2 + r_0^2$$

so that $\qquad s_\mu = \text{cov} \, (x_t^2, \, x_{t+\mu}^2) = e \sum_{\nu = -\infty}^{\infty} a_{t-\nu}^2 a_{t+\mu-\nu}^2 + 2 \, r_\mu^2.$

$$\text{Then} \qquad e = \frac{\sum\limits_{\mu=-\infty}^{\infty} s_\mu - 4\pi \int\limits_{-\pi}^{\pi} f^2(\lambda)\, d\lambda}{\left[\int\limits_{-\pi}^{\pi} f(\lambda)\, d\lambda\right]^2}, \qquad (3)$$

so that e is identifiable. One can in fact construct a consistent estimate for e using (3). However this estimate will not converge rapidly.

6.6. The Normal Case

Theorem 4 is of special interest when x_t is a normal process. The following corollary rephrases the content of the theorem in this special context.

COROLLARY 1. *When x_t is a normal process with a positive spectral density having an integrable second dervative, Theorem 4 reduces to the following statement*

$$\lim_{N\to\infty} P\left\{\max_{0\le\lambda\le\pi} \sqrt{N}\,|F_N^*(\lambda) - F(\lambda)| \le \alpha\right\}$$

$$= \sum_{k=-\infty}^{\infty} (-1)^k\,[\Phi((2k+1)\,\alpha/x) - \Phi((2k-1)\,\alpha/x)] = \Delta\left(\frac{\alpha}{x}\right),$$

where $\Phi(u)$ is the normal distribution function and

$$x = \sqrt{2\,\pi\,G(\pi)}.$$

Proof. If the spectral density of x_t is positive and has an integrable second derivative conditions 1 and 2 of Theorem 4 are both satisfied. One can easily see that the second condition is satisfied on choosing $a(\lambda) = \sqrt{2\pi f(\lambda)}$. The parameter $e = 0$ since x_t is a normal process. But then $\eta(\lambda)$ reduces to the model of linear Brownian motion discussed in section 1.1 with the following changed scale of time

$$t = 2\pi G(\lambda), \ \ 0\le\lambda\le\pi$$

so that $\qquad P\left\{\max_{0\le\lambda\le\pi} |\eta(\lambda)| \le \alpha\right\} = P\left\{\max_{0\le t\le 2\pi G(\pi)} |B(t)| \le \alpha\right\}, \qquad (1)$

where $B(t)$ is the linear Brownian notion. The reader may note that (1) is the probability that a particle in Brownian motion on the line is not absorbed by the barriers $\alpha, -\alpha$ in the time interval $(0, 2\pi G(\pi))$ given that the particle starts from 0 at time 0. Consider the fundamental solution $p(t,x)$ of the heat equation $\partial p/\partial t = \frac{1}{2}\partial^2 p/\partial x^2$ which is zero at $x = -\alpha, \alpha$ and behaves like a δ-function at $x = 0$ when $t \to 0$. The absorbing barrier probability considered above is

$$\int_{-a}^{a} p(t,x)\,dx,$$

where $t = 2\pi G(\pi)$. This absorbing barrier probability can be elegantly obtained by the method of images (see Sommerfeld [1], pp. 74–79). Table 1 is a table of the percentiles of $\Delta(\alpha)$.

TABLE 1.

Table of percentiles of $\Delta(\alpha)$.

$\Delta(\alpha)$	α	$\Delta(\alpha)$	α
.999	3.4808	.55	1.2126
.99	2.8070	.50	1.1490
.95	2.2414	.45	1.0892
.90	1.9600	.40	1.0322
.85	1.7805	.35	.9774
.80	1.6449	.30	.9238
.75	1.5341	.18524	.8
.70	1.4395	.10267	.7
.65	1.3562	.04136	.6
.60	1.2812	.00916	.5

The corollary of Theorem 4 lends itself to important statistical applications. However, we first have to estimate $G(\pi)$ which is in general unknown. Note that

$$G(\pi) = \frac{1}{4\pi} \sum_{-\infty}^{\infty} r_\nu^2.$$

The statistics C_ν/N are consistent estimates of r_ν. It is natural to consider an estimate of the form

$$G^*(\pi) = \frac{1}{4\pi}\left\{\left(\frac{C_0}{N}\right)^2 + 2\sum_{\nu=1}^{[kN^\alpha]}\left(\frac{C_\nu}{N}\right)^2\right\}, \quad 0 < \alpha < 1, \; k > 0.$$

One reason for this particular choice is that in practice one will try to avoid the cumbersome calculation of all the lagged product sums C_ν.

Lemma 2. *If $a_\nu = 0(\nu^\beta)$, $\beta < -1$, the statistic $G^*(\pi)$ is a consistent estimate of $G(\pi)$.*

Proof. We write $G^*(\pi)$ as the sum of two terms

$$G^*(\pi) = \frac{1}{4\pi}\left\{\left(\frac{C_0}{N}\right)^2 + 2\sum_{\nu=1}^m \left(\frac{C_\nu}{N}\right)^2\right\} + \frac{1}{2\pi}\sum_{\nu=m+1}^{[kN^\alpha]} \left(\frac{C_\nu}{N}\right)^2. \tag{2}$$

On using the representation of x_t as a linear process, the expectation of the second term can be seen to be less than or equal to

$$\sum_{\nu=m+1}^{[kN^\alpha]} \sum_{j,k=1}^N \sum_{\beta_1,\beta_2} \left\{\left|a_{j-\beta_1}a_{j+\nu-\beta_1}a_{k-\beta_2}a_{k+\nu-\beta_2}\right| + \left|a_{j-\beta_1}a_{j+\nu-\beta_2}a_{k-\beta_1}a_{k+\nu-\beta_2}\right| + \right.$$

$$\left. + \left|a_{j-\beta_1}a_{j+\nu-\beta_2}a_{k-\beta_2}a_{k+\nu-\beta_1}\right|\right\}(4+\mu_4)$$

$$= (\Sigma_1 + \Sigma_2 + \Sigma_3)(4+\mu_4).$$

Let the covariances of the process $\sum_{\nu=-\infty}^{\infty}|a_{n-\nu}|\xi_\nu$ be denoted by ϱ_ν. The spectral density $\frac{1}{2}|\sum|a_\nu|e^{i\nu\lambda}|^2$ of this process is continuous and therefore quadratically integrable so that $\sum_{-\infty}^{\infty}\varrho_\nu^2 < \infty$. But then

$$|\Sigma_1| = \sum_{\nu=m+1}^{[kN^\alpha]}N^2\varrho_\nu^2 \le N^2\sum_{\nu=m+1}^{\infty}\varrho_\nu^2$$

so that

$$\frac{1}{N^2}|\Sigma_1| < \varepsilon$$

for m sufficiently large as $N \leftarrow \infty$. We also see that

$$\frac{1}{N^2}|\Sigma_2| = \frac{1}{N^2}\sum_{\nu=m+1}^{[kN^\alpha]}\sum_{j,k=1}^N \varrho_{j-k}^2 \le \frac{1}{N}\sum_{m+1}^{[kN^\alpha]}\sum_{n=-\infty}^{\infty}\varrho_n^2 \le \frac{kN^\alpha+1}{N}\sum_{-\infty}^{\infty}\varrho_n^2 \to 0$$

as $N \to \infty$. The third sum Σ_3 can be handled in very much the same way using the Schwarz inequality. Choose m so large that the last sum in (2) is less than δ with probability larger than $1-\delta$ as $N \to \infty$. The first sum in (2) consists of a fixed number of terms, each of which converges in probability to the corresponding term in the expression for $G(\pi)$. The lemma is proved.

Corollary 1 states that the asymptotic distribution of $\max_{0\le\lambda\le\pi}\sqrt{N}|F_N^*(\lambda) - F(\lambda)|$ depends only on the parameter $G(\pi)$ when x_t is a normal process with a regular spectrum. This corollary and lemma 2 enable us to construct confidence bands for $F(\lambda)$.

THEOREM 5. *Suppose that x_t is a normal process and that its spectral density is positive and has an integrable second derivative. Then*

$$F_N^*(\lambda) - \alpha \sqrt{\frac{2\pi G^*(\pi)}{N}} \leq F(\lambda) \leq F_N^*(\lambda) + \alpha \sqrt{\frac{2\pi G^*(\pi)}{N}}$$

is an asymptotic confidence band of the spectral distribution function $F(\lambda)$ with confidence coefficient $\Delta(\alpha)$.

The proof follows immediately from Corollary 1 and Lemma 2 since $\Delta(\alpha)$ is continuous.

Theorem 5 also gives a test of significance for the simple hypothesis of a completely specified spectrum. Another interesting case however is the following.

THEOREM 6. *Consider a stochastic process x_t satisfying the assumptions of Theorem 5. Assume that two independent time series of length N_1 and length N_2 generated by this process are observed and that the corresponding estimates $F_{N_1}^*(\lambda)$, $F_{N_2}^*(\lambda)$, $G_1^*(\pi)$, $G_2^*(\pi)$ are computed. Then if $N_1/N_2 \to c > 0$,*

$$\frac{\max\limits_{0 \leq \lambda \leq \pi} \sqrt{N} \left| F_{N_1}^*(\lambda) - F_{N_2}^*(\lambda) \right|}{\sqrt{G_1^*(\pi) + G_2^*(\pi)}} > \alpha, \qquad N = \frac{2N_1 N_2}{N_1 + N_2},$$

is asymptotically a critical region of size $1 - \Delta(\alpha)$, as $N \to \infty$, for testing the hypothesis $F_1(\lambda) \equiv F_2(\lambda)$.

The proof is analogous to that of Theorem 5. Both these theorems are of considerable methodological interest. They correspond to nonparametric statistical techniques since the parameter space of the class of admissible processes is the space of regular spectral distribution functions (with a distance function given for example by the maximum of the difference between two points of the space). But this space is properly speaking an infinite dimensional space since it cannot be mapped onto a finite dimensional space by a continuous mapping.

6.7. Remarks on the Nonnormal Case

In the case $e \neq 0$ we know very little. However a little bit can be said and it is worth while stating.

First of all there is an inequality for absorbing barrier probablities of the type we are considering that is of some interest. Let $\eta_1(\lambda)$, $\eta_2(\lambda)$ be two normal processes with moments

$$F \eta_k (\lambda) \equiv 0$$

$$E \eta_k (\lambda) \eta_k (\mu) = e_k \, F_k (\lambda) \, F_k (\mu) + 2 \pi \int\limits_0^{\min (\lambda, \mu)} f_k^2 (l) \, d \, l,$$

$k = 1, 2$. Assume that $e_1 \geq e_2 \geq -2$ (the expression for $E \eta_k (\lambda) \eta_k (\mu)$ will not be a covariance function unless $e_k \geq -2$) and that $f_1 (\lambda) \geq f_2 (\lambda) \geq 0$ for all λ. Of course

$$F_k (\lambda) = \int\limits_0^\lambda f_k (l) \, d \, l.$$

If the functions $f_k(\lambda)$ satisfy the regularity conditions we have imposed on the spectral density in the previous sections, one can choose representations of the processes $\eta_k(\lambda)$ that have continuous sample functions with probability one. The absorbing barrier probabilities

$$P \, (\max_{0 \leq \lambda \leq \pi} | \eta_k (\lambda) | < \alpha)$$

are then well defined. Note that

$$E \eta_1(\lambda)\eta_1(\mu) - E\eta_2(\lambda)\eta_2(\mu) \tag{1}$$

is a nonnegative definite function. This implies that

$$\eta_1 (\lambda) = \eta_2 (\lambda) + a (\lambda)$$

where $a(\lambda)$ is a normal process with covariance function (1) independent of $\eta_2(\lambda)$. Intuitively it then seems reasonable that

$$P \, (\max_{0 \leq \lambda \leq \pi} | \eta_1 (\lambda) | < \alpha) \leq P \, (\max_{0 \leq \lambda \leq \pi} | \eta_2 (\lambda) | < \alpha). \tag{2}$$

This inequality is valid and follows from a result of T. W. Anderson [2]. Thus if $e < 0$ we know that

$$P \, (\max_{0 \leq \lambda \leq \pi} | \eta (\lambda) | < \alpha) \geq P \, (\max_{0 \leq t \leq 2\pi G(\pi)} | B (t) | < \alpha) = \Delta \left(\frac{\alpha}{x} \right),$$

where $x = \sqrt{2 \pi G(\pi)}$, so that one is acting conservatively if one sets up confidence regions based on the limit theorem for normal x_t.

There are a few cases in which the limiting probability (6.5.2) can be explicitly evaluated. They can be used together with inequality (2) to get bounds on the absorbing barrier probability of interest.

When the process x_t is pure white noise (so that $f(\lambda) \equiv$ constant, say 1) the limiting probability of interest is given by

$$P \{ \max_{0 \le \lambda \le \pi} | \zeta (\lambda) | \le \alpha \} \tag{3}$$

$$E \, \zeta (\lambda) \equiv 0$$

$$E \, \zeta (\lambda) \, \zeta (\mu) = e \, \lambda \, \mu + 2 \, \pi \min (\lambda, \, \mu).$$

and can be explicitly evaluated.

THEOREM 7.

$$P \{ \max_{0 \le \lambda \le \pi} | \zeta (\lambda) | \le \alpha \}$$
$$= \sum_{k = -\infty}^{\infty} (-1)^k \, e^{-\frac{k^2 \alpha^2}{2} \left(1 - \frac{\gamma}{2} \right)} \left[\Phi \left(\frac{\sqrt{\gamma} \, \alpha}{\pi} \left(k + \frac{1}{\eta} \right) \right) - \Phi \left(\frac{\sqrt{\gamma} \, \alpha}{\pi} \left(k - \frac{1}{\gamma'} \right) \right) \right]$$

where $\gamma = e + 2$.

Proof. Let $\tau = \lambda / \pi$. We first introduce the following notation. Let x be a normal stochastic variable with mean zero and variance one. Let $x(\tau)$ be a normal process with

$$E x (\tau) \equiv 0$$

$$E x (\tau) x (\tau') = \min (\tau, \tau') - \tau \tau',$$

that is, $x(\tau)$ is the linear Brownian motion conditioned so that $x(1) = 0$. x and $x(\tau)$ are assumed to be independent of each other. Now consider the process

$$u (\tau) = \sqrt{\gamma} \, \pi \, x \, \tau + \pi \, \sqrt{2} \, x (\tau).$$

The process $u (\tau)$ has the same probability distribution as $\zeta (\lambda)$ so that

$$P \{ \max_{0 \le \lambda \le \pi} | \zeta (\lambda) | \le \alpha \} = P \{ \max_{0 \le \tau \le 1} | u (\tau) | \le \alpha \}.$$

But

$$P \{ \max_{0 \le \tau \le 1} | u (\tau) | \le \alpha \}$$
$$= \int_{-\infty}^{\infty} P \left\{ \frac{-\alpha - \sqrt{\gamma} \, \pi \, \tau \, x}{\pi \sqrt{2}} \le x (\tau) \le \frac{\alpha - \sqrt{\gamma} \, \pi \, \tau \, x}{\pi \sqrt{2}}; \, 0 \le \tau \le 1 \right\} \varphi (x) \, d x \tag{4}$$

where $\varphi (x)$ is the normal frequency function. Let

$$Y (t) = (t + 1) \, x \left(\frac{t}{t + 1} \right), \quad 0 \le t < \infty.$$

Then $Y (t)$ is the linear Brownian motion (see J. L. Doob [1]), $0 \le t < \infty$. Now consider

$$P\{-a-(a+b)\,t\le y\,(t)\le a+(a-b)\,t;\ 0\le t<\infty\}, \tag{5}$$

where $a=\alpha/\pi\sqrt{2}$, $b=\sqrt{\gamma}\,x/\sqrt{2}$. The integrand in (4) is zero unless $|\sqrt{\gamma}\,x|\le\alpha/\pi$. Suppose that this inequality holds. Doob[1] has then evaluated (5) as

$$1-\sum_{m=1}^{\infty}\{e^{-2[(2m-1)^2a^2-(2m-1)ba]}+e^{-2[(2m-1)^2a^2+(2m-1)ba]}-$$

$$-e^{-2[(2m)^2a^2-2mba]}-e^{-2[(2m)^2a^2+2mba]}\}$$

$$=1-2\sum_{n=1}^{\infty}(-1)^{n+1}e^{-2n^2a^2}\cos h\,2nba.$$

Then (3) is equal to

$$\Phi\left(\frac{\alpha}{\pi\sqrt{\gamma}}\right)-\Phi\left(\frac{-a}{\pi\sqrt{\gamma}}\right)-2\sum_{n=1}^{\infty}(-1)^{n+1}e^{-\frac{n^2a^2}{\pi^2}}\int_{\frac{-a}{\pi\sqrt{\gamma}}}^{\frac{a}{\pi\sqrt{\gamma}}}\varphi\,(x)\cos h\,n\,\frac{\sqrt{\gamma}\,\alpha}{\pi}x\,d\,x$$

$$=\Phi\left(\frac{\alpha}{\pi\sqrt{\gamma}}\right)-\Phi\left(\frac{-\alpha}{\pi\sqrt{\gamma}}\right)-\sum_{n=1}^{\infty}(-1)^{n+1}e^{-n^2\left[\frac{\alpha^2}{\pi^2}-\frac{\gamma}{2}\frac{\alpha^2}{\pi^2}\right]}\cdot\left\{\Phi\left(\frac{n\sqrt{\gamma}\,\alpha}{\pi}+\frac{\alpha}{\pi\sqrt{\gamma}}\right)-\right.$$

$$\left.-\Phi\left(\frac{n\sqrt{\gamma}\,\alpha}{\pi}-\frac{\alpha}{\pi\sqrt{\gamma}}\right)+\Phi\left(\frac{-n\sqrt{\gamma}\,\alpha}{\pi}+\frac{\alpha}{\pi\sqrt{\gamma}}\right)-\Phi\left(\frac{-n\sqrt{\gamma}\,\alpha}{\pi}-\frac{\alpha}{\pi\sqrt{\gamma}}\right)\right\}$$

$$=\sum_{n=-\infty}^{\infty}(-1)^n e^{-\frac{n^2\alpha^2}{\pi^2}\left(1-\frac{\gamma}{2}\right)}\left[\Phi\left(\frac{\sqrt{\gamma}\,\alpha}{\pi}\left(n+\frac{1}{\gamma}\right)\right)-\Phi\left(\frac{\sqrt{\gamma}\,\alpha}{\pi}\left(n-\frac{1}{\gamma}\right)\right)\right].$$

Note that the fourth cumulant $e>-2$. Let the limiting distribution discussed above be denoted by $\Delta_e(\alpha)$. In the previous section, this limiting distribution had been written in down in the case of a normal process x_t, that is, $\Delta(\alpha)=\Delta_0(\alpha)$ had been obtained. Table 2 and Graph 1 describe the dependence of $\Delta_e(\alpha)$ on e and α.

TABLE 2.

Table of α for fixed e and $\Delta_e(\alpha)$.

	e						
$\Delta_e(a)$	-2	-1	0	1	3	5	10
.900	1.224	1.603	1.960	2.271	2.943	3.375	4.264
.950	1.358	1.800	2.241	2.624	3.396	3.923	5.001
.990	1.628	2.194	2.807	3.333	4.307	5.019	6.464
.999	1.949	2.664	3.481	4.174	5.390	6.315	8.183

6.8. Spectral Analysis with a Regression Present

Theorems 5 and 6 are somewhat restricted in their applicability as they stand since x_t is a linear process with mean value zero. In many contexts the observed process $y_t = x_t + m_t$ where $m_t = E y_t$ is not identically zero. Consider the case in which

$$m_t = d_1 \varphi_t^{(1)} + \cdots + d_p \varphi_t^{(p)},$$

where $\varphi_t^{(1)}$, $\varphi_t^{(2)}, \ldots, \varphi_t^{(p)}$ are given real-valued sequences and the regression coefficients d_ν are unknown. Let $d_1^*, \ldots, d_p^*$ be the least square estimates of $d_1, \ldots, d_p$. It then seems intuitively plausible that Theorems 5 and 6 will still hold if $F_N^*(\lambda)$ is computed using $y_t - d_1^* \varphi_t^{(1)} - \cdots - d_p^* \varphi_t^p$ in place of x_t. This is shown to be true. To avoid unnecessary complications we confine ourselves to the case $p = 2$, which will illustrate the general situation. We have to introduce the following condition which prevents the two regression variables $\varphi_t^{(1)}$ and $\varphi_t^{(2)}$ from becoming linearly dependent in the limit

$$R = \varlimsup_{N \to \infty} \frac{\left(\sum\limits_1^N \varphi_t^{(1)} \varphi_t^{(2)} \right)^2}{\sum\limits_1^N \varphi_t^{(1)^2} \sum\limits_1^N \varphi_t^{(2)^2}} < 1. \tag{1}$$

THEOREM 8. *Under the conditions of Theorems 5 and 6 and (1), these theorems remain valid if $F_N^*(\lambda)$ is computed using $y_t - d_1^* \varphi_t^{(1)} - d_2^* \varphi_t^{(2)}$ in place of x_t.*

Proof. It is sufficient to prove that

$$\max_{0 \leq \lambda \leq \pi} \sqrt{N} \left| \frac{1}{2 \pi N} \int\limits_0^\lambda \left| \sum\limits_1^N (y_t - d_1^* \varphi_t^{(1)} - d_2^* \varphi_t^{(2)}) e^{-itl} \right|^2 dl - \right.$$

$$\left. - \frac{1}{2 \pi N} \int\limits_0^\lambda \left| \sum\limits_1^N x_t e^{-itl} \right|^2 dl \right|$$

tends to zero in probability as $N \to \infty$. The expression inside the absolute value sign is

$$\frac{1}{2 \pi N} \sum\limits_{\nu, \mu = 1}^N [-2 (d_1^* - d) \varphi_\nu^{(1)} x_\mu - 2 (d_2^* - d_2) \varphi_\nu^{(2)} x_\mu + (d_1^* - d_1)^2 \varphi_\nu^{(1)} \varphi_\mu^{(1)} +$$

$$+ (d_2^* - d_2)^2 \varphi_\nu^{(2)} \varphi_\mu^{(2)} + 2 (d_1^* - d_1) (d_2^* - d_2) \varphi_\nu^{(1)} \varphi_\mu^{(2)}] \frac{\sin (\nu - \mu) \lambda}{\nu - \mu}$$

$$= \Sigma_1 + \Sigma_2 + \Sigma_3 + \Sigma_4 + \Sigma_5,$$

where the usual convention is used for terms with $\nu = \mu$. The least square estimates d_1^*, d_2^* are unbiased linear estimates with coefficients depending only upon the $\varphi^{(1)}$'s and $\varphi^{(2)}$'s. Now

$$d_1^* = \frac{\sum\limits_{t=1}^{N} y_t \left[\varphi_t^{(2)} \sum\limits_{\tau=1}^{N} \varphi_\tau^{(1)} \varphi_\tau^{(2)} - \varphi_t^{(1)} \sum\limits_{\tau=1}^{N} \varphi_\tau^{(2)^2} \right]}{\left(\sum\limits_{t=1}^{N} \varphi_t^{(1)} \varphi_t^{(2)} \right)^2 - \sum\limits_{t=1}^{N} \varphi_t^{(1)^2} \varphi_t^{(2)^2}}$$

and d_2^* is obtained by interchanging $\varphi_t^{(1)}$ and $\varphi_t^{(2)}$ in the expression for d_1^*.

A simple argument using the fact that the spectral density is bounded shows that

$$\operatorname{var} d_1^* \leq 2\pi \max_{0 \leq \lambda \leq \pi} f(\lambda) \frac{\sum \varphi_\nu^{(2)^2}}{\sum \varphi_\nu^{(1)^2} \sum \varphi_\nu^{(2)^2} - \left(\sum \varphi_\nu^{(1)} \varphi_\nu^{(2)} \right)^2}$$

$$\leq \frac{2\pi \max\limits_{0 \leq \lambda \leq \pi} f(\lambda)}{1 - R} \cdot \frac{1}{\sum\limits_{1}^{N} \varphi_\nu^{(1)^2}}. \tag{2}$$

But

$$\pi \sqrt{N} \max_{0 \leq \lambda \leq \pi} |\Sigma_1| \leq \frac{1}{\sqrt{N}} \left\{ \left| d_1^* - d_1 \right| \left| \sum_{p=1}^{N-1} \frac{1}{p} \right| \sum_{\nu=1}^{N-p} x_\nu \varphi_{\nu+p}^{(1)} \right| + $$

$$+ \left| d_1^* - d_1 \right| \pi \left| \sum_{\nu=1}^{N} x_\nu \varphi_\nu^{(1)} \right|^2 + \left| d_1^* - d_1 \right| \sum_{p=-N+1}^{1} \frac{1}{|p|} \left| \sum_{\nu=1-p}^{N} x_\nu \varphi_{\nu+p}^{(1)} \right| \right\}.$$

Moreover,

$$E \left| \sum_{\nu=1}^{N-p} x_\nu \varphi_{\nu+p}^{(1)} \right|^2 \leq 2\pi \max_{0 \leq \lambda \leq \pi} f(\lambda) \sum_{\nu=1}^{N} \varphi_\nu^{(1)^2}. \tag{3}$$

From (2) we know that with as large a probability as desired $\left| d_1^* - d_1 \right|$ is less than $k / \sqrt{\sum\limits_{\nu=1}^{N} \varphi_\nu^{(1)^2}}$. It then follows from the Schwarz inequality and (3) that with large probability

$$\pi \sqrt{N} \max_{0 \leq \lambda \leq \pi} |\Sigma_1| < k' \log N / \sqrt{N} \to 0.$$

The sum Σ_2 can be handled in the same way. Now

$$2\pi \sqrt{N} \max_{0 \leq \lambda \leq \pi} |\Sigma_3| = \frac{(d_1^* - d_1)^2}{\sqrt{N}} \int_0^\lambda \left| \sum_1^N \varphi_\nu^{(1)} e^{i\nu l} \right|^2 dl \leq \frac{(d_1^* - d_1)^2}{\sqrt{N}} \sum_1^N \varphi_\nu^{(1)^2}$$

and the expectation of this tends to zero as $N^{-\frac{1}{4}}$. Σ_4 and Σ_5 can be treated in a similar manner and this proves the theorem.

An important special case is that in which $\varphi_\nu \equiv 1$. This corresponds to an unknown mean value of the process. Another situation of some interest arises when the spectrum of the process has a discrete component with frequencies $\lambda_1, \lambda_2, \ldots, \lambda_p$. We then take the φ_ν's as trigonometric functions with these frequencies.

6.9. Alternative Estimates of the Spectral Distribution Function

It is of great interest to see whether Theorems 4–6, 8 are still valid if the estimate $F_N^*(\lambda)$ is replaced by a truncated estimate

$$
F_{N,\,tr}^*(\lambda) = \frac{C_0\,\lambda}{2\,\pi\,N} + \frac{1}{\pi\,N} \sum_{\nu=1}^{h_N} C_\nu \frac{\sin \nu\lambda}{\nu}
$$

$$
= \frac{1}{2\,\pi} \int\limits_0^\lambda \int\limits_{-\pi}^\pi I_N(l)\, \frac{\sin\left(h_N + \frac{1}{2}\right)(l-\mu)}{\sin \dfrac{l-\mu}{2}}\, dl\, d\mu \tag{1}
$$

where $h_N \to \infty$ as $N \to \infty$. Here the weighting factors are 1 from $\nu = 0$ up to $\nu = h_N$ and are zero from that point on. The estimate $F_{N,\,tr}^*(\lambda)$, in general, is not nondecreasing with probability 1 and this can at times be an unpleasant feature. One might be interested in choosing $h_N = [k\,N^\alpha]$. Such estimates are of considerable interest because they reduce the computational work as one only needs to compute the C_ν's for $\leq [k\,N^\alpha]$.

We shall now consider a class of estimates of the spectral distribution function with nondecreasing weight functions. Let

$$
W_N(\lambda) = \int\limits_{-\pi}^\lambda w_N(l)\, dl,
$$

where $w_N(l) \geq 0$ in $(-\pi, \pi)$

$$
\int\limits_{-\pi}^\pi w_N(l)\, dl = 1 \quad \text{and}
$$

$$
\lim_{N\to\infty} W_N(\lambda) = \begin{cases} 0 & \text{if } \lambda < 0 \\ 1 & \text{if } \lambda > 0. \end{cases}
$$

Let
$$F_N^* (\lambda, \, W_N) = \int\limits_0^\pi I_N(l) \, W_N(\lambda - l) \, dl$$

$$F(\lambda, \, W_N) = \int\limits_0^\pi f(l) \, W_N(\lambda - l) \, dl.$$

We prove the following theorem.

THEOREM 9. *Under the conditions of Theorem 4*

$$\lim_{N\to\infty} P\{ \max_{0\le\lambda\le\pi} \sqrt{N} \, | F_N^*(\lambda, \, W_N) - F(\lambda, \, W_N)| \le \alpha\} = P\{ \max_{0\le\lambda\le\pi} |\eta(\lambda)| \le \alpha\}.$$

Proof. On integrating by parts we have

$$\sqrt{N} \, [F_N^*(\lambda, \, W_N) - F(\lambda, \, W_N)]$$

$$= \sqrt{N} \int\limits_0^\pi [I_N(l) - f(l)] \, dl \, W_N(\lambda - \pi) +$$

$$+ \int\limits_0^\pi \sqrt{N} \int\limits_0^l [I_N(\mu) - f(\mu)] \, d\mu \, w_N(\lambda - l) \, dl. \qquad (2)$$

By Theorem 2 we can replace (2) by

$$\sqrt{N} \int\limits_0^\pi f(l) \, [2\pi I_{N,\xi}(l) - 1] \, dl \, W_N(\lambda - \pi) +$$

$$+ \int\limits_0^\pi \sqrt{N} \int\limits_0^l [2\pi I_{N,\xi}(\mu) - 1] \, f(\mu) \, d\mu \, w_N(\lambda - l) \, dl,$$

committing an error of at most $\varepsilon > 0$ uniformly in λ with probability $1 - \varepsilon$. On integrating by parts twice we obtain

$$\sqrt{N} \, 2\pi \, [F_{N,\xi}^*(\lambda) - 1/2] \, f(\pi) \, W_N(\lambda - \pi) -$$

$$- \int\limits_0^\pi \sqrt{N} \, 2 \left[F_{N,\xi}^*(l) - \frac{l}{2} \right] \frac{d}{dl}(f(l) \, W_N(\lambda - l)) \, dl. \qquad (3)$$

But

$$\sqrt{N} \max_{0\le\lambda\le\pi} \left| F_{N,\xi}^*(\lambda) - \frac{\lambda}{2\pi} - \frac{1}{\sqrt{N}} s_{N,m}(\lambda) \right| < \varepsilon$$

with probability $1 - \varepsilon$ where m is a large but fixed number. We can than replace (3) by

205

$$\int_0^\pi f(l)\,W_N\,(\lambda-l)\,s'_{N,\,m}\,(l)\,dl$$

$$= \frac{c_0-N}{2\pi\sqrt{N}}\int_0^\pi f(l)\,W_N\,(\lambda-l)\,dl\,+$$

$$+\frac{1}{\pi}\sum_1^m\int_0^\pi\frac{c_\nu}{\sqrt{N}}\cos\nu l f(l)\,W_N\,(\lambda-l)\,dl$$

with an error of at most ε uniformly in λ. Reasoning as in Theorem 4 we have

$$\lim_{N\to\infty}P\left\{\max_{0\le\lambda\le\pi}\left|\int_0^\pi f(l)\,W_N\,(\lambda-l)\,s'_{N,\,m}\,(l)\,dl\right|\le\alpha\right\}$$

$$=P\left\{\max_{0\le\lambda\le\pi}\left|\int_0^\lambda f(l)\,s'_m\,(l)\,dl\right|\le\alpha\right\}$$

making use of the fact that

$$\max_{0\le\lambda\le\pi}\left|\int_0^\pi\cos\nu l f(l)\,W_N\,(\lambda-l)\,dl-\int_0^\lambda\cos\nu l f(l)\,dl\right|$$

$$\le\max_{0\le\lambda\le\pi}f(\lambda)\left\{\int_{-\pi}^0 W_N\,(l)\,dl+\int_0^\pi|\,W_N\,(l)-1\,|\,dl\right\}\to 0$$

as $N\to\infty$. But

$$\max_{0\le\lambda\le\pi}\left|\int_0^\lambda f(l)\,s'_m\,(l)\,dl-\eta\,(\lambda)\right|<\varepsilon$$

with large probability if m is sufficiently large and the theorem follows immediately.

One is usually more interested in estimating $F(\lambda)$ than $F(\lambda,W_N)$. The following corollary enables us to do this.

COROLLARY 2. *Theorems 4–6, 8 remain valid when* $F_N^*(\lambda)$ *is replaced by* $F_N^*(\lambda,W_N)$ *if*

$$\int_{-\pi}^0 W_N\,(\lambda)\,d\lambda+\int_0^\pi[1-W_N\,(\lambda)]\,d\lambda=o\,(N^{-1/2}). \tag{4}$$

Proof. The proof follows immediately as

$$\max_{0\le\lambda\le\pi} \sqrt{N}\,|F(\lambda) - F(\lambda,\, W_N)|$$

$$\le \sqrt{N} \max_{0\le\lambda\le\pi} f(\lambda) \left\{ \int_{-\pi}^{0} W_N(\lambda)\, d\lambda + \int_{0}^{\pi} [1 - W_N(\lambda)]\, d\lambda \right\} = o(1).$$

It is clear from the above comments that the time series analyst has a large class of estimates of the spectral distribution function at his disposal. It is worth while noting that the Fejér kernel

$$\frac{1}{2\pi h_N}\, \frac{\sin^2 \dfrac{h_N}{2}\lambda}{\sin^2 \dfrac{\lambda}{2}} = w_N(\lambda).$$

satisfies (4) if $\log h_N / h_N = o(N^{-\frac{1}{2}})$, so that we can choose the truncation point h_N as $h_N = [K N^\alpha]$, $\frac{1}{2} < \alpha < 1$. The estimate corresponding to this kernel is

$$F_N^*(\lambda,\, W_N) = \frac{C_0}{2\pi N} + \frac{1}{\pi N} \sum_{\nu=1}^{h_N} C_\lambda \frac{\sin \nu\lambda}{\nu} \left(1 - \frac{\nu}{h_N}\right).$$

This estimate of the spectral distribution function is closely related to an estimate of the spectral density given by Bartlett (see section 4.6). It is nondecreasing and does not require the computation of all the C_ν's.

Using an argument analogous to that given above one can easily see that Theorems 4–6, 8 are still valid if $F_N^*(\lambda)$ is replaced by $F_{N,\,tr}^*(\lambda)$, where $(\log h_N)/h_N = o(N^{-\frac{1}{2}})$. If the spectral density $f(\lambda)$ is continuous and analytic for all λ in $(-\pi, \pi)$ where $-\pi$ is identified with π, Theorems 4–6, 8 are valid with $F_N^*(\lambda)$ replaced by $F_{N,\,tr}^*(\lambda)$ when $h_N = [k N^\alpha]$, $0 < \alpha < 1$.

6.10. Alternative Statistics and the Corresponding Limit Theorems

In some cases one might prefer to consider statistics other than $\max_{0\le\lambda\le\pi}$ $|F_N^*(\lambda) - F(\lambda)|$ in dealing with the spectral distribution function $F(\lambda)$. We shall consider some alternative statistics in this section.

Consider the linear space consisting of continuous functions $c = c(\lambda)$ on $0 \le \lambda \le \pi$ with the norm $\|c\| = \sup |c(\lambda)|$. Let $\varphi(c)$ be a functional uniformly continuous in this topology.

THEOREM 10. *Under the conditions of Theorem 4,*

$$\lim_{N\to\infty} P\{\varphi(\sqrt{N}\,[F_N^*(\lambda) - F(\lambda)]) \le \alpha\} = P\{\varphi(\eta(\lambda)) \le \alpha\}.$$

207

Proof. Writing

$$\sqrt{N}\,[F_N^*(\lambda) - F(\lambda)] = s_{N,k}(\lambda) + r_{N,k}(\lambda)$$

as before, we note that

$$\|r_{N,k}(\lambda)\| < \varepsilon$$

with probability $1 - \varepsilon$ if k is chosen sufficiently large. We therefore commit only a small error by considering instead the probability of the event

$$\{\varphi(s_{N,k}(\lambda)) \le \alpha\}$$

which is a closed set in $(k+1)$-space. This probability converges to

$$P\,\{\varphi(s_k(\lambda)) \le \alpha\}$$

as $N \to \infty$. But choose k so large that

$$\|s_k(\lambda) - \eta(\lambda)\| < \delta$$

with probability $1 - \delta$. This together with the uniform continuity of $\varphi(c)$ proves the theorem.

An example of some interest is

$$\varphi(c) = \left\{\int_0^\lambda |c(\lambda)|^p\, d\mu(\lambda)\right\}^{1/p}, \quad p > 1$$

where $\mu(\lambda)$ is bounded and nondecreasing. This will give a statistic of the von Mises type.

It is also of interest to consider the estimated spectral mass in several fixed nonoverlapping λ-intervals. Both $\sqrt{N}\,[F_N^*(\lambda) - F(\lambda)]$ and $\eta(\lambda)$ can be extended to interval functions in the usual sense, that is

$$\sqrt{N}\,[F_N^*(I) - F(I)] = \sqrt{N}\,[F_N^*(\lambda_2) - F(\lambda_2)] - \sqrt{N}\,[F_N^*(\lambda_1) - F(\lambda_1)]$$

$$\eta(I) = \eta(\lambda_2) - \eta(\lambda_1),$$

where $I = (\lambda_1, \lambda_2)$. Then it is clear that the joint distribution of $\sqrt{N}\,[F_N^*(I_1) - F(I_1)], \ldots, \sqrt{N}\,[F_N^*(I_k) - F(I_k)]$ where $I_1, \ldots, I_k$ are nonoverlapping intervals in $(0, \pi)$ is asymptotically that of $\eta(I_1), \ldots, \eta(I_k)$ as $N \to \infty$.

6.11. Confidence Band for the Spectral Density

In the previous sections the distribution theory associated with the estimation of the spectral distribution function $F(\lambda)$ was discussed in some detail.

In particular, in Section 6.6, confidence bands for $F(\lambda)$ are set up, when the observed process x_t is normal. The results are less appealing in the nonnormal case because they depend on the parameter e. The computation of limiting probabilities becomes much more complicated and it does not seem as if they could easily be put into a form that is nonparametric. Moreover, even though e can be estimated consistently we have not been able to find an estimate that would be useful in practice (see section 6.5).

In this section we shall discuss heuristically the setting up of confidence bands for the spectral density $f(\lambda)$. It is significant that the asymptotic distribution associated with these confidence bands does not depend on e and can be given a nonparametric form for the class of linear processes with regular spectra. This might have been anticipated since we have already seen in section 4.2 that the limiting covariance of spectrograph estimates does not depend on e. This is of interest from an applied point of view because it means that estimation of the spectral density can be carried out within bounds without worrying about e. We do not have rigorous proofs of many of the results in this section. However, they are of considerable interest and so we have given a heuristic derivation. We shall indicate conditions we believe to be intuitively plausible. However the reader should take these with the customary grain of salt. In this discussion consider

$$\frac{1}{h} \int_{kh}^{(k+1)h} I_N(\lambda)\,d\lambda$$

as an estimate of $f((k+\frac{1}{2})h)$ and confidence bands for $f(\lambda)$ about this estimate. It will also be clear that one can consider truncated estimates or estimates of the form

$$\frac{1}{h} \int_{kh}^{(k+1)h} \int_{-\pi}^{\pi} I_N(x) w_N(x - \lambda)\ dx\ d\lambda,$$

where $w_N(x)$ is a weight function which approaches a delta function at $x = 0$ as $N \to \infty$. We are interested in these estimates as $N, 1/h \to \infty$ simultaneously but where $1/h \to \infty$ more slowly than N. However, we shall only prove a limit theorem for the case in which $N \to \infty$ first and then $1/h \to \infty$. Of course, the gap in the argument will arise when we claim that we can then let $N, 1/h \to \infty$ simultaneously, $1/h = o\,(N)$, and obtain the same limit theorem. This is the case of practical interest. If a modified estimate of the type indicated above with weight function $w_N(x)$ is used, it seems

6.11

intuitively plausible that $w_N(x)$ should approach a delta function at $x = 0$ slower than $(1/N)$ and faster than (h).

We shall now make use of Theorem 4 in the plausibility argument. Consider the stochastic variables

$$Z_k = \sqrt{N} \left[\int_{kh}^{(k+1)h} I_N(\lambda)\, d\lambda - \int_{kh}^{(k+1)h} f(\lambda)\, d\lambda \right],$$

where $h = \pi/m$ and $k = 0, 1, \ldots, m-1$. They have the same joint distribution in the limit $N \to \infty$ as the stochastic variables

$$\eta((k+1)h) - \eta(kh), \quad k = 0, 1, \ldots, m-1,$$

that is, they are normal with mean zero and covariance

$$e \int_{kh}^{(k+1)h} f(\lambda)\, d\lambda \int_{jh}^{(j+1)h} f(\lambda)\, d\lambda + 2\pi\, \delta_{jk} \int_{kh}^{(k+1)h} f^2(\lambda)\, d\lambda.$$

The stochastic variables $\eta((k+1)h) - \eta(kh)$, $k = 0, 1, \ldots, m-1$ almost behave like independent normal variables and it is worth while seeing how they differ from independent variables. Consider a normal variable X, independent of the process $\eta(\lambda)$, with mean zero and variance 1. The stochastic variables

$$X\sqrt{2} \int_{kh}^{(k+1)h} f(\lambda)\, d\lambda + \eta((k+1)h) - \eta(kh), \quad k = 0, 1, \ldots, m-1 \qquad (1)$$

are normal with mean zero and covariance

$$(e+2) \int_{kh}^{(k+1)h} f(\lambda)\, d\lambda \int_{jh}^{(j+1)h} f(\lambda)\, d\lambda + 2\pi\, \delta_{jk} \int_{kh}^{(k+1)h} f^2(\lambda)\, d\lambda.$$

Let $Y, Y_1, \ldots, Y_m$ be independent normal variables with mean zero and variance 1. Then the stochastic variables (1) have the same probability structure as

$$Y\sqrt{e+2} \int_{kh}^{(k+1)h} f(\lambda)\, d\lambda + \sqrt{2\pi \int_{kh}^{(k+1)h} f^2(\lambda)\, d\lambda}\; Y_k, \quad k = 0, 1, \ldots, m-1,$$

since $e + 2 \geq 0$. If all these stochastic variables are appropriately defined on the same probability space, we can write

$$\eta\left((k+1)\,h\right)-\eta\left(k\,h\right)=\sqrt{2\,\pi\int\limits_{kh}^{(k+1)h}f^2\left(\lambda\right)d\,\lambda}\ Y_k+$$

$$+\sqrt{e+2}\int\limits_{kh}^{(k+1)h}f\left(\lambda\right)d\,\lambda\ Y-\sqrt{2}\int\limits_{kh}^{(k+1)h}f\left(\lambda\right)d\,\lambda\,X. \tag{2}$$

We are interested in the following limiting probability

$$\lim_{h\to 0}P\left\{\max_k\frac{\left|\eta\left((k+1)\,h\right)-\eta\left(k\,h\right)\right|}{\sqrt{2\,\pi\int\limits_{kh}^{(k+1)h}f^2\left(\lambda\right)d\,\lambda}}\le\Phi^{-1}\left(1-\frac{\alpha}{m}\right)\right\}, \tag{3}$$

where $h=\pi/m$ and $\Phi\left(x\right)$ is the normal distribution function. Here Φ^{-1} denotes the inverse function. However the probability of the set

$$\max_k\frac{\left|\eta\left((k+1)\,h\right)-\eta\left(k\,h\right)\right|}{\sqrt{2\,\pi\int\limits_{kh}^{(k+1)h}f^2\left(\lambda\right)d\,\lambda}}\le\Phi^{-1}\left(1-\frac{\alpha}{m}\right)$$

given any fixed pair of values for X and Y converges to

$$\lim_{m\to\infty}P\left\{\max_k|\,Y_k\,|\le\Phi^{-1}\left(1-\frac{\alpha}{m}\right)\right\}=e^{-2\alpha}$$

as $m\to\infty$. This is clear since the coefficient of Y_k in (2) is essentially $\sqrt{2\,\pi\,h}\,f\left(k\,h\right)$ while the coefficients of Y and X are essentially $\sqrt{e+2}\,h\,f\left(k\,h\right)$, $\sqrt{2}\,h\,f\left(k\,h\right)$ respectively. But the limiting probability (3) is then $e^{-2\alpha}$. We have thus shown that

$$\lim_{m\to\infty}\ \lim_{N\to\infty}P\left\{\max_k\frac{\left|\sqrt{N}\left[\int\limits_{kh}^{(k+1)h}I_N\left(\lambda\right)d\,\lambda-\int\limits_{kh}^{(k+1)h}f\left(\lambda\right)d\,\lambda\right]\right|}{\sqrt{2\,\pi\int\limits_{kh}^{(k+1)h}f^2\left(\lambda\right)d\,\lambda}}\right.$$

$$\left.\le\Phi^{-1}\left(1-\frac{\alpha}{m}\right)\right\}=e^{-2\alpha}.$$

The stochastic variables

$$\sqrt{N}\,\log\left[\int\limits_{kh}^{(k+1)h}I_N\left(\lambda\right)d\,\lambda\,\bigg/\int\limits_{kh}^{(k+1)h}f\left(\lambda\right)d\,\lambda\right],\quad k=0,1,\ldots,m-1$$

have the same distribution when $N\to\infty$ as

$$\frac{\eta((k+1)h)-\eta(kh)}{\int\limits_{kh}^{(k+1)h} f(\lambda)\,d\lambda}, \quad k=0,\,1,\,\ldots,\,m-1.$$

Using an argument similar to that given above one obtains the following limit theorem

$$\lim_{m\to\infty}\lim_{N\to\infty} P\left\{\max_k \sqrt{\frac{Nh}{2\pi}}\left|\log\left[\int\limits_{kh}^{(k+1)h} I_N(\lambda)\,d\lambda\bigg/\int\limits_{kh}^{(k+1)h} f(\lambda)\,d\lambda\right]\right|\right.$$
$$\left.\le \Phi^{-1}\left(1-\frac{\alpha}{m}\right)\right\}=e^{-2\alpha}. \quad (4)$$

The different forms of the limit theorem given above suggest confidence bands for the spectral mass. Perhaps the last form is the most interesting because the logarithm of the ratio of the spectral mass and its estimate is considered. This is a rather natural statistic.

In the limit theorem given above we first let $N\to\infty$ and then let $m\to\infty$. A limit theorem of much greater interest from the applied point of view is that in which both N and m increase simultaneously. It is clear that the limit theorem is still true when N and m increase simultaneously, if $m\to\infty$ sufficiently slowly with respect to N. A simple diagonalization argument will show this. The question of greatest interest is *how slowly should $m\to\infty$ with respect to N.*

In any case, as noted before, one must *at least* have $m\to\infty$ more slowly than $N\to\infty$ if such a limit theorem is to hold. Moreover, if one were to deal with an estimate of the form

$$\frac{1}{h}\int\limits_{kh}^{(k+1)h}\int\limits_{-\pi}^{\pi} I_N(x)\,w_N(x-\lambda)\,dx\,d\lambda,$$

where $w_N(x)$ approaches a delta function at $x=0$ as $N\to\infty$ and expect such a limit theorem to be valid, one would *at least* have

$$\int\limits_{-h/2}^{h/2} w_N(x)\,dx=1+o(1) \quad \text{and} \quad \int\limits_{-1/N}^{1/N} w_N(x)\,dx=o(1)$$

as $m,\,N\to\infty$. Note that if one could let $m\to\infty$ faster than $N^{2/7}$, the limit theorem (4) could be put in the following form

$$P\left\{\max_k \left|\sqrt{\frac{N\,h}{2\,\pi}}\, \log\left[\frac{1}{h}\int\limits_{kh}^{(k+1)h} I_N(\lambda)\,d\lambda \Big/ f\left(\left(k+\frac{1}{2}\right)h\right)\right]\right|\right.$$

$$\left. \leq \Phi^{-1}\left(1-\frac{\alpha}{m}\right)\right\} \rightarrow e^{-2\alpha}.$$

This is a rather convenient form since it would lead to the following asymptotic confidence band

$$\exp\left\{-\sqrt{\frac{2\,\pi\,m}{N}}\,\Phi^{-1}\left(1-\frac{\alpha}{m}\right)\right\}\frac{m}{\pi}\int\limits_{\frac{k\,\pi}{m}}^{\frac{(k+1)\pi}{m}} I_N(\lambda)\,d\lambda \leq f\left(\left(k+\frac{1}{2}\right)\frac{\pi}{m}\right)$$

$$\leq \exp\left\{\sqrt{\frac{2\,\pi\,m}{N}}\,\Phi^{-1}\left(1-\frac{\alpha}{m}\right)\right\}\frac{m}{\pi}\int\limits_{\frac{k\,\pi}{m}}^{\frac{(k+1)\pi}{m}} I_N(\lambda)\,d\lambda$$

for the spectral density $f(\lambda)$ at the points $\lambda = \pi/2m,\ 3\pi/2m, \ldots, ((2m-1)/2m)\pi$. Of course one would expect to get the same type of confidence band in the case of an estimate

$$\frac{1}{h}\int\limits_{kh}^{(k+1)h}\int\limits_{-\pi}^{\pi} I_N(x)\,w_N(x-\lambda)\,d\lambda$$

where $w_N(x)$ is a weight function satisfying conditions of the type spoken of above. Again convenient choices for $w_N(x)$ would be either the Dirichlet kernel

$$w_N(x) = \frac{1}{2}\,\frac{\sin\left(\left[N^\alpha\right]+\frac{1}{2}\right)x}{\sin\frac{1}{2}\,x}$$

or the Fejer kernel

$$w_N(x) = \frac{1}{2\,\pi\,[N^\alpha]}\,\frac{\sin^2\frac{1}{2}\,[N^\alpha]\,x}{\sin^2\frac{1}{2}\,x},$$

where $0 < \alpha < 1$ and $h N^\alpha \rightarrow \infty$.

If the observed process has a nonzero regression of the form given in section 6.8, one could subtract the estimated regression from the observed time series as one did in section 6.8 and compute the estimate of the spectral density from the resultant series of numbers. The limit theorem for the asymptotic confidence band would again be expected to be of the same form.

We have noted that the limit theorems conjectured and discussed here are independent of e. However, it is clear that the speed of convergence to the limiting form would be affected by the magnitude of e.

6.12. Spectral Analysis of Some Artificially Generated Time Series

Ten time series were generated for us in Stockholm, Sweden, under auspices of the Institute of Mathematical Statistics of the Stockholms Högskola. Before commenting on the results of the spectral analysis of the time series, we will describe the way in which they were generated and discuss the reasons for choosing this mode of generation.

In every case the computation started with the choice of a sequence of random numbers $\xi_{-4}, \xi_{-3}, \xi_{-2}, \ldots, \xi_t, \ldots, \xi_M$. These random numbers should be regarded as independent observations from a population with a given probability distribution. There are three probability distributions for ξ that were chosen. They are

N: Normal with mean zero and variance one.

R: Rectangular distribution on the interval $0 \leq \xi \leq 100$.

T: A three-point distribution

$$\xi = \begin{cases} 1 & \text{with probability } 1/10 \\ 0 & \text{,,} \qquad \text{,,} \qquad 8/10 \\ -1 & \text{,,} \qquad \text{,,} \qquad 1/10. \end{cases}$$

The time series x_t is computed by applying a moving average

$$x_t = a_0 \xi_t + a_1 \xi_{t-1} + a_2 \xi_{t-2} + a_3 \xi_{t-3} + a_4 \xi_{t-4} + a_5 \xi_{t-5}$$

to the sequence $\xi_{-4}, \xi_{-3}, \ldots, \xi_M$ of $M + 5$ random numbers. There are two alternative schemes for the coefficients of the moving average that we shall call alternatives A and B.

Coefficients						
Alternatives	a_0	a_1	a_2	a_3	a_4	a_5
A	0.1	0.5	0.2	-0.1	0.2	0.1
B	0.3	0.3	-0.2	0.1	0.1	0.1

Graphs 2 and 3 give the spectral distribution function of the process x_t in the case of alternatives A and B respectively. Graphs 4 and 5 give the form of the spectral density of x_t for the alternatives A and B. The values of the spectral distribution function and spectral density respectively for alternatives A and B at $\lambda = (k\pi/16)$, $k = 1,\ldots, 16$ are given in Tables 3 and 4. In all these cases the variance of ξ_t is assumed to be one. To get the proper scale one must multiply the values by σ_ξ^2.

TABLE 3.

Table of values of the spectral distribution function.

	Alternatives	
λ	A	B
$\pi/16$	.030275	.007409
$2\,\pi/16$	.055277	.012703
$3\,\pi/16$	.072249	.015088
$4\,\pi/16$	.082063	.015548
$5\,\pi/16$	.088370	.016161
$6\,\pi/16$	.095450	.018814
$7\,\pi/16$	.106045	.024160
$8\,\pi/16$	.120346	.031465
$9\,\pi/16$	.136423	.039287
$10\,\pi/16$	.151591	.046430
$11\,\pi/16$	.163748	.052538
$12\,\pi/16$	.172063	.058048
$13\,\pi/16$	.176871	.063712
$14\,\pi/16$	.179136	.070086
$15\,\pi/16$	.179897	.077282
$16\,\pi/16$	.180000	.085000

The time series are of length $M = 104$ or $M = 200$. The following notation has been adopted for the time series. Time series $NA2$ is the time series of length 200 generated from normally distributed random numbers under alternative A. Time series $RB1$ is the time series of length 104 generated from rectangularly distributed random numbers under alternative B. Time series $RB3$ has the same properties as time series $RB1$, that is, $M = 104$, and the suffix 3 has been used only to distinguish it from $RB1$. The following time series have been generated and analyzed:

$$RA1 \qquad RB1 \qquad NA1 \qquad NB1 \qquad TA1$$

$$RA3 \qquad RB3 \qquad NA2 \qquad NB2 \qquad TB1.$$

We have noted that the limiting distribution of $\max\limits_{0 \leq \lambda \leq \pi} \big| F_N^*(\lambda) - F(\lambda) \big| /$ $G^*(\pi)$ (see sections 6.5 and 6.6) depends on e and the spectral density $f(\lambda)$.

215

Table 4.

Table of values of the spectral density.

	Alternatives	
λ	A	B
$\pi/16$	.144518	.033755
$2\,\pi/16$	.107707	.019452
$3\,\pi/16$	.065994	.005749
$4\,\pi/16$	.037265	.000819
$5\,\pi/16$	.030809	.007125
$6\,\pi/16$	.043723	.020461
$7\,\pi/16$	.064318	.033306
$8\,\pi/16$	.079577	.039789
$9\,\pi/16$	.081785	.038813
$10\,\pi/16$	.070868	.033651
$11\,\pi/16$	.052271	.028981
$12\,\pi/16$	.032763	.027829
$13\,\pi/16$	.017087	.030357
$14\,\pi/16$	.006884	.034661
$15\,\pi/16$	.001584	.038364
$16\,\pi/16$	.000000	.039789

In the case of a normal process x_t, $e = 0$ and there is no dependence on $f(\lambda)$. Graph 1 suggests that in general the dependence on e is much more important than the dependence on $f(\lambda)$. It is clear that confidence bands for the spectral distribution function based on the limit theorem in the normal case are conservative if $e < 0$ and optimistic if $e > 0$ (see section 6.7).

The suggested limiting distribution of $\max_k |\log(\Delta(F^*(kh)/\Delta F(kh))|$ (see section 6.11) is independent of e and $f(\lambda)$. Here $\Delta F^*(kh)$ and $\Delta F(kh)$ are the estimated spectral mass and true spectral mass in the interval $(kh, (k+1)h)$ where $h = \pi/m$ and $k = 0, 1, \ldots, m-1$. However, for a finite sample the distribution will certainly depend on e and $f(\lambda)$. Within bounds, it seems clear that the dependence of the distribution on $f(\lambda)$ will be much greater than the dependence on e since $\Delta F^*(kh)$ is a local estimate. If $f(\lambda)$ changes very rapidly in magnitude over a given λ range, for a fixed sample size M, one cannot expect $\Delta F^*(kh)$ to be as good an estimate of the spectral mass in intervals in this range as when $f(\lambda)$ has slow changes in magnitude. The same comment is valid for estimates of the spectral density. We shall discuss an interesting and relevant suggestion of J. W. Tukey in section 8.8.

A spectral analysis of ten time series cannot give much information about the distribution of the statistics of interest. However, it may give some interesting hints about the dependence of the distribution of the statistics on e and $f(\lambda)$. In order to get some idea of the dependence on e we have used three types of random numbers in the generation of the time series. In the case R of rectangularly distributed random numbers, $e = -6/5 < 0$. In the case N of normally distributed random numbers $e = 0$ while in the case T of a three point distribution $e = 2 > 0$. Alternatives A and B give two different spectral densities $f(\lambda)$. The spectral density of alternative A is more irregular than that of alternative B. The decrease of the spectral density of alternative A to zero at $\lambda = \pi$ is very rapid.

The product lag moments

$$C_\nu = \sum_{\nu=0}^{M-\nu} x_t\, x_{t+\nu}$$

$\nu = 0, 1, \ldots, 15$ were computed for the time series of length $M = 104$. For time series of length $M = 200$, C_ν, $\nu = 0, 1, \ldots, 20$ were computed.

The estimate $F^*(\lambda)$ of $F(\lambda)$ is given by

$$F^*(\lambda) = \frac{C_0}{M}\frac{\lambda}{2\pi} + \frac{1}{\pi M}\sum_{\nu=1}^{15} C_\nu \frac{\sin \nu\lambda}{\nu}\left(1 - \frac{\nu}{15}\right)$$

when $M = 104$ and by

$$F^*(\lambda) = \frac{C_0}{M}\frac{\lambda}{2\pi} + \frac{1}{\pi M}\sum_{\nu=1}^{20} C_\nu \frac{\sin \nu\lambda}{\nu}\left(1 - \frac{\nu}{20}\right)$$

when $M = 200$. Both these estimates are constructed by using Fejer kernels (see section 6.9). We have chosen these estimates because they are nondecreasing functions of λ of a simple form. The estimates $F^*(\lambda)$ of $F(\lambda)$ have been computed at $\lambda = (k\pi/16)$, $k = 1, \ldots, 16$ for each of the time series and are given in Table 5. Our estimate of $G(\pi)$ is

$$G^*(\pi) = \frac{1}{4\pi}\frac{C_0^2}{M^2} + \frac{1}{2\pi}\sum_{\nu=1}^{15} \frac{C_\nu^2}{M^2}\left(1 - \frac{\nu}{15}\right)^2$$

when $M = 104$ and

$$G^*(\pi) = \frac{1}{4\pi}\frac{C_0^2}{M^2} + \frac{1}{2\pi}\sum_{\nu=1}^{20} \frac{C_\nu^2}{M^2}\left(1 - \frac{\nu}{20}\right)^2$$

when $M = 200$. The values of $G^*(\pi)$ for the different time series are given in Table 6.

TABLE 5.

Table of values of $F^*(\lambda)$.

λ	Series									
	TB1	TA1	NB2	NB1	NA2	NA1	RB1	RB3	RA3	RA1
$\pi/16$	.00067	.0049	.0052	.0049	.0227	.0143	5.84	1.74	15.87	27.85
$2\,\pi/16$	.00118	.0087	.0103	.0096	.0447	.0305	11.56	4.60	37.44	53.07
$3\,\pi/16$	.00156	.0117	.0139	.0121	.0626	.0457	14.54	6.99	52.76	69.52
$4\,\pi/16$	.00177	.0138	.0154	.0132	.0730	.0541	15.61	8.15	61.78	80.71
$5\,\pi/16$	.00201	.0156	.0171	.0143	.0803	.0600	16.74	9.06	68.37	88.93
$6\,\pi/16$	.00247	.0171	.0205	.0170	.0897	.0677	18.80	11.22	72.51	96.84
$7\,\pi/16$	.00310	.0191	.0270	.0216	.1057	.0767	22.22	15.24	77.36	109.60
$8\,\pi/16$	.00406	.0219	.0318	.0264	.1202	.0885	26.59	20.69	85.38	124.00
$9\,\pi/16$	.00550	.0242	.0380	.0309	.1338	.1018	31.41	26.09	94.04	135.34
$10\,\pi/16$	.00679	.0259	.0468	.0374	.1503	.1126	37.65	30.52	103.40	145.91
$11\,\pi/16$	.00766	.0277	.0521	.0446	.1674	.1222	45.30	34.68	114.52	154.72
$12\,\pi/16$	.00847	.0296	.0571	.0499	.1773	.1322	52.13	39.69	122.49	160.59
$13\,\pi/16$	.00928	.0311	.0621	.0558	.1822	.1406	58.11	45.14	126.93	165.08
$14\,\pi/16$	.01008	.0319	.0670	.0625	.1844	.1461	64.00	49.75	130.00	167.49
$15\,\pi/16$	.01078	.0322	.0752	.0684	.1860	.1487	69.69	55.39	131.86	169.12
$16\,\pi/16$	.01130	.0325	.0879	0761	.1868	.1499	75.60	63.68	132.86	170.32

TABLE 6.

Table of values of $G^*(\pi)$.

Series	$G^*(\pi)$
TB1	4.9748×10^{-4}
TA1	4.4685×10^{-4}
NB2	3.0757×10^{-3}
NB1	2.1746×10^{-3}
NA2	1.4994×10^{-2}
NA1	8.6001×10^{-2}
RB1	2.1404×10^{3}
RB3	1.6017×10^{3}
RA3	8.0661×10^{3}
RA1	1.2293×10^{4}

The true and estimated spectral distribution functions of time series TA1, NB1, RA3 are given in graphs 6 to 8. Confidence bands about the estimated distribution function, computed on the basis of the limit theorem in the case of a normal process x_t, have been set up. In each case the narrowest confidence band containing the true distribution function has been drawn so as to give a measure of the deviation between the true and estimated distribution function. Note that the true distribution functions of all the time series except TB1 are contained in confidence bands of confidence coefficient .90. It is not surprising that the exceptional time series is TB1 since then $e = 2 > 0$.

In section 6.11 one noted that in estimating the spectral mass in an interval, the length of the interval ought to be larger than the bandwidth of the weight function $w_m(x)$ used. In this case it then seems reasonable to estimate the mass in intervals of length $\pi/8$. Here

$$\Delta F^* \left(k \frac{\pi}{8} \right) = F^* \left((k+1) \frac{\pi}{8} \right) - F^* \left(k \frac{\pi}{8} \right)$$

is an estimate of

$$\Delta F \left(k \frac{\pi}{8} \right) = F \left((k+1) \frac{\pi}{8} \right) - F \left(\frac{k\pi}{8} \right)$$

$k = 0, 1, \ldots, 7$. The estimated and true spectral masses are given in Tables 7 and 8 respectively. In the case of all the time series computed under alternative B the true spectral masses are contained in a confidence band of confidence coefficient .90 about the estimated spectral masses. However, in the case of the time series computed under alternative A the true spectral masses are not even contained in a confidence band of confidence coefficient

TABLE 7.

Table of the estimated spectral mass ΔF^* in the intervals
$((k-1)(\pi/8), \ k(\pi/8)), k = 1, 2, \ldots, 8.$

k	Series									
	TB1	TA1	NB2	NB1	NA2	NA1	RB1	RB3	RA3	RA1
1	.00118	.0087	.0103	.0096	.0447	.0305	11.36	4.60	37.44	53.07
2	.00059	.0051	.0051	.0036	.0283	.0236	4.05	3.55	24.34	27.64
3	.00070	.0033	.0051	.0038	.0167	.0136	3.19	3.07	10.73	16.13
4	.00159	.0048	.0113	.0094	.0305	.0208	7.79	9.47	12.87	27.16
5	.00273	.0040	.0150	.0110	.0301	.0241	11.06	9.83	18.02	21.91
6	.00168	.0037	.0103	.0125	.0270	.0196	14.48	9.17	19.09	14.68
7	.00161	.0023	.0099	.0126	.0071	.0139	11.87	10.06	7.51	6.90
8	.00122	.0006	.0209	.0136	.0024	.0038	11.60	13.93	2.86	2.83

TABLE 8.

Table of the true spectral mass ΔF in the intervals
$((k-1)\,(\pi/8),\ k\,(\pi/8)),\ k=1,\,2,\,...,\,8.$

k	Series					
	$TB1$	$TA1$	$NB1\ \&\ NB2$	$NA1\ \&\ NA2$	$RB1\ \&\ RB3$	$RA1\ \&\ RA3$
1	.002541	.011055	.012703	.055277	10.5858	46.0642
2	.000569	.005358	.002845	.026786	2.3709	22.3217
3	.000653	.002677	.003266	.013387	2.7216	11.1559
4	.002530	.004979	.012651	.024896	10.5426	20.7466
5	.002993	.006249	.014965	.031245	12.4709	26.0375
6	.002324	.004095	.011618	.020572	9.6816	17.0600
7	.002407	.001414	.012038	.007073	10.0317	5.8942
8	.002983	.000173	.014914	.000864	12.4283	0.7200

.99. However, this is not too surprising. We had already noted that the spectral density of alternative A decreases to zero at $\lambda = \pi$. If we omit consideration of the spectral mass in interval $(7\pi/8, \pi)$, a confidence band of confidence coefficient .90 will contain the true spectral masses in every case.

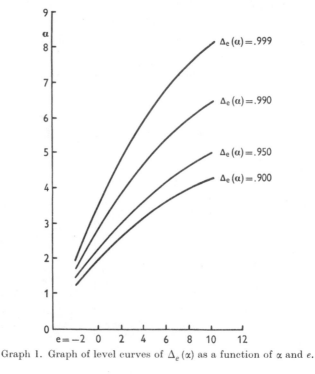

Graph 1. Graph of level curves of $\Delta_\varrho\,(\alpha)$ as a function of α and e.

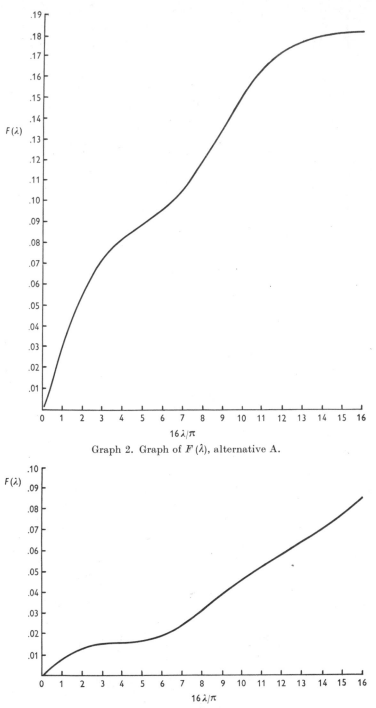

Graph 2. Graph of $F(\lambda)$, alternative A.

Graph 3. Graph of $F(\lambda)$, alternative B.

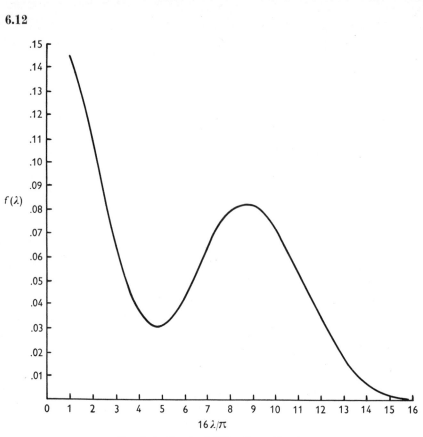

Graph 4. Graph of $f(\lambda)$, alternative A.

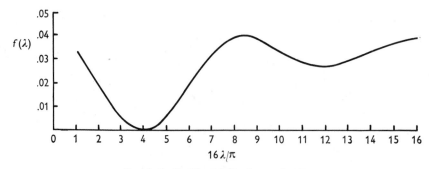

Graph 5. Graph of $f(\lambda)$, alternative B.

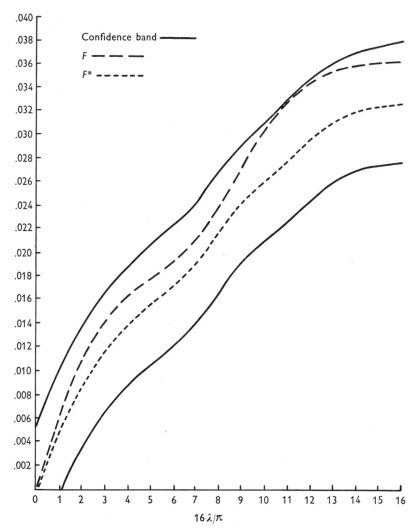

Graph 6. True and estimated spectral distribution function of series $TA1$. Confidence band corresponding to $\Delta(\alpha) = .35$ and $\alpha = .982$.

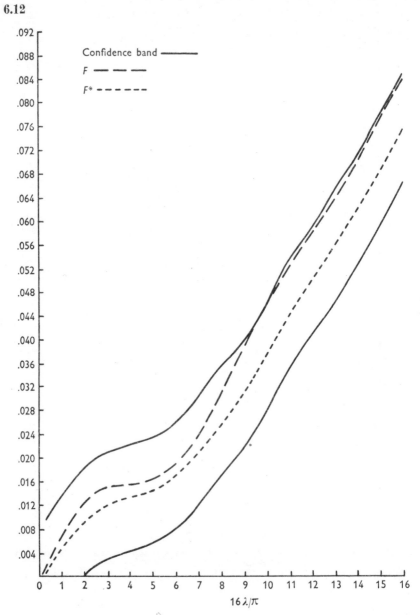

Graph 7. True and estimated spectral distribution function of series $NB1$. Confidence band corresponding to $\Delta(\alpha) = .173$ and $\alpha = .785$.

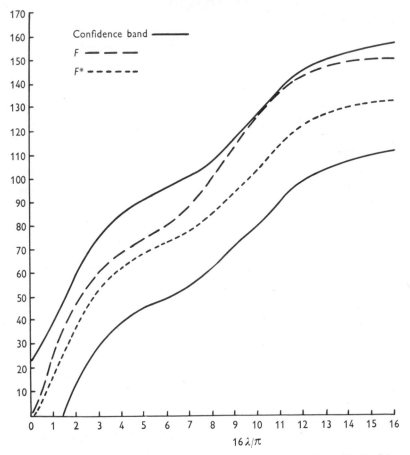

$16\lambda/\pi$

Graph 8. True and estimated spectral distribution function of series $RA3$. Confidence band corresponding to $\Delta(\alpha) = .41$ and $\alpha = 1.039$.

CHAPTER 7

PROBLEMS IN LINEAR ESTIMATION

7.0. Preliminary Discussion

We discuss a variety of problems associated with regression analysis in this chapter. One of the first problems that comes to mind is that of distinguishing between two regressions. For simplicity let us consider the two simple hypotheses

$$H_j; \quad y_t = x_t + m_t^{(j)}, \quad j = 0, 1,$$

where x_t is assumed to be normally distributed with mean zero and spectral distribution function $F(\lambda)$. The two regression column vectors $m^{(0)} = (m_t^{(0)};$ $t = 1, 2, \ldots, n)$ and $m^{(1)} = (m_t^{(1)}; t = 1, 2, \ldots, n)$ are assumed to have real components. After having observed $y_1, y_2, \ldots, y_n$ we may want to test hypothesis H_0 against hypothesis H_1. Assume that the covariance matrix R of the disturbance x_t is nonsingular. Consider the two frequency functions corresponding to H_0 and H_1

$$f_j(y_1, y_2, \ldots, y_n) = \frac{1}{(2\pi)^{\frac{n}{2}} |R|^{1/2}} \exp\left\{ -\tfrac{1}{2}(y - m^{(j)})^* R^{-1}(y - m^{(j)}) \right\}, \quad j = 0, 1.$$

We know that a most powerful test of H_0 against H_1 has the critical region (see Cramér [3])

$$W = \{ y^* R^{-1}(m^{(1)} - m^{(0)}) > K \}.$$

We shall now assume the special form

$$m_t^{(j)} = \int_{-\pi}^{\pi} e^{it\lambda} d\varphi_j(\lambda), \quad j = 0, 1, \tag{1}$$

for the regression sequences where $\varphi_0(\lambda)$, $\varphi_1(\lambda)$ are of bounded variation. Although this choice of $m_t^{(j)}$ includes the important case of a trigonometric regression, it is somewhat restricted. We shall see in the later sections how to deal with regressions of a more general form.

Introduce the expected values

$$E_j y^* R^{-1}(m^{(1)} - m^{(0)}) = \mu_j, \quad j = 0, 1,$$

and the variance

$$D^2[y^* R^{-1}(m^{(1)} - m^{(0)})] = v$$

which is the same for both hypotheses. Then it is clear that there will exist a consistent test of H_0 against H_1 if and only if the quantity

$$\tau = \frac{(\mu_1 - \mu_0)^2}{v}$$

tends to infinity with n.

We have by straightforward computation

$$\tau = \frac{[(m^{(1)} - m^{(0)})^* R^{-1}(m^{(1)} - m^{(0)})]^2}{(m^{(1)} - m^{(0)})^* R^{-1}(m^{(1)} - m^{(0)})} = (m^{(1)} - m^{(0)})^* R^{-1}(m^{(1)} - m^{(0)}).$$

Now recall the estimation problem dealt with in section 2.6. There we considered the minimization of a quadratic form with a linear restraint

$$\left. \begin{array}{c} c^* R c = \min \\ c^* \gamma = 1 \end{array} \right\},$$

with
$$c = \begin{pmatrix} c_1 \\ c_2 \\ \vdots \\ c_n \end{pmatrix} \quad \text{and} \quad \gamma = \begin{pmatrix} \gamma_1 \\ \gamma_2 \\ \vdots \\ \gamma_n \end{pmatrix},$$

where the γ's are given by

$$\gamma_t = \int_{-\pi}^{\pi} e^{it\lambda} d\gamma(\lambda).$$

In section 2.6 the time parameter ranges was $-n$ to n but it is easily seen that the same result holds with the range 1 to n. Setting

$$R^{1/2} c = x$$

we have

$$\|x\|^2 = \min$$
$$x^* R^{-1/2} \gamma = 1$$

so that x has to be perpendicular to the plane $x^* R^{-1/2} \gamma = 1$, i.e., of the form

$$x = b R^{-1/2} \gamma,$$

where b is a constant. The constant b must then be

$$b = \frac{1}{\gamma^* R^{-1} \gamma}$$

so that the minimum value is

$$\| x \|^2 = b^2 \gamma^* R^{-1} \gamma = \frac{1}{\gamma^* R^{-1} \gamma} \cdot$$

Now putting

$$\gamma(\lambda) = \varphi_1(\lambda) - \varphi_0(\lambda)$$

we see that τ is just the inverse of $\| x \|^2$. But we have seen in section 2.6 that this minimum value converges to

$$\frac{1}{\displaystyle\int_{-\pi}^{\pi} \frac{|d\gamma(\lambda)|^2}{dF(\lambda)}}$$

as $n \to \infty$. Hence there exists a consistent test of H_0 against H_1 if and only if the Hellinger integral diverges

$$\int_{-\pi}^{\pi} \frac{|(d(\varphi_1(\lambda) - \varphi_0(\lambda)))|^2}{dF(\lambda)} = +\infty. \tag{2}$$

This is in agreement with what one would guess; there is a consistent test only if $dF(\lambda)$ is small with respect to $|d(\varphi_1(\lambda) - \varphi_0(\lambda))|^2$ at frequencies λ where $d\varphi_0(\lambda)$ and $d\varphi_1(\lambda)$ differ.

For example, if we are testing a constant mean $m_t^{(0)} \equiv m_0$ against $m_t^{(1)} \equiv m_1$, then $\varphi_1(\lambda) - \varphi_0(\lambda)$ has as its only point of variation $\lambda = 0$ with the saltus $m_1 - m_0$. The value of the integral in (2) is

$$\lim_{\varepsilon \to 0} \frac{(m_1 - m_0)^2}{F(\varepsilon) - F(-\varepsilon)},$$

so that there is a consistent test of the hypothesis if and only if the spectral distribution function is continuous at $\lambda = 0$. We will now see why this is so. Otherwise $\lambda = 0$ would be a discrete line in the spectrum of x_t. The process x_t has the spectral representation $x_t = \int_{-\pi}^{\pi} e^{it\lambda} dz(\lambda)$. Since there is a discrete line in the spectrum at $\lambda = 0$, $z_0 = z(0+) - z(0-) \neq 0$, we can write $x_t = z_0 + x_t'$. The process $x_t' = x_t - z_0$ has a spectral distribution function continuous at $\lambda = 0$ since the jump z_0 of $z(\lambda)$ at $\lambda = 0$ has been removed. Under the two hypotheses we have

$$H_j: y_t = m_j + z_0 + x'_t, \quad j = 1, 2.$$

It is clear that the stochastic variable z_0 for a given realization is just a constant independent of t, i.e., it behaves just like m_j. The presence of z_0 then makes the discrimination between H_0, H_1 much harder and it is clearly impossible to find a consistent test. One can similarly discuss trigonometric regression. What has been said above is clearly related to the discussion in section 2.5.

In the rest of this chapter we shall deal with stationary disturbances that have an absolutely continuous spectrum and a positive and piecewise continuous spectral density. A typical problem is that of estimating the regression coefficient γ when

$$y_t = x_t + \gamma \varphi_t,$$

where φ_t is a given regression sequence, not necessarily of the form (1), and x_t is stationary with mean zero. We shall restrict ourselves to estimates of regression coefficients that are linear in the observations $y_t, t = 1, \ldots, n$. There are various reasons one can give for this restriction. Linear estimates are reasonable when the residual x_t is a normal process and we shall discuss this point at greater length in the next paragraph. In many cases x_t will not be normal and there will be nonlinear estimates of γ better than the linear estimates. Nonetheless, one rarely has much detailed information about the probability structure of the process x_t. In such a case linear estimates are particularly appealing because they are of a simple form and their characteristics can be studied in great detail. This is not true of other classes of estimates. Moreover, the methods of this book are mainly linear methods so that a detailed study of linear estimates is particularly appropriate.

If x_t were normally distributed and the covariance matrix R of $x_1, \ldots, x_n$ were fixed and known, $\varphi^* R^{-1} y$ would be a minimal sufficient statistic for the class of probability distributions of interest. Here φ is the regression column vector. The linear estimate

$$c = (\varphi^* R^{-1} \varphi)^{-1} \varphi^* R^{-1} y \tag{3}$$

is an unbiased estimate of γ. In this chapter mean square error is the criterion by which we judge estimates. In formal statistical language the mean square error

$$E|c - \gamma|^2$$

is the risk function. One can then show that (3) is a minimax estimate of γ and is an admissible estimate of γ. This can be shown by using the tech-

7.0

niques employed in Lehmann-Hodges [1]. In this chapter, we will be interested in finding out when there are good linear estimates whose form does not depend on R.

Suppose there is a sequence of linear consistent estimates c_n of γ

$$c_n = \sum_1^n a_t^{(n)} y_t,$$

where by consistency we mean that $E|c_n - \gamma|^2 \to 0$ as $n \to \infty$. Note that this is not quite the usual statistical usage of the term consistency. Then mean square error is

$$E|c_n - \gamma|^2 = E|c_n - Ec_n|^2 + |Ec_n - \gamma|^2$$

$$= \int_{-\pi}^{\pi} \left| \sum_1^n a_t^{(n)} e^{it\lambda} \right|^2 f(\lambda)\, d\lambda + |\gamma|^2 \left| \sum_1^n a_t^{(n)} \varphi_t - 1 \right|^2.$$

As this has to tend to zero

$$\lim_{n \to 0} \sum_1^n a_t^{(n)} \varphi_t = 1,$$

i.e., we must have an asymptotically unbiased estimate. As

$$\int_{-\pi}^{\pi} \left| \sum_1^n a_t^{(n)} a^{it\lambda} \right|^2 f(\lambda)\, d\lambda \geq 2\pi \min_\lambda f(\lambda) \sum_1^n |a_t^{(n)}|^2$$

we also have

$$\lim_{n \to \infty} \sum_1^n |a_t^{(n)}|^2 = 0.$$

But Schwarz' inequality then tells us that

$$\lim_{n \to \infty} \sum_1^n |\varphi_t|^2 = \infty \tag{4}$$

is a necessary condition for an asymptotically unbiased estimate. This is immediately seen to be also a sufficient condition for a consistent estimate as

$$c_n = \frac{\sum\limits_1^n \bar{\varphi}_t\, y_t}{\sum\limits_1^n |\bar{\varphi}_t|^2}$$

has a mean square error less than

230

$$2\pi \max_{\lambda} f(\lambda) \frac{1}{\frac{1}{n} \sum_{1}^{n} |\varphi_t|^2} \to 0$$

as $n \to \infty$. It is therefore appropriate to introduce the condition (4) in the following discussion.

We have already restricted ourselves to estimates linear in the observations. The additional assumption of *unbiasedness* is now introduced. This restriction can be motivated by noting that the linear unbiased estimates are the only estimates of γ whose mean square error is a bounded function of γ. This is not a serious restriction for the type of estimation problem we deal with. It is only when we have rather precise *a priori* information concerning the true value of c that it would be advantageous to allow the estimates under consideration to be biased.

7.1. Estimating Regression Coefficients

We have already noted that in many cases the observed process cannot be assumed to have mean value zero. For example, in measuring the current at some place in a noisy network there might be a dominating direct current or alternating current component different from zero.

Let the observed process be $y_t = m_t + x_t$, where $m_t = E\,y_t$ is the mean value sequence and x_t, $E\,x_t \equiv 0$, is the stationary residual. There are in general the two following problems. In characterizing the statistical structure of the noise x_t, one is quite often content with knowledge of the spectrum. The other problem is to estimate the mean value component m_t. It is clear that if m_t is completely arbitrary one cannot get any consistent estimate of it. On the other hand, in many situations one is helped by the fact that the mean value sequence can be given in the *regression* form (see section 2.5)

$$m_t = \sum_{\nu=1}^{p} \gamma_\nu \, \varphi_t^{(\nu)}$$

or
$$m = \Phi \gamma = (\varphi^{(1)}, \varphi^{(2)}, \dots, \varphi^{(p)}) \, \gamma,$$

where

$$m = \begin{pmatrix} m_1 \\ m_2 \\ \vdots \\ m_n \end{pmatrix} \text{ is the mean value vector,}$$

231

$$\varphi^{(j)} = \begin{pmatrix} \varphi_1^{(j)} \\ \vdots \\ \varphi_n^{(j)} \end{pmatrix} \quad j = 1, \ldots, p \text{ are the known regression vectors, and}$$

$$\gamma = \begin{pmatrix} \gamma_1 \\ \vdots \\ \gamma_p \end{pmatrix} \text{ is the vector whose components, the } \textit{regression coefficients,}$$

are in general unknown. As one example we mention the important case where

$$\left. \begin{aligned} \varphi_t^{(1)} &= 1 \\ \varphi_t^{(\nu)} &= \cos (\lambda_\nu t + \phi_\nu) \end{aligned} \right\}.$$

γ_1 is the direct current amplitude and γ_ν, $\nu = 2,3,\ldots, p$, are the alternating current amplitudes corresponding to the frequencies λ_ν. This is a *trigonometric regression*. Another case is the so-called *polynomial regression*, where $\varphi_t^{(\nu)} = t^\nu$. We should also mention the important case of *pulse regression*; here $\varphi_t^{(\nu)}$ is periodic in t but is not a simple cosine or sine term.

One way to look upon these regression problems is to consider them as questions related to the construction of a device optimal in the linear sense for the detection of signals in a noisy channel (i.e., testing a linear hypothesis) or for measuring the strength of the signal (linear estimation). In the last few years problems of this type have attracted a good deal of attention on the part of physicists and communication engineers (see e.g., Lawson-Uhlenbeck [1] and papers in issues of the *Journal of Applied Physics* from 1952 to the present).

When estimating the noise spectrum we have to eliminate the signal and then treat the remainder by methods like those described in the previous chapters. The linear estimates of the regression coefficients used for this purpose in section 6.8 will be shown to be asymptotically optimal among linear estimates in the present chapter when the regression is a polynomial or trigonometric regression.

As the class of admissible estimates we will choose those which are *linear* in the observed variables and *unbiased*

$$c_\nu = \sum_{t=1}^n a_t^{(\nu)} x_t, \quad \nu = 1, 2, \ldots, p, \tag{1}$$

$$E c = \gamma.$$

Here $c = \begin{pmatrix} c_1 \\ \vdots \\ c_p \end{pmatrix}$. By a consistent estimate (in the linear sense) we mean an estimate of the form (1) each of whose components c_ν converges in the mean square to the true value γ_ν as $n \to \infty$.

Consider the covariance matrix $\Gamma(c)$ of the estimate of γ

$$\Gamma = \{E(c_\nu - \gamma_\nu)\overline{(c_\mu - \gamma_\mu)}; \quad \nu, \mu = 1, 2, \dots, p\}.$$

In section 2.6 we proved that if the covariance matrix R of the process x_t is nonsingular (this assumption will be adhered to throughout this chapter) there is at least one estimate c_0 such that

$$\Gamma(c_0) \leq \Gamma(c)$$

for every unbiased linear estimate c. Such an estimate c_0 is called an *efficient estimate* of γ (in the linear sense).

One could then define efficiency as the ratio $\det\Gamma(c_0^*)/\det\Gamma(c^*)$ and asymptotic efficiency as the limit of this ratio as $n \to \infty$ if it exists. We refer to Grenander [4] who uses a method similar to that of this chapter.

7.2. The Regression Spectrum

Consider for a fixed r the sequence

$$\Phi_n^{(r)} = \sum_{t=1}^{n} |\varphi_t^{(r)}|^2.$$

We have to assume that $\Phi_n^{(r)}$ approaches infinity with n, since otherwise no consistent estimate of γ_r exists, as has been shown. On the other hand $\Phi_n^{(r)}$ must not increase too fast. We assume that

$$\lim_{n \to \infty} \frac{\Phi_{n+h}^{(r)}}{\Phi_n^{(r)}} = 1 \tag{1}$$

for each h. If the limiting relation (1) holds for $h = 1$, it holds for all integral h. If (1) holds, $\Phi_n^{(r)}$ is said to be *slowly increasing*. This terminology differs somewhat from the customary one. We will also assume the existence of the limits

$$R_h^{(r,s)} = \lim_{n \to \infty} \frac{\sum_{t=1}^{n} \varphi_{t+h}^{(r)} \, \bar{\varphi}_t^{(s)}}{\sqrt{\Phi_n^{(r)} \Phi_n^{(s)}}} \tag{2}$$

for $1 \leq r, s \leq p$ and all nonnegative integers h. In order to deal with negative values of h we define $\varphi_t^{(r)} = 0$ for $t < 0$, and then $R_h^{(r,s)}$ is defined by (2) for all integral values of h. For $h \geq 0$ we have

233

$$\frac{\sum_{t=1}^{n} \varphi_{t-h}^{(r)} \, \bar{\varphi}_t^{(s)}}{\sqrt{\Phi_n^{(r)} \, \Phi_n^{(s)}}} = \frac{\sum_{1}^{n-h} \bar{\varphi}_{u+h}^{(s)} \, \varphi_u^{(r)}}{\sqrt{\Phi_{n-h}^{(r)} \, \Phi_{n-h}^{(s)}}} \sqrt{\frac{\Phi_{n-h}^{(r)} \, \Phi_{n-h}^{(s)}}{\Phi_n^{(r)} \, \Phi_n^{(s)}}}$$

and on taking the limits of both sides and using the slowly increasing character of $\Phi_n^{(r)}$ (see (1)) we have

$$R_{-h}^{(r,\,s)} = \bar{R}_h^{(s,\,r)}, \quad \text{i.e.,} \quad R_{-h} = R_h^*.$$

Let α be an arbitrary p-vector and consider the quadratic form

$$\sigma_{\nu-\mu} = \alpha^* R_{\nu-\mu} \alpha = \lim_{n\to\infty} \sum_{r,\,s=1}^{p} \frac{\bar{\alpha}_r}{\sqrt{\Phi_n^{(r)}}} \sum_{t=1}^{n} \varphi_{t+\nu}^{(r)} \, \bar{\varphi}_{t+\mu}^{(s)} \frac{\alpha_s}{\sqrt{\Phi_n^{(s)}}}.$$

This relation is proved just as before using the slowly increasing character of $\Phi_n^{(r)}$. Let k be an m-vector, where m is arbitrary. Then

$$\sum_{\nu,\,\mu=1}^{m} \bar{k}_\nu \, \sigma_{\nu-\mu} \, k_\mu = \lim_{n\to\infty} \sum_{t=1}^{n} \left| \sum_{\nu,\,r} \frac{\bar{\alpha}_r \, \bar{k}_\nu}{\sqrt{\Phi_n^{(r)}}} \varphi_{t+\nu}^{(r)} \right|^2 \geq 0,$$

so that $\alpha^* R_\nu \alpha$ is a nonnegative definite sequence. It then follows (see section 1.8) that

$$R_h = \int_{-\pi}^{\pi} e^{ih\lambda} \, dM(\lambda), \tag{3}$$

where $\Delta M(\lambda) = M(\lambda_2) - M(\lambda_1)$ is a nonnegative definite matrix for every interval (λ_1, λ_2).

Assume in the following that $R_0 = M(\pi) - M(-\pi) = M$ is nonsingular. The converse would imply that the n-vectors $\varphi^{(1)}, \varphi^{(2)}, \ldots, \varphi^{(p)}$ would in a sense be asymptotically linearly dependent. By this we do not mean a strict linear correlation for finite n. It is then intuitively plausible that one could not estimate all the regression coefficients consistently, but only some linear functions of them.

$M(\lambda)$ is called the spectral distribution function of the regression vectors $\varphi^{(1)}, \varphi^{(2)}, \ldots, \varphi^{(p)}$.

We are interested in comparing the least square estimates c_L and the minimum variance unbiased estimates c_0 of γ as $n\to\infty$. Their covariance matrices are

$$E(c_L - \gamma)(c_L - \gamma)^* = (\Phi^*\Phi)^{-1}\Phi^* R \Phi (\Phi^*\Phi)^{-1}$$

and

$$E(c_0 - \gamma)(c_0 - \gamma)^* = (\Phi^* R^{-1}\Phi)^{-1}$$

respectively where R is the covariance matrix of $x_1, \ldots, x_n$ (see section 2.5). We know that

$$E(c_L - \gamma)(c_L - \gamma)^* = (\Phi^* \Phi)^{-1} \Phi^* R \Phi (\Phi^* \Phi)^{-1}$$

$$\geq E(c_0 - \gamma)(c_0 - \gamma)^* = (\Phi^* R^{-1} \Phi)^{-1}.$$

We introduce the diagonal matrix

$$D_n = \left\{ \begin{array}{cccc} \Phi_n^{(1)\,1/2} & 0 \ldots & & \\ 0 & \Phi_n^{(2)\,1/2} \ldots & & \\ \cdot & \cdot \quad \cdot \quad \cdot & \cdot & \cdot \\ & 0 & & \Phi_n^{(p)\,1/2} \end{array} \right\},$$

and say that the estimate c_L is *asymptotically efficient* if

$$\lim_{n \to \infty} D_n E(c_L - \gamma)(c_L - \gamma)^* D_n = \lim_{n \to \infty} D_n E(c_0 - \gamma)(c_0 - \gamma)^* D_n. \qquad (4)$$

We have pre and post multiplied by D_n in this definition of asymptotic efficiency to insure that the matrices remain finite (do not vanish or diverge) as $n \to \infty$. We would use the same definition of asymptotic efficiency for a general linear unbiased estimate c. In our discussion of asymptotic efficiency we shall for mathematical convenience and simplicity allow the stochastic process y_t and the regression components $\varphi_t^{(j)}$ to be complex-valued. The case of greatest interest is of course that in which y_t and $\varphi_t^{(j)}$ are real-valued. We shall specialize to the real-valued case after discussions on the complex-valued case and discuss the corresponding results for the real-valued case. Let λ be a point such that for any interval $I = (\lambda_1, \lambda_2), \lambda_1 < \lambda < \lambda_2$, containing λ, $M(\lambda_2) - M(\lambda_1) = \Delta M(I) > 0$. Note that $\Delta M(I) > 0$ means that $\Delta M(I)$ is a nonnegative definite matrix and is not the null matrix. The set of all such points λ is called the *regression spectrum* and will be denoted by S.

7.3. Asymtotic Expressions for the Covariance Matrices

When estimating the regression coefficients γ, one should in theory use the best linear estimate which is given by (see section 2.5)

$$c_0 = (\Phi^* R^{-1} \Phi)^{-1} \Phi^* R^{-1} x.$$

This has minimum variance among all unbiased linear estimates. Now this is usually not a very practical procedure. First of all, R is in general not known although it can be estimated if we have a sufficiently large sample.

Secondly, even when we know R the expression for c_0 is often quite compli-cated and requires tedious numerical computations involving the inversion of two matrices of high order.

Fortunately in the case of some important types of regression we can find a simple estimate that is asymptotically efficient for all positive and piece-wise continuous spectral densities $f(\lambda)$. This is the least squares estimate which is given by

$$c_L = (\Phi^*\Phi)^{-1}\Phi^*x.$$

The matrix $\Phi^*\Phi$ (of order $p\times p$) is usually much easier to invert than R (of order $n\times n$). We know (see section 2.5) that c_L is unbiased. The covari-ance matrix of the least squares estimate is given in the previous section. We shall first consider the asymptotic behavior of the matrix

$$D_n E(c_L - \gamma)(c_L - \gamma)^* D_n = D_n(\Phi^*\Phi)^{-1}\Phi^* R\Phi(\Phi^*\Phi)^{-1}D_n,$$

for large samples. First let us assume that the disturbance is of the moving average type

$$x_t = \sum_1^\alpha a_\nu \eta_{t-\nu},$$

where $\{\eta_t\}$ is white noise with variance one. Then the spectral density is a trigonometric polynomial

$$f(\lambda) = \sum_{-\alpha}^\alpha f_\nu e^{i\nu\lambda}.$$

Here
$$r_\nu = \begin{cases} 2\pi f_\nu, & |\nu| \leq \alpha \\ 0 & |\nu| > \alpha. \end{cases}$$

Then

$$\{D_n^{-1}\Phi^* R\Phi D_n^{-1}\}_{\nu\mu} = \sum_{u,v=1}^n \frac{\bar{\varphi}_u^{(\nu)} r_{u-v} \varphi_v^{(\mu)}}{\sqrt{\Phi_n^{(\nu)}\Phi_n^{(\mu)}}}$$

$$= 2\pi\sum_{m=0}^\alpha f_m \sum_{v=1}^{n-m} \frac{\varphi_v^{(\mu)}\bar{\varphi}_{m+v}^{(\nu)}}{\sqrt{\Phi_n^{(\nu)}\Phi_n^{(\mu)}}} + 2\pi\sum_{m=-1}^{-\alpha} f_m \sum_{u=1}^{n+m} \frac{\varphi_{n-m}^{(\mu)}\bar{\varphi}_u^{(\nu)}}{\sqrt{\Phi_n^{(\nu)}\Phi_n^{(\mu)}}}$$

for $n > \alpha$. As $n\to\infty$ each of the $2\alpha+1$ terms tends to a finite limit as is easily seen by using the slowly increasing character of the $\Phi_n^{(\nu)}$'s. The limit is

$$2\pi\sum_{m=-\alpha}^\alpha f_m R_{-m}^{(\mu,\nu)}$$

so that on using the representation (7.2.3) we have

$$\lim_{n\to\infty} D_n^{-1} \Phi^* R \Phi D_n^{-1} = 2\pi \int_{-\pi}^{\pi} f(-\lambda) \, dM(\lambda).$$

Now
$$\lim_{n\to\infty} D_n^{-1} \Phi^* \Phi D_n^{-1} = R_0 = M$$

so that

$$\lim_{n\to\infty} D_n E(c_L - \gamma)(c_L - \gamma)^* D_n = M^{-1} 2\pi \int_{-\pi}^{\pi} f(-\lambda) \, dM(\lambda) M^{-1}$$

as M is nonsingular.

From now on we shall assume that the spectral density $f(\lambda)$ is piecewise continuous and positive. To avoid trivial complications we shall not allow the possible discontinuities of $f(-\lambda)$ to coincide with those of $M(\lambda)$. We can then approximate $f(\lambda)$ from above and below

$$f_1(\lambda) \le f(\lambda) \le f_2(\lambda),$$

where $f_1(\lambda)$ and $f_2(\lambda)$ are finite trigonometric polynomials. It is clear that for the corresponding covariance matrices we have

$$R_1 \le R \le R_2.$$

This is seen immediately by considering the corresponding quadratic forms

$$Z^* R_j Z = \int_{-\pi}^{\pi} \left| \sum_1^n Z_\nu e^{i\nu\lambda} \right|^2 f_j(\lambda) \, d\lambda, \quad j = 1, 2,$$

$$Z^* R Z = \int_{-\pi}^{\pi} \left| \sum_1^n Z_\nu e^{i\nu\lambda} \right|^2 f(\lambda) \, d\lambda.$$

Then clearly for any vector Z

$$Z^* M^{-1} \int_{-\pi}^{\pi} f_1(-\lambda) \, dM(\lambda) M^{-1} Z \le \varliminf_{n\to\infty} \varlimsup_{n\to\infty} Z^* D_n E(c_L - \gamma)(c_L - \gamma)^* D_n Z$$

$$\le Z^* M^{-1} \int_{-\pi}^{\pi} f_2(-\lambda) \, dM(\lambda) M^{-1} Z.$$

But as $\max[f_2(\lambda) - f_1(\lambda)]$ can be made as small as required except in small neighborhoods of the points of discontinuity of $f(\lambda)$, it follows that

$$\lim_{n\to\infty} D_n \, E \, (c_L - \gamma) \, (c_L - \gamma)^* \, D_n = M^{-1} \, 2\pi \int_{-\pi}^{\pi} f(-\lambda) \, d M(\lambda) \, M^{-1}. \qquad (1)$$

We now derive an analogous expression for the optimal estimate c_0. We deal at first with a disturbance of the autoregressive type

$$b_0 x_t + b_1 x_{t+1} + \cdots + b_\alpha x_{t+\alpha} = \eta_{t+\alpha}$$

with the roots of the characteristic equation $\sum_{k=0}^{\alpha} b_k z^k = 0$ inside the unit circle. This corresponds (see section 1.6) to a spectral density

$$f(\lambda) = \frac{1}{2\pi} \frac{1}{\left| \sum_0^\alpha b_\nu \, e^{i\nu\lambda} \right|^2}.$$

Consider the space spanned by the stochastic variables $x_1, x_2, \ldots, x_n$. The vectors $\eta_{\alpha+1}, \eta_{\alpha+2}, \ldots, \eta_n$ are orthonormal and orthogonal to $x_1, x_2, \ldots, x_\alpha$ (see section 1.6). Using the Gram-Schmidt orthogonalization procedure on the latter vectors we see that there are numbers $d_{\nu\mu}$ so that

$$d_{11} x_1 = \varepsilon_1$$
$$d_{21} x_1 + d_{22} x_2 = \varepsilon_2$$

$$\cdots \cdots \cdots$$

$$d_{\alpha 1} x_1 + d_{\alpha 2} x_2 + \cdots + d_{\alpha\alpha} x_\alpha = \varepsilon_\alpha$$
$$b_0 x_1 + b_1 x_2 + \cdots + b_\alpha x_{\alpha+1} = \varepsilon_{\alpha+1} = \eta_{\alpha+1}$$
$$0 \cdot x_1 + b_0 x_2 + \cdots + b_\alpha x_{\alpha+2} = \varepsilon_{\alpha+2} = \eta_{\alpha+2}$$

$$\cdots \cdots \cdots \cdots \cdots \cdots \cdots$$

$$0 \cdot x_1 + 0 \cdot x_2 + \cdots + b_0 x_{n-\alpha} + \cdots + b_\alpha x_n = \varepsilon_n = \eta_n.$$

where the ε's are orthonormal vectors. Denoting the subdiagonal matrix premultiplying $x = \begin{pmatrix} x_1 \\ \vdots \\ x_n \end{pmatrix}$ by Δ we see that the equations above can be written

$$\Delta x = \varepsilon. \qquad (2)$$

Thus Δ is a nonsingular transformation carrying $x_1, \ldots, x_n$ into the orthonormal system $\varepsilon_1, \varepsilon_2, \ldots, \varepsilon_n$. On taking the covariance matrix of both sides of (2) we have

$$\Delta\,R\Delta^* = I$$

so that
$$R^{-1} = \Delta^*\Delta.$$

Hence except for $4\alpha^2$ elements in the matrix we have

$$\{R^{-1}\}_{\nu\mu} = \sum_{u=-\infty}^{\infty} \bar{b}_{\nu+u}\,b_{\mu+u}$$

where we have set $b_\nu = 0$ if $\nu < 0$ or $\nu > \alpha$. But

$$\sum_{u=-\infty}^{\infty} \bar{b}_{\nu+u}\,b_{\mu+u} = \frac{1}{4\pi^2}\int_{-\pi}^{\pi} e^{i\,(\nu-\mu)\,\lambda}\,\frac{1}{f(\lambda)}\,d\,\lambda.$$

Consider

$$\{D^{-1}\,\Phi^*\,R^{-1}\,\Phi\,D^{-1}\}_{\nu\mu} = \sum_{u,v=1}^{n} \frac{\bar{\varphi}_u^{(\nu)}\,r_{u,v}^{(-1)}\,\varphi_v^{(\mu)}}{\sqrt{\Phi_n^{(\nu)}\,\Phi_n^{(\mu)}}}$$

$$= \sum_{m=0}^{\alpha} \varrho_m \sum_{v=1}^{n-m} \frac{\varphi_v^{(\mu)}\,\bar{\varphi}_{m+v}^{(\nu)}}{\sqrt{\Phi_n^{(\nu)}\,\Phi_n^{(\mu)}}} + \sum_{m=-1}^{-\alpha} \varrho_m \sum_{u=1}^{n+m} \frac{\varphi_{u-m}^{(\mu)}\,\bar{\varphi}_u^{(\nu)}}{\sqrt{\Phi_n^{(\nu)}\,\Phi_n^{(\mu)}}} + \delta_n. \qquad (3)$$

Here $\{r_{u,v}^{(-1)}\} = R^{-1}$, $\varrho_m = \dfrac{1}{4\pi^2}\displaystyle\int_{-\pi}^{\pi} e^{i\,m\,\lambda}\,\dfrac{1}{f(\lambda)}\,d\,\lambda$, and δ_n tends to zero as n increases. Indeed δ_n is the sum of at most $4\alpha^2$ terms of the form

$$r_{u,v}^{(-1)}\,\frac{\bar{\varphi}_u^{(\nu)}\,\varphi_v^{(\mu)}}{\sqrt{\Phi_n^{(\nu)}\,\Phi_n^{(\mu)}}}\,.$$

The first factor is bounded uniformly in n as seen from the relation $R^{-1} = \Delta^*\,\Delta$. In fact

$$\left|r_{u,v}^{(-1)}\right| \le (\alpha+1)\,M^2, \quad \text{where } M = \max_{0\le i,j,k\le\alpha}\{d_{ij},\,b_k\}.$$

Moreover

$$\frac{\left|\varphi_{u+1}^{(\nu)}\right|^2}{\Phi_n^{(\nu)}} = \left[\frac{\Phi_{u+1}^{(\nu)}}{\Phi_u^{(\nu)}} - 1\right]\frac{\Phi_u^{(\nu)}}{\Phi_n^{(\nu)}}\,.$$

Either u is bounded and then the second term tends to zero or it is not and then the first term tends to zero since $\Phi_u^{(\nu)}$ is slowly increasing.

On letting $n\to\infty$ it follows from (3) that

$$\lim_{n\to\infty} D_n^{-1}\,\Phi^*\,R^{-1}\,\Phi\,D_n^{-1} = \frac{1}{2\pi}\int_{-\pi}^{\pi}\frac{1}{f(-\lambda)}\,d\,M\,(\lambda). \qquad (4)$$

7.3

Given a general $f(\lambda)$ we approximate it from above and below by spectral densities of autoregressive schemes and an argument of the same type as before shows that (4) is valid.

As

$$\int_{-\pi}^{\pi} \frac{1}{f(-\lambda)} \, d M(\lambda) \geq \frac{M}{\min\limits_{\lambda} f(\lambda)}$$

and M is nonsingular it follows that the matrix on the left side is also nonsingular so that

$$\lim_{n \to \infty} D_n E(c_0 - \gamma)(c_0 - \gamma)^* D_n = 2\pi \left\{ \int_{-\pi}^{\pi} \frac{1}{f(-\lambda)} \, d M(\lambda) \right\}^{-1}. \tag{5}$$

It follows from the construction that

$$M^{-1} \int_{-\pi}^{\pi} f(-\lambda) \, d M(\lambda) \, M^{-1} \geq \left\{ \int_{-\pi}^{\pi} \frac{1}{f(-\lambda)} \, d M(\lambda) \right\}^{-1}.$$

Let us now look at the case of greatest interest where the process y_t and the regression components $\varphi_t^{(j)}$ are real-valued. Since x_t is real-valued the spectral density $f(\lambda)$ is symmetric about zero, that is $f(\lambda) = f(-\lambda)$. The fact that the regression components $\varphi_t^{(j)}$ are real implies that

$$d M(\lambda) = \overline{d M(-\lambda)}.$$

It is then convenient to introduce the nondecreasing matrix-valued function

$$T(\lambda) = M(\lambda +) - M(\lambda -), \quad 0 \leq \lambda \leq \pi,$$

with real elements. Results (1) and (5) can then be rewritten as

$$\lim_{n \to \infty} D_n E(c_L - \gamma)(c_L - \gamma)^* D_n = T^{-1} 2\pi \int_0^{\pi} f(\lambda) \, d T(\lambda) \, T^{-1} \tag{6}$$

and

$$\lim_{n \to \infty} D_n E(c_0 - \gamma)(c_0 - \gamma)^* D_n = 2\pi \left\{ \int_0^{\pi} \frac{1}{f(\lambda)} \, d T(\lambda) \right\}^{-1} \tag{7}$$

respectively, where $T = T(\pi) = M$.

The regression spectrum S in the real-valued case is defined just as in the complex-valued case. Let λ be a point such that for any interval I containing $\lambda, \Delta T(I) > 0$. The set of all such points λ is the regression spectrum. Now S is a set of points in the interval $0 \leq \lambda \leq \pi$ instead of a set of points in the interval $-\pi \leq \lambda \leq \pi$.

7.4. Elements of the Spectrum: Asymptotic Conditions for the Efficiency of a Least Squares Estimate

In the study of the least squares estimates an important role is played by the *elements of the spectrum S*. The elements of the spectrum are defined by the following construction. The matrix-valued function

$$N(\lambda) = M^{-1/2} M(\lambda) M^{-1/2}$$

is a nondecreasing function since for $\lambda_1 > \lambda_2$

$$N(\lambda_1) - N(\lambda_2) = M^{-1/2}[M(\lambda_1) - M(\lambda_2)] M^{-1/2} > 0.$$

$N(\lambda)$ is normed so that

$$N(\pi) - N(-\pi) = I.$$

We say that a set H has zero N measure if $\int_H dN(\lambda) = 0$ and we identify sets differing only on a set of zero N measure. Note that N measure zero and M measure zero (analogously defined) are equivalent. Let $E_1 \subset S$, $E_2 = S - E_1$. If there is no set $E_1 \subset S$ such that the matrices $N(E_1) = \int_{E_1} dN(\lambda)$, $N(E_2) = \int_{E_2} dN(\lambda) > 0$ and are orthogonal

$$N(E_1)N(E_2) = 0,$$

we say that S has one element, the set S itself. If there are sets E_1, E_2 satisfying the above conditions, we can ask whether they can be decomposed again in the same manner. A sequence of such decompositions will end in a finite number of steps. The order p of I is finite, so that there can be at most $p - 1$ such decompositions and at most p elements E_i in the final decomposition since

$$N(E_i) > 0$$
$$\Sigma N(E_i) = I,$$
$$N(E_i)N(E_j) = 0, \quad i \neq j.$$

Let there be q elements $E_1, \ldots, E_q$, $q \leq p$, in the final decomposition. Then

$$
\left.
\begin{aligned}
&N(E_j) = \int_{E_j} dN(\lambda) > 0, \quad j = 1, 2, \ldots, q, \\
&\sum_{j=1}^{q} N(E_j) = I, \\
&N(E_i)N(E_j) = 0 \text{ for } i \neq j,
\end{aligned}
\right\}
$$

where none of the E_j can be decomposed further. Multiplying the second of these relations by $N(E_i)$ we obtain $N^2(E_i) = N(E_i)$, i.e., $N(E_i)$ is a projection operator. Of course this could have been deduced directly from the orthogonality between $N(E_i)$ and $\sum_{j \neq i} N(E_j)$. By the elements of S we mean the sets E_i of such a maximal decomposition of S into nonoverlapping sets with orthogonal nonnegative definite increments $N(E_i)$ of $N(\lambda)$.

We now have to show that the construction just given defines the elements of S uniquely. Suppose the opposite is true; there are then two distinct collections $\{E_j\}$, $\{E'_j\}$ which form maximal decompositions of S into nonoverlapping sets with orthogonal N increments. Then there must be sets E_k, E'_i, E'_j such that

$$\left. \begin{array}{l} N(E_k \cap E'_i) > 0 \\ N(E_k \cap E'_j) > 0 \end{array} \right\}.$$

We now need the following result. If M_1, M_2, N_1, N_2 are Hermitian nonnegative definite $p \times p$ matrices,

$$\left. \begin{array}{l} M = M_1 + M_2 \\ N = N_1 + N_2 \end{array} \right\}$$

and $MN = 0$, then $M_i N_j = 0$, $i, j = 1, 2$. Assume that a unitary transformation has been used to carry M into diagonal form with the first m diagonal elements $d_1, d_2, \ldots, d_m \neq 0$. The first m diagonal elements $\{N\}_{ll}, l = 1, 2, \ldots, m$ of N are then zero. The same is clearly true of N_1 and N_2. On using the nonnegative definiteness of the matrices, we see that the only nonvanishing elements of N_1, N_2 are those with subscripts (r, s) where $m + 1 \leq r, s \leq p$. But then $M_i N_j = 0$.

Let us write $E_k = (E'_i \cap E_k) \cup F = D \cup F$. As $N(E_k) = N(D) + N(F)$ is orthogonal to every $N(E_l)$ with $l \neq k$ it follows that the same holds for $N(D)$ and $N(F)$. But as $N(E'_i) N(\bigcup_{j \neq i} E'_j) = 0$ it also follows that $N(E'_i \cap E_k)$ $N(F) = 0$ so that $\{E_i\}$ can be decomposed further contrary to our assumption. This proves the uniqueness of the elements as constructed above.

We have shown in section 7.3 that a necessary and sufficient condition for the asymptotic efficiency of the least squares estimate is that

$$\int_{-\pi}^{\pi} f(-\lambda) \, dN(\lambda) \int_{-\pi}^{\pi} \frac{1}{f(-\mu)} \, dN(\mu) = I. \tag{1}$$

Using the decomposition of S into elements we see that (1) is equivalent to

$$\sum_{j=1}^{q} \int_{E_j} f(-\lambda) \, dN(\lambda) \int_{E_j} \frac{1}{f(-\mu)} \, dN(\mu) = I.$$

If $f(-\lambda) = c_j > 0$ on E_j, the above sum reduces to

$$\sum_{j=1}^{q} N^2(E_j) = \sum_{j=1}^{q} N(E_j) = I,$$

so that *we have asymptotic efficiency*.

The converse is also true. Suppose that (1) holds. Using a unitary transformation U we simultaneously diagonalize the matrices

$$\int_{-\pi}^{\pi} f(-\lambda) \, dN(\lambda) \quad \text{and} \quad \int_{-\pi}^{\pi} \frac{1}{f(-\mu)} \, dN(\mu).$$

Then

$$\int_{-\pi}^{\pi} f(-\lambda) \, d\{UN(\lambda)U^*\}_{ii} \int_{-\pi}^{\pi} \frac{1}{f(-\mu)} \, d\{UN(\lambda)U^*\}_{ii} = 1, \; i = 1, 2, \ldots, p.$$

We know that the Schwarz inequality reduces to an equality if and only if the integrands are proportional on the set on which the nondecreasing function $N_i(\lambda) = \{UN(\lambda)U^*\}_{ii}$, with respect to which we integrate, increases. Hence $f(-\lambda)$ has to be a constant c_i on each of these p sets A_i, $i = 1, 2, \ldots, p$. Consider any chain of sets $A_1, A_{i_1}, \ldots, A_{i_k}$ such that

$$N_1(A_1 \cap A_{i_1}) > 0$$
$$N_{i_1}(A_{i_1} \cap A_{i_2}) > 0$$
$$\cdot \quad \cdot \quad \cdot$$
$$N_{i_{k-1}}(A_{i_{k-1}} \cap A_{i_k}) > 0$$
$$N_{i_k}(A_{i_{k-1}} \cap A_{i_k}) > 0.$$

It is clear that $f(-\lambda)$ must equal the same constant $\gamma_1 = c_1$ on every set in the chain. Let B_1 be the union of all sets A_i which are links in any such chain containing the set A_1. Then $f(-\lambda) = \gamma_1 = c_1$ on B_1. For every set A_i construct the union of all sets A_j which are links in such a chain containing A_i. We will then get nonoverlapping sets B_i, $i = 1, 2, \ldots, r \leq p$ and $f(-\lambda) = \gamma_i$ is a constant on each of these sets.

Then (1) reduces to

$$\sum_{i=1}^{r} N^2(B_i) = I. \qquad (2)$$

But as $N(B_i) \geq 0$ and

$$\sum_{i=1}^{r} N(B_i) = I$$

we have $N(B_i) \leq I$ and $N^2(B_i) \leq N(B_i)$. This together with (2) implies that $N^2(B_i) = N(B_i)$, i.e., the $N(B_i)$ are projection operators. But as their sum is the projection I they must be orthogonal (see Halmos [2], p. 53). Each B_i is then the union of a number of elements of the spectrum S. Hence $f(-\lambda)$ is constant on each element as was to be proved. We restate what has been proved in terms of $M(\lambda)$.

The spectrum S of the regression can be decomposed into disjoint sets E_j, $j = 1, 2, \ldots, q \leq p$ such that

$$M(E_i) M^{-1} M(E_j) = \delta_{ij} M(E_i), M(E_i) > 0,$$

and this is the finest such decomposition. The sets E_j are called the elements of the regression spectrum.

The least squares estimate c_L of the regression coefficients is asymptotically efficient if and only if the spectral density is constant on each of the elements of S.

It is of especial interest to find out when the least squares estimate c_L of γ will be asymptotically efficient for every positive piecewise continuous spectral density $f(\lambda)$, that is, asymptotically efficient for most stationary processes met in practice. From the above it is clear that this will be valid if and only if the spectrum S of $M(\lambda)$ has q elements which are distinct points $\lambda_1, \lambda_2, \ldots, \lambda_q$, $q \leq p$. *The least squares estimate c_L of γ is asymptotically efficient for any process x_t with a positive piecewise continuous spectral density $f(\lambda)$ if and only if the spectrum S of $M(\lambda)$ has elements which are q distinct points $\lambda_1, \ldots, \lambda_p$, $q \leq p$.*

For a treatment of the analogous problem for vector-valued processes see Rosenblatt [1].

The results are completely analogous in the real-valued case. We state them for completeness. *The spectrum S of the regression can be decomposed into disjoint sets E_j, $j = 1, \ldots, q \leq p$ such that*

$$T(E_i) T^{-1} T(E_j) = \delta_{ij} T(E_i), T(E_i) > 0,$$

and this is the finest such decomposition. The sets E_j are called the elements of the regression spectrum. The least squares estimate c_L of the regression coefficients is asymptotically efficient if and only if the spectral density is constant on each of the elements of S. The least squares estimate c_L of γ is asymptotically *efficient for any real-valued process with a positive piecewise continuous spectral density if and only if the spectrum S of $T(\lambda)$ has elements which are q distinct points $\lambda_1, \lambda_2, \ldots, \lambda_q$, $q \leq p$.*

7.5. Polynomial and Trigonometric Regression

We shall first consider the following rather simple but important case. Let the regression variables

$$\varphi_t^{(\nu)} = t^\nu e^{it\lambda_1}, \quad \nu = 0, 1, 2, \ldots, p_1$$

$$\varphi_t^{(p_1+\nu+1)} = t^\nu e^{it\lambda_2}, \quad \nu = 0, 1, 2, \ldots, p_2$$

$$\cdot \quad \cdot \quad \cdot \quad \cdot \quad \cdot \quad \cdot \quad \cdot \quad \cdot \quad \cdot \quad \cdot \quad \cdot \quad \cdot$$

$$\varphi_t^{(p_1+p_2+\cdots+p_{m-1}+m-1+\nu)} = t^\nu e^{it\lambda_m}, \quad \nu = 0, 1, \ldots, p_m,$$

where $\lambda_1, \lambda_2, \ldots, \lambda_m$ are distinct frequencies in $(-\pi, \pi)$. In this enumeration scheme a superscript k corresponds to a pair of integers (ν, s), where ν is the power to which t is raised and s is the index of the frequency. Of course we could leave out certain pairs (ν, s) but it is easy to see how the following discussion should be modified.

Here
$$\Phi_n^{(k)} = \sum_{t=1}^n t^{2\nu} \sim \frac{n^{2\nu+1}}{2\nu+1}$$

is a slowly increasing sequence. We have

$$R_h^{(k,\,k')} = \lim_{n\to\infty} \frac{1}{\sqrt{\Phi_n^{(k)}\,\Phi_n^{(k')}}} \sum_{t=1}^n t^{\nu+\nu'} e^{it(\lambda_s-\lambda_{s'})} e^{ih\lambda_{s'}}$$

$$= \frac{\sqrt{(2\nu+1)(2\nu'+1)}}{(\nu+\nu'+1)} \delta_{ss'}\, e^{ih\lambda_{s'}}$$

as is easily verified. In the spectral representation

$$R_h = \int_{-\pi}^{\pi} e^{ih\lambda}\, dM(\lambda),$$

the matrix function $M(\lambda)$ is constant except at the points λ_s. To each λ_s there corresponds a jump

$$\Delta M(\lambda_s) = \begin{bmatrix} \overbrace{}^{p_1+p_2+\cdots+p_{s-1}+s-1} & & \\ 0 & 0 & 0 \\ 0 & M_s & 0 \\ 0 & 0 & 0 \end{bmatrix}$$

where M_s is the nonsingular matrix

$$M_s = \left\{ \frac{\sqrt{(2\nu+1)(2\nu'+1)}}{(\nu+\nu'+1)}; \ \nu, \nu' = 0, 1, \ldots, p_s \right\}.$$

Thus $M = M(\pi) - M(-\pi)$ is the direct sum of the nonsingular matrices $M_1, \ldots, M_m$.

As each matrix M_s is nonsingular it follows that $M = R_0$ is also nonsingular. One can see that M_s is nonsingular in the following manner. Now

$$M_s = D \left\{ \frac{1}{\nu+\nu'+1}; \ \nu, \nu' = 0, 1, \cdots, p_s \right\} D = D A_s D,$$

where D is the diagonal matrix with the nonzero elements $\sqrt{2\nu+1}$, $\nu = 0$, $1, \ldots, p_s$, in the main diagonal. If A_s were singular there would exist a non-trivial $(p_s + 1)$-vector z such that

$$0 = z^* A_s z = \sum_{\nu, \nu'=0}^{p_s} \bar{z}_\nu z_{\nu'} \frac{1}{\nu+\nu'+1} = \int_0^1 \left| \sum_0^{p_s} z_\nu x^\nu \right|^2 dx,$$

implying that
$$\sum_0^{p_s} z_\nu x^\nu \equiv 0.$$

But then $z = 0$ contrary to our assumption. The regression spectrum S of $M(\lambda)$ consists of the elements $\lambda_1, \ldots, \lambda_m$ with corresponding orthogonal saltuses $\Delta M(\lambda_1), \ldots, \Delta M(\lambda_m)$. Since the elements of the spectrum S are the distinct points λ_s, it is clear that *the least squares estimate c_L of the vector of regression coefficients γ is asymptotically efficient in this context*, whatever the spectral density is.

Consider for example, the simplest case of *trigonometric* regression

$$y_t = \gamma_1 e^{it\lambda_1} + \gamma_2 e^{it\lambda_2} + \cdots + \gamma_p e^{it\lambda_p} + x_t.$$

If the frequencies $\lambda_1, \lambda_2, \ldots, \lambda_p$ are different the above result holds, so that the least squares estimates of $\gamma_1, \gamma_2, \ldots, \gamma_p$ are asymptotically efficient. The covariances of these estimates will be given by the asymptotic expressions (see (7.3.1))

$$\mathrm{cov}\,(c_j, c_k) \sim \frac{2\pi}{n} f(\lambda_j)\,\delta_{jk} + o\left(\frac{1}{n}\right).$$

Hence they are approximately uncorrelated with variances depending only upon the spectral density at the points $\lambda_1, \lambda_2, \ldots, \lambda_p$ for large samples.

When we have *polynomial regression*

$$y_t = c_0 + c_1 t + \cdots + c_p t^p + x_t$$

we see that the spectrum consists of only one point, $\lambda = 0$, with the corresponding jump of $M(\lambda)$

$$\Delta M(0) = \left\{ \frac{\sqrt{(2\nu+1)(2\nu'+1)}}{\nu+\nu'+1}; \quad \nu, \nu' = 0, 1, \cdots, p \right\}.$$

It follows that the least squares estimates are again asymptotically efficient and have the covariances

$$\text{cov}(c_j, c_k) \sim \frac{2\pi f(0) m_{jk}}{n^{\nu+\nu'+1}},$$

where

$$m_{jk} = \left\{ \frac{1}{\nu+\nu'+1}; \quad \nu, \nu' = 0, 1, \ldots, p \right\}_{jk}^{-1}.$$

The real-valued case is again analogous though somewhat more tedious. We shall state some of the analogous results. Suppose the regression sequences are of the form

$$_1\varphi_t^{(\nu)} = t^\nu \cos t\lambda_1 \qquad \nu = 0, 1, \ldots, {}_1p_1$$

$$_2\varphi_t^{(\nu)} = t^\nu \sin t\lambda_1 \qquad \nu = 0, 1, \ldots, {}_2p_1$$

$$\cdot \quad \cdot \quad \cdot$$

$$_1\varphi_t^{({}_1p_1+\cdots+{}_1p_{m-1}+m-1+\nu)} = t^\nu \cos t\lambda_m \qquad \nu = 0, 1, \ldots, {}_1p_m$$

$$_2\varphi_t^{({}_2p_1+\cdots+{}_2p_{m-1}+m-1+\nu)} = t^\nu \sin t\lambda_m \qquad \nu = 0, 1, \ldots, {}_2p_m,$$

where $\lambda_1, \ldots, \lambda_m$ are distinct frequencies in $(0, \pi)$. The sine terms for the frequency λ_s do not appear if $\lambda_s = 0$. Since we have already discussed the case $\lambda_s = 0$, we shall assume that none of the frequencies λ_s are zero. One finds that $T(\lambda)$ is constant except at the points λ_s. At the point λ_s there is a jump

$$_1p_1 + {}_2p_1 + \cdots + {}_1p_{s-1} + {}_2p_{s-1} + 2s - 2$$

$$\Delta T(\lambda_s) = \overbrace{\begin{bmatrix} 0 & 0 & 0 & 0 \\ 0 & {}_1T_s & 0 & 0 \\ 0 & 0 & {}_2T_s & 0 \\ 0 & 0 & 0 & 0 \end{bmatrix}},$$

where

$$_1T_s = \left\{ \frac{\sqrt{(2\,\nu+1)\,(2\,\nu'+1)}}{\nu+\nu'+1} ;\ \nu,\nu'=0,\ \ldots,\ _1p_s \right\}$$

$$_2T_s = \left\{ \frac{\sqrt{(2\,\nu+1)\,(2\,\nu'+1)}}{\nu+\nu'+1} :\ \nu,\nu'=0,\ \ldots,\ _2p_s \right\}.$$

Note that for the types of regression dealt with in this section one has asymptotic efficiency of the least squares estimate for all positive piecewise continuous $f(\lambda)$.

7.6. More General Trigonometric and Polynomial Regression

We shall now generalize the type of regression sequence considered but will for convenience restrict ourselves to the case of only two such sequences. The two regression sequences are

$$\varphi_t^{(1)} = P(t) \int\limits_{-\pi}^{\pi} e^{i t \lambda} d\alpha(\lambda)$$

$$\varphi_t^{(2)} = Q(t) \int\limits_{-\pi}^{\pi} e^{i t \lambda} d\beta(\lambda),$$

where $P(t)$, $Q(t)$ are polynomials $P(t) = \sum\limits_{\nu=0}^{u} p_\nu t^\nu$, $Q(t) = \sum\limits_{\nu=0}^{v} q_\nu t^\nu$ and $\alpha(\lambda)$, $\beta(\lambda)$ are functions of bounded variation. We also assume that $\alpha(\lambda)$, $\beta(\lambda)$ both have jumps and denote the denumerable number of λ values at which either $\alpha(\lambda)$ or $\beta(\lambda)$ have jumps by $\lambda_1, \lambda_2, \ldots, \lambda_s, \ldots$. The magnitude of the jumps of $\alpha(\lambda)$, $\beta(\lambda)$ at λ_s are given by a_s, b_s respectively. Let the jumpfree parts of $\alpha(\lambda)$, $\beta(\lambda)$ be given by $\alpha_1(\lambda)$, $\beta_1(\lambda)$, that is,

$$\alpha_1(\lambda) = \alpha(\lambda) - \sum_{\lambda_s \leq \lambda} a_s = \alpha(\lambda) - \alpha_2(\lambda)$$

$$\beta_1(\lambda) = \beta(\lambda) - \sum_{\lambda_s \leq \lambda} b_s = \beta(\lambda) - \beta_2(\lambda).$$

We shall show that only the jumps of $\alpha(\lambda)$, $\beta(\lambda)$ can contribute to $M(\lambda)$. It will be enough to show that

$$\sum_{t=1}^{n} \left| \int\limits_{-\pi}^{\pi} e^{i t \lambda} d\alpha_1(\lambda) \right|^2 = o(n). \tag{1}$$

Now

$$\sum_{t=1}^{n} \left| \int_{-\pi}^{\pi} e^{it\lambda} \, d\alpha_1(\lambda) \right|^2 = \int_{-\pi}^{\pi}\int_{-\pi}^{\pi} e^{i(\lambda-\lambda')} \frac{e^{in(\lambda-\lambda')}-1}{e^{i(\lambda-\lambda')}-1} \, d\alpha_1(\lambda) \, \overline{d\alpha_1(\lambda')}$$

$$\leq n \iint_{|\lambda-\lambda'|<\epsilon} |d\alpha_1(\lambda)||d\alpha_1(\lambda')| + \frac{1}{\epsilon}[\mathrm{Var}\,(|\alpha_1(\lambda)|)]^2.$$

But $\displaystyle\iint_{|\lambda-\lambda'|<\epsilon} |d\alpha_1(\lambda)||d\alpha_1(\lambda')| \to 0$ as $\epsilon\to 0$, since $\alpha_1(\lambda)$ has no jumps. Thus (1) has been proven. The same result holds for $\beta_1(\lambda)$. Now

$$\Phi_n^{(1)} = \sum_{1}^{n} |P(t)|^2 \left[\left| \int_{-\pi}^{\pi} e^{it\lambda} \, d\alpha_1(\lambda) \right|^2 \right.$$

$$\left. + 2\,Re\left(\int_{-\pi}^{\pi} e^{it\lambda} \, d\alpha_1(\lambda) \int_{-\pi}^{\pi} e^{-it\lambda} \, \overline{d\alpha_2(\lambda)} \right) + \left| \int_{-\pi}^{\pi} e^{it\lambda} \, d\alpha_2(\lambda) \right|^2 \right].$$

But

$$\sum_{1}^{n} |P(t)|^2 \left| \int_{-\pi}^{\pi} e^{it\lambda} \, d\alpha_1(\lambda) \right|^2 = |P(n)|^2 \sum_{t=1}^{n} \left| \int_{-\pi}^{\pi} e^{it\lambda} \, d\alpha_1(\lambda) \right|^2 -$$

$$- \sum_{t=1}^{n-1} (|P(t+1)|^2 - |P(t)|^2) \sum_{k=1}^{t} \left| \int_{-\pi}^{\pi} e^{ik\lambda} \, d\alpha_1(\lambda) \right|^2.$$

Using the fact that $|P(t+1)|^2 - |P(t)|^2 = 0\,(t^{2u-1})$ and (1) we see that

$$\sum_{k=1}^{n} |P(t)|^2 \left| \int_{-\pi}^{\pi} e^{it\lambda} \, d\alpha_1(\lambda) \right|^2 = o\,(n^{2u+1}).$$

Now

$$\sum_{1}^{n} |P(t)|^2 \left| \int_{-\pi}^{\pi} e^{it\lambda} \, d\alpha_2(\lambda) \right|^2 \sim |p_u|^2 \frac{n^{2u+1}}{2u+1} \sum |a_s|^2.$$

It is then clear that

$$\sum_{1}^{n} |P(t)|^2 \left| 2\,Re\left(\int_{-\pi}^{\pi} e^{it\lambda} \, d\alpha_1(\lambda) \int_{-\pi}^{\pi} e^{-it\lambda} \, \overline{d\alpha_2(\lambda)} \right) \right|$$

$$\leq 2\left[\sum_{1}^{n} |P(t)|^2 \left| \int_{-\pi}^{\pi} e^{it\lambda} \, d\alpha_1(\lambda) \right|^2 \sum_{1}^{n} |P(t)|^2 \left| \int_{-\pi}^{\pi} e^{it\lambda} \, d\alpha_2(\lambda) \right|^2 \right]^{\frac{1}{2}}$$

$$= o\,(n^{2u+1}).$$

But then

$$\Phi_n^{(1)} = \left(\frac{|p_u|^2}{2\,u+1} \sum |a_s|^2 + o\,(1) \right) n^{2u+1}.$$

In the same way one can show that

$$\Phi_n^{(2)} = \left(\frac{|q_v|^2}{2\,v+1} \sum |b_s|^2 + o\,(1) \right) n^{2v+1}.$$

A similar argument implies that

$$\sum_{t=1}^{n} \varphi_{t+h}^{(1)}\,\overline{\varphi_t^{(2)}} \sim \left(\frac{p_u\,\overline{q}_v}{u+v+1} \sum a_s\,\overline{b}_s\,e^{i\,h\,\lambda_s} + o\,(1) \right) n^{u+v+1}.$$

It is clear that

$$M(\lambda) = D^{-1} \begin{pmatrix} \dfrac{|p_u|^2}{2\,u+1} \displaystyle\sum_{\lambda_s \leq \lambda} |a_s|^2, & \dfrac{p_u\,\overline{q}_v}{u+v+1} \displaystyle\sum_{\lambda_s \leq \lambda} a_s\,\overline{b}_s \\[4mm] \dfrac{\overline{p}_u\,q_v}{u+v+1} \displaystyle\sum_{\lambda_s \leq \lambda} \overline{a}_s\,b_s, & \dfrac{|q_v|^2}{2\,v+1} \displaystyle\sum_{\lambda_s \leq \lambda} |b_s|^2 \end{pmatrix} D^{-1}$$

where D is the diagonal matrix

$$D = \begin{pmatrix} \dfrac{|p_u|\,(\sum |a_s|^2)^{1/2}}{\sqrt{2\,u+1}} & 0 \\[4mm] 0 & \dfrac{|q_v|\,(\sum |b_s|^2)^{1/2}}{\sqrt{2v+1}} \end{pmatrix}.$$

We do not want to have $M = M(\pi) - M(-\pi)$ singular. But M can be singular if and only if $\sum |a_s|^2 \sum |b_s|^2 = |\sum a_s \overline{b}_s|^2$, that is, if and only if the sequences a_s and b_s respectively are linearly related or equivalently if and only if the functions $\alpha_2(\lambda)$, $\beta_2(\lambda)$ are linearly related. We assume that this is not the case.

The spectrum S of $M(\lambda)$ consists of the denumerable set of points λ_1, $\lambda_2, \ldots, \lambda_s, \ldots$. We shall find the elements of the spectrum S. There can be at most two elements E_1, E_2. If there are two elements E_1, E_2 then $E_1 \cap E_2 = 0$, $E_1 \cup E_2 = S$ and the corresponding increments

$$M_1 = \int_{E_1} d\,M\,(\lambda), \quad M_2 = \int_{E_2} d\,M\,(\lambda)$$

satisfy

$$M_i\,M^{-1}\,M_j = \delta_{ij}\,M_i$$

(see section 7.4). Moreover the manifolds corresponding to M_1, M_2 are each of dimension one. In the two dimensional case, consider any nonsingular positive matrix M and a decomposition $M = M_1 + M_2$ of M into two positive matrices M_1, M_2 whose manifolds are of dimension one and have only the null vector in common. We show that

$$M_i M^{-1} M_j = \delta_{ij} M_i.$$

Let U be the transformation that simultaneously diagonalizes M_1, M_2 and hence also M. Then $U M_1 U^*$, $U M_2 U^*$, $U^{*-1} M^{-1} U^{-1}$ are simultaneously diagonal. But

$$M_i M^{-1} M_j = U^{-1} U M_i U^* U^{*-1} M^{-1} U^{-1} U M_j U^* U^{*-1}$$

$$= \delta_{ij} U^{-1} U M_i U^* U^{*-1} = \delta_{ij} M_i$$

since the manifolds corresponding to M_1, M_2 have only the null vector in common. But there are two elements E_1, E_2 of the spectrum S if and only if there is a decomposition of the spectrum into two sets E_1, E_2 such that the corresponding increments M_1, M_2 over these sets have dimension one. This is true if and only if the matrices

$$\begin{pmatrix} |p_u|^2 \sum_{\lambda_s \in E_i} |a|^2 & \dfrac{p_u \bar{q}_v}{u+v+1} \sum_{\lambda_s \in E_i} a_s \bar{b}_s \\[2ex] \bar{p}_u q_v \sum_{\lambda_s \in E_i} \bar{a}_s b_s & \dfrac{|q_v|^2}{2v+1} \sum_{\lambda_s \in E_i} |b_s|^2 \end{pmatrix} \quad i = 1, 2$$

are singular. This can happen if and only if

$$\frac{1}{(2u+1)(2v+1)} \sum_{\lambda_s \in E_i} |a_s|^2 \sum_{\lambda_s \in E_i} |b_s|^2$$

$$= \frac{1}{(u+v+1)^2} \left| \sum_{\lambda_s \in E_i} a_s \bar{b}_s \right|^2, \quad i = 1, 2. \tag{2}$$

There are two ways in which this can occur. We could have $a_s \equiv 0$, $s \in E_i$, and $b_s \equiv 0$, $s \in E_j$, $i \neq j$. If this is not so then $a_s = 0$, $s \in E_i$ $i = 1, 2$. Then both sides of equation (2) must be positive for either E_1 or E_2 (say E_1) and equality implies that $u = v$ and that $\{a_s\}$, $\{b_s\}$ $s \in E_1$ are linearly related (Schwarz inequality). In any case we must also have $\{a_s\}$, $\{b_s\}$ $s \in E_2$ linearly related. Thus, *if there are two elements E_1, E_2 of the spectrum, we must either have $a_s \equiv 0$, $s \in E_i$, and $b_s \equiv 0$, $s \in E_j$, where $i \neq j$ or the orders $u = v$ and the sequences $\{a_s\}$, $\{b_s\}$, $s \in E_i$, are linearly related $i = 1, 2$. Note that the linear relationship between $\{a_s\}$ and $\{b_s\}$ must not be the same on both E_1 and E_2 for the matrix M would then be singular. It is also clear that if $\{a_s\}$,*

$\{b_s\}$ *satisfy either of these two conditions, there are two elements* E_1 *and* E_2 *of the spectrum.*

We now discuss the cases in which one does have asymptotic efficiency for every $f(\lambda)$. We know that there can be one or two elements. In either case, each of the elements is a point. If there is one element, the whole regression spectrum S is one point, say μ, and the only condition for asymptotic efficiency is that $\Delta M(\mu) = M$ be nonsingular. The nonsingularity of M implies that $u \neq v$. If there are two elements, the spectrum S consists of two points λ_1, λ_2 and each of these points is an element of the spectrum. There are then two possibilities corresponding to the dichotomy discussed above. The first possibility is that $\alpha_2(\lambda)$ has the one jump λ_1 and $\beta_2(\lambda)$ has the one jump λ_2. The second possibility is that $\alpha_2(\lambda)$, $\beta_2(\lambda)$ both have the jumps λ_1, λ_2 but that $u = v$ and that $a_1 b_2 \neq b_1 a_2$. Thus *we have asymptotic efficiency when*

$$\varphi_t^{(1)} = P(t) \int_{-\pi}^{\pi} e^{it\lambda} d\alpha(\lambda)$$

$$\varphi_t^{(2)} = Q(t) \int_{-\pi}^{\pi} e^{it\lambda} d\beta(\lambda)$$

for all positive and piecewise continuous $f(\lambda)$ *if and only if one of the three following cases arises*

(1)
$$\varphi_t^{(1)} = P(t) \left[e^{it\mu} + \int_{-\pi}^{\pi} e^{it\lambda} d\alpha_1(\lambda) \right]$$

$$\varphi_t^{(2)} = Q(t) \left[e^{it\mu} + \int_{-\pi}^{\pi} e^{it\lambda} d\beta_1(\lambda) \right],$$

where $u \neq v$.

(2)
$$\varphi_t^{(1)} = P(t) \left[e^{it\lambda_1} + \int_{-\pi}^{\pi} e^{it\lambda} d\alpha_1(\lambda) \right]$$

$$\varphi_t^{(2)} = Q(t) \left[e^{it\lambda_2} + \int_{-\pi}^{\pi} e^{it\lambda} d\beta_1(\lambda) \right],$$

where $\lambda_1 \neq \lambda_2$.

(3)
$$\varphi_t^{(1)} = P(t) \left[a_1 e^{it\lambda_1} + a_2 e^{it\lambda_2} + \int_{-\pi}^{\pi} e^{it\lambda} d\alpha_1(\lambda) \right]$$

$$\varphi_t^{(2)} = Q(t) \left[b_1 e^{it\lambda_1} + b_2 e^{it\lambda_2} + \int_{-\pi}^{\pi} e^{it\lambda} d\beta_1(\lambda) \right],$$

where $u = v$, $\lambda_1 \neq \lambda_2$ and $a_1 b_2 \neq a_2 b_1$.

We now look at the real-valued case. Let

$$\varphi_t^{(1)} = P(t) \int_{-\pi}^{\pi} e^{it\lambda} d\alpha(\lambda)$$

(3)

$$\varphi_t^{(2)} = Q(t) \int_{-\pi}^{\pi} e^{it\lambda} d\beta(\lambda),$$

where $P(t)$, $Q(t)$ are polynomials of order u, v respectively with real coefficients and $\int_{-\pi}^{\pi} e^{it\lambda} d\alpha(\lambda)$, $\int_{-\pi}^{\pi} e^{it\lambda} d\beta(\lambda)$ are real. The functions $\alpha(\lambda)$, $\beta(\lambda)$ are both assumed to have jumps. Let $\alpha_1(\lambda)$, $\beta_1(\lambda)$ again denote the jumpfree parts of $\alpha(\lambda)$, $\beta(\lambda)$. An argument similar to that given above indicates that one has asymptotic efficiency when the regression sequences are of form (3) if and only if one of the following cases arise:

(1) $\quad \varphi_t^{(1)} = P(t) \left[a_1 \cos t\lambda + a_2 \sin t\lambda + a_3 \cos t\mu + a_4 \sin t\mu + \right.$

$$\left. + \int_{-\pi}^{\pi} e^{it\lambda} d\alpha_1(\lambda) \right]$$

$$\varphi_t^{(2)} = Q(t) \left[b_1 \cos t\lambda + b_2 \sin t\lambda + b_3 \cos t\mu + b_4 \sin t\mu + \right.$$

$$\left. + \int_{-\pi}^{\pi} e^{it\lambda} d\beta_1(\lambda) \right],$$

where

$$\lambda, \ \mu \neq 0, \ \lambda \neq \mu, \ u = v \quad \text{and} \quad \begin{pmatrix} a_1 & a_2 \\ b_1 & b_2 \end{pmatrix}, \ \begin{pmatrix} a_3 & a_4 \\ b_3 & b_4 \end{pmatrix}$$

are matrices of rank one.

(2) $\quad\quad \varphi_t^{(1)} = P(t) \left[a_1 \cos t\lambda + a_2 \sin t\lambda + \int_{-\pi}^{\pi} e^{it\lambda} d\alpha_1(\lambda) \right]$

$$\varphi_t^{(2)} = Q(t) \left[b_1 \cos t\lambda + b_2 \sin t\lambda + \int_{-\pi}^{\pi} e^{it\lambda} d\beta_1(\lambda) \right],$$

where $\lambda \neq 0$ and $u \neq v$ or $a_1 b_2 \neq a_2 b_1$.

(3) $$\varphi_t^{(1)} = P(t) \left[a_1 + a_2 \cos t\lambda + a_3 \sin t\lambda + \int\limits_{-\pi}^{\pi} e^{it\lambda} d\alpha_1(\lambda) \right]$$

$$\varphi_t^{(2)} = Q(t) \left[b_1 + b_2 \cos t\lambda + b_3 \sin t\lambda + \int\limits_{-\pi}^{\pi} e^{it\lambda} d\beta_1(\lambda) \right],$$

where $\lambda \neq 0$, $u = v$ and $\begin{pmatrix} a_2 & a_3 \\ b_2 & b_3 \end{pmatrix}$ is of rank one.

(4) $$\varphi_t^{(1)} = P(t) \left[a + \int\limits_{-\pi}^{\pi} e^{it\lambda} d\alpha_1(\lambda) \right]$$

$$\varphi_t^{(2)} = Q(t) \left[b + \int\limits_{-\pi}^{\pi} e^{it\lambda} d\beta_1(\lambda) \right],$$

where $u \neq v$.

7.7. Some Other Types of Regression

Suppose for simplicity that we deal with just one regression variable, $p = 1$, say φ_t. It is of interest to study what happens if the regression variable is periodic so that $\varphi_{t+q} = \varphi_t$, where q is the period and is a positive integer. We shall then say that the regression variable forms a periodic pulse train with the pulse shape $\{\varphi_1, \varphi_2, \ldots, \varphi_q\}$. It can then be written as

$$\varphi_t = b_1 + b_2 e^{2\pi i \frac{t}{q}} + \cdots b_q e^{2\pi i \frac{t(q-1)}{q}}.$$

The matrix $\{e^{2i(t\nu/q)}; t, \nu = 0, 1, \ldots, q-1\}$ is nonsingular. The spectrum S consists of those points $2\pi\nu/q$ for which the constant b_ν does not vanish. As $p = 1$ the spectrum is indecomposable. Only if the spectral density is the same for these points will the least squares estimate

$$c_L = \frac{\sum\limits_1^n y_t \varphi_t}{\Phi_n}$$

be asymptotically efficient. This will in general not happen. The variance of the estimate will be

$$D^2[c_L] \sim \frac{\sum\limits_{\nu=0}^{q-1} 2\pi f\left(2\pi \frac{\nu}{q}\right) |b_\nu|^2}{\left[\sum\limits_0^{q-1} |b_\nu|^2\right]^2 n}$$

asymptotically.

In another case of interest the regression variable φ_t has been obtained as an observation of a strictly stationary process with a spectrum $\varphi(\lambda)$. Assuming this process to be ergodic, it is known (see e.g., Doob [1]) that φ_1 has a spectrum in the sense of section 7.2 with probability one and that this spectrum coincides with $\varphi(\lambda)$. Hence, as $\varphi(\lambda)$ will have more than one point of increase, the least squares estimate of γ will not be asymptotically efficient in general. The asymptotic variance will be

$$D^2[c_L^*] \sim \frac{2\pi \int\limits_{-\pi}^{\pi} f(\lambda)\, d\varphi(\lambda)}{\left[\int\limits_{-\pi}^{\pi} d\varphi(\lambda)\right]^2 n} \cdot$$

Note that after having observed φ_t it is regarded as a sequence of known constants and we act as if we had completely forgotten that φ_t forms a stochastic process. This is a special case of the *fixed variate case*, which is sometimes dealt with in econometrics.

7.8. Detection of Signals in Noise

We will show in this section how some of the results obtained in this chapter have an immediate application to an important problem in the theory of communication. It will be most convenient to word the statements in terms of a continuous time parameter.

A message $y(t)$, $0 < t < T$, has been received, but due to disturbances in the channel of communication, we cannot reconstruct the original signal $s(t)$ directly. Suppose that we know that

$$y(t) = s(t) + x(t),$$

and that the noise $x(t)$ is a stationary process with an absolutely continuous spectrum and a continuous spectral density.

Consider the case of

$$s(t) = \gamma$$

an unknown constant mean value γ. What is the best way to find a reasonable estimate of γ? The result of section 7.5 tells us immediately that as this corresponds to a regression spectrum having only one element, the point $\lambda = 0$, we will get an asymptotically best estimate (in the sense used throughout this chapter) by constructing the least squares estimate,

$$c_L = \frac{1}{T} \int\limits_0^T y(t)\, dt.$$

Strictly speaking this was shown only for the case of a discrete time parameter, but a proof of the asymptotic optimality of c_L can be found in
Grenander [1]. Various physical devices can be thought of to find c_L. We
might average $y(t)$ in a d. c. meter.

Now one could make the following objection. It is quite true that c_L is
a best estimate in the large sample sense, but in practice it will be desirable
to keep T fairly small. This may be because the noise cannot be assumed
to be stationary over very long time intervals, or because γ has a slow secular
variation. Anyhow it would then be natural to ask whether we could then
find a better estimate.

The following case is simple but illustrative. Suppose that $x(t)$ is generated
by white noise passed through a passive linear network, with a finite number of loops. We then know (see section 1.8) that the spectral density will
be of the form

$$f(\lambda) = \frac{K}{\left| \sum\limits_{\nu=0}^n a_\nu (i\lambda)^\nu \right|^2}. \tag{1}$$

Then the linear unbiased estimate of minimum variance of γ can be explicitly
given. It is

$$c_0 = \frac{1}{2a_1 + a_0 T} \left\{ \sum\limits_0^{n-1} a_{\nu+1} [(-1)^\nu y^{(\nu)}(0) + y^{(\nu)}(T)] + a_0 \int\limits_0^T y(t)\, dt \right\} \tag{2}$$

(see Grenander [1], p. 242). We see that it differs from c_L mainly in that
we have added the values of $y(t)$ and some of its derivatives (which exist in
the mean up to the order $n-1$) at the points $t=0$ and $t=T$. The variance
turns out to be

$$D^2[c_0] = \frac{2\pi K}{a_0(2a_1 + a_0 T)}.$$

On the other hand we have an asymptotic expression for the variance of
the least squares estimate in general

$$D^2[c_L] = \frac{1}{T^2} \int\limits_{-\infty}^{\infty} \frac{\sin^2 \dfrac{T\lambda}{2}}{\left(\dfrac{\lambda}{2}\right)^2} f(\lambda)\, d\lambda.$$

Now c_L asymptotically behaves like (2), as we know it should. The expression (2) is not very easy to handle and as $D^2[c_L]$ is not appreciably smaller than $D^2(c_0)$ unless T is quite small it does not seem worthwhile in general to use c_0 instead of c_L. If we assume that $f(\lambda)$ has a bounded second derivative in $(-\varepsilon, \varepsilon)$

$$T D^2[c_L] = \frac{1}{T} \int\limits_{|\lambda|>\varepsilon} + \frac{1}{T} \int\limits_{|\lambda|<\varepsilon} \frac{\sin^2 \dfrac{T\lambda}{2}}{\left(\dfrac{\lambda}{2}\right)^2} f(\lambda)\, d\lambda$$

$$= 0\left(\frac{1}{T}\right) + \frac{1}{T} \int\limits_{|\lambda|<\varepsilon} \frac{\sin^2 \dfrac{T\lambda}{2}}{\left(\dfrac{\lambda}{2}\right)^2} [f(0) + f'(0)\lambda]\, d\lambda + 0\left(\frac{1}{T}\right)$$

$$= 2\pi f(0) + 0\left(\frac{1}{T}\right)$$

so that
$$D^2[c_L] = \frac{2\pi f(0)}{T} + 0\left(\frac{1}{T^2}\right).$$

The conclusion holds *a fortiori* if $f(\lambda)$ is of a more complicated form than (1) as it is then not known whether there exists any closed form for the best estimate.

If we instead choose $s(t)$ as a periodic pulse train with an unknown regression sequence, the same conclusion cannot be drawn. We have seen in section 7.7 that the least squares estimate is then not asymptotically efficient so that even for a very long interval of observation it is possible to get a substantially better estimate. It would then be of interest to find an expression for such an estimate in closed form. We would have to know the spectral density at the frequencies characteristic of the pulse but these values could be estimated by the methods described in Chapters 4 and 6.

The reader interested in this topic should read the papers by Davis [1], Rudnick [1], Stone [1] and the book of Lawson-Uhlenbeck [1].

7.9. Confidence Intervals and Tests

So far in this chapter we have only dealt with point estimation. In a practical situation it will also be desirable to find *confidence intervals for the regression coefficients*. To illustrate how this can be done in the present context we choose the following simple case.

We suppose that the regression consists of a constant and a trigonometric component of frequency $\lambda \neq 0$,

$$y_t = \gamma_1 + \gamma_2 \cos t\lambda + x_t.$$

The least squares estimates are given by (see section 7.3)

$$c_L = \begin{pmatrix} c_1 \\ c_2 \end{pmatrix} = A \begin{pmatrix} \sum\limits_1^n y_t \\ \sum\limits_1^n \cos t\lambda \, y_t \end{pmatrix},$$

where

$$A = (\Phi^* \Phi)^{-1} = \begin{pmatrix} n & , & \sum\limits_1^n \cos t\lambda \\ \sum\limits_1^n \cos t\lambda, & & n \end{pmatrix}^{-1}$$

$$= \frac{1}{n} \begin{pmatrix} 1 + o(1), & o(1) \\ o(1), & 1 + o(1) \end{pmatrix}.$$

We have seen in section 7.5 that c_L is asymptotically efficient with variances of the order $1/n$. It follows then immediately from the asymptotic form of A that the estimate $m = (m_1, m_2)$ with

$$m_1 = \frac{1}{n} \sum_1^n y_t = \bar{y}$$

$$m_2 = \frac{1}{n} \sum_1^n \cos t\lambda \, y_t$$

is also asymptotically efficient with the covariances

$$\left. \begin{aligned} D^2[m_1] &\sim \frac{2\pi}{n} f(0) + o(n^{-1}) \\ D^2[m_2] &\sim \frac{4\pi}{n} f(\lambda) + o(n^{-1}) \\ \operatorname{cov}[m_1, m_2] &= o(n^{-1}). \end{aligned} \right\} \tag{1}$$

They are a bit easier to compute than c_L.

In any case m is asymptotically efficient and it seems reasonable to use it for the construction of confidence intervals. Assuming that the noise x_t is a linear process with a positive and continuous spectral density $f(\lambda)$ we know (see Moran [2]) that m is asymptotically normal with mean (γ_1, γ_2)

and covariances given by (1). Let us take a consistent estimate of the spectral density $f(\lambda)$ (see Chapter 4) say $f^*(\lambda)$. Then, on setting

$$\sqrt{n}\,\frac{m_1 - \gamma_1}{\sqrt{2\pi f^*(0)}} = z_1$$

$$\sqrt{n}\,\frac{m_2 - \gamma_2}{\sqrt{4\pi f^*(\lambda)}} = z_2$$

we know that for large samples z_1, z_2 are approximately normally distributed and independent with means zero and standard deviation one. We then have the two-dimensional confidence interval

$$m_1 - \alpha_1 \sqrt{\frac{2\pi f^*(0)}{n}} \leq \gamma_1 \leq m_1 + \alpha_1 \sqrt{\frac{2\pi f^*(0)}{n}}$$

$$m_2 - \alpha_2 \sqrt{\frac{4\pi f^*(\lambda)}{n}} \leq \gamma_2 \leq m_2 + \alpha_2 \sqrt{\frac{4\pi f^*(0)}{n}}$$

with a confidence coefficient $P = P_1 P_2$, where

$$\frac{1}{\sqrt{2\pi}} \int_{-a_j}^{a_j} e^{-\frac{z^2}{2}} dz = P_j, \quad j = 1, 2.$$

The above statement should of course be interpreted as a large sample relation.

The above can be extended in an obvious way to more general situations. While this method will serve as a reasonable first approximation it would be useful to have a careful examination of the range in which this approximation is valid. If one is interested in obtaining tests for linear hypotheses in time series analysis it is easy to see how such can be obtained by slightly modifying the above procedure.

CHAPTER 8

ASSORTED PROBLEMS

8.0. Introduction

Assorted problems that are of interest are discussed in this chapter. Some of the problems are clearly related to topics discussed in previous chapters. We felt it would be best to include them in a separate chapter as they could not be well motivated without the extended development given before. Other problems were included because they deserve discussion even though they are not related to topics discussed earlier. At times the discussion may be heuristic due to our inability to supply a rigorous proof; whenever this occurs it is clearly indicated. Such heuristic results are included whenever they are of sufficient interest. The problem of greatest interest is that of constructing the linear predictor for a stationary and purely nondeterministic process when the spectrum is not known but has to be estimated from the sample.

8.1. Prediction When the Conjectured Spectrum is Not the True One

We have seen in Chapter 2 how to construct the best linear predictor for a stationary and purely nondeterministic process, under the assumption that its spectral density is known. As the true spectrum is not known very often *a priori*, it is of considerable interest to see what happens when a predictor is computed on the basis of a conjectured spectral density $g(\lambda)$ when the true one is $f(\lambda)$. We know that the mean square error of the best linear predictor of x_1 given that $\ldots, x_{-2}, x_{-1}, x_0$ have been observed is

$$\sigma^2 = 2\pi \exp\left\{\frac{1}{2\pi} \int\limits_{-\pi}^{\pi} \log f(\lambda)\, d\lambda\right\} > 0.$$

If the spectrum is not known but is assumed to be

$$g(\lambda) \not\equiv f(\lambda), \quad \int\limits_{-\pi}^{\pi} |\log g(\lambda)|\, d\lambda < \infty,$$

prediction based on this assumption will of course not be as good as prediction making use of knowledge of the true spectrum. We can in fact write down explicitly the predictor which appears to be the best if $g(\lambda)$ is assumed to be the true spectral density. It is (see section 2.2)

$$x_1^* = \int_{-\pi}^{\pi} e^{i\lambda} \frac{c(e^{-i\lambda}) - c(0)}{c(e^{-i\lambda})} \, dz(\lambda), \tag{1}$$

where $z(\lambda)$ is the spectral process with orthogonal increments corresponding to x_t. The function $c(z)$ was defined in section 2.2 and we remind the reader of the relation

$$|c(e^{-i\lambda})|^2 = 2\pi g(\lambda).$$

Here $c(z)$ is constructed from $g(\lambda)$, not $f(\lambda)$. The function $c(e^{-i\lambda})$ should be interpreted as the boundary value of the function $c(z)$ at the unit circle in the complex plane as approached radially from within.

Another condition necessary to give integral (1) meaning is

$$\int_{-\pi}^{\pi} \frac{f(\lambda)}{g(\lambda)} \, d\lambda < \infty.$$

Then the integrand in (1) is quadratically integrable with respect to $f(\lambda)$ so that integral (1) is well defined as an element of $\mathcal{M}_\infty$. As the integrand is essentially a trigonometric series involving only the nonpositive powers of $e^{i\lambda}$, x_1^* belongs to $\mathcal{M}_0$.

The mean square error of prediction is then

$$E \, |x_1^* - x_1|^2 = \frac{|c(0)|^2}{2\pi} \int_{-\pi}^{\pi} \frac{f(\lambda)}{g(\lambda)} \, d\lambda$$

$$= \int_{-\pi}^{\pi} \frac{f(\lambda)}{g(\lambda)} \, d\lambda \, \exp\left\{ \frac{1}{2\pi} \int_{-\pi}^{\pi} \log g(\lambda) \, d\lambda \right\}$$

$$= \frac{1}{2\pi} \int_{-\pi}^{\pi} \frac{f(\lambda)}{g(\lambda)} \, d\lambda \, \exp\left\{ \frac{1}{2\pi} \int_{-\pi}^{\pi} \log \frac{g(\lambda)}{f(\lambda)} \, d\lambda \right\} \sigma^2. \tag{2}$$

The factor multiplying σ^2 is greater than or equal to one by Jensen's inequality. Equality is obtained if and only if $f(\lambda)$ and $g(\lambda)$ are such that

$$\frac{f(\lambda)}{g(\lambda)} = k \neq 0$$

almost everywhere.

8.2. Uniform Convergence of the Estimated Spectral Density to the True Spectral Density

Suppose that we use a spectrograph estimate $f_N^*(\lambda)$ as described in Chapter 4 to estimate the unknown spectral density $f(\lambda)$. We assume that the spectral density $f(\lambda)$ is positive and has a bounded second derivative. Let $f_N^*(\lambda)$ be a spectrograph estimate with positive weight function

$$w_N(x-\lambda) = \frac{1}{2\pi} \sum_{\nu=-N}^{N} w_\nu^{(N)} e^{i\nu(x-\lambda)}, \quad w_\nu^{(N)} = w_{-\nu}^{(N)}; \quad \int_{-\pi}^{\pi} w_N(x-\lambda)\, dx \equiv 1.$$

The mass of the weight function must concentrate in the neighborhood of λ as $N \to \infty$ to ensure consistency of the estimate, but it should not do this too fast. We therefore assume that

$$\sum_{|\nu| \leq N} |w_\nu^{(N)}| = o(\sqrt{N}). \tag{1}$$

The observed process is supposed to be linear.

Under these assumptions we will show that $f_N^*(\lambda)$ converges in probability to $f(\lambda)$ uniformly in λ. In fact

$$2\pi[f(\lambda) - f_N^*(\lambda)] = \sum_{|\nu| \leq N} r_\nu(1 - w_\nu^{(N)}) e^{i\nu\lambda} + \sum_{|\nu| > N} r_\nu e^{i\nu\lambda} + \sum_{|\nu| \leq N} (r_\nu - r_\nu^*) e^{i\nu\lambda} w_\nu^{(N)}$$

$$= S_1 + S_2 + S_3,$$

where $r_\nu^* = C_\nu/N$. But

$$|S_1| \leq \sum_{|\nu| \leq N} |r_\nu| |1 - w_\nu^{(N)}|.$$

As $\sum_{-\infty}^{\infty} |r_\nu| < \infty$ $(r_\nu = 0(\nu^{-2})$ since $f''(\lambda)$ is bounded) and for each fixed ν $w_\nu^{(N)} \to 1$ with increasing sample size, it follows that

$$\lim_{N \to \infty} \max_{\lambda} |S_1| = 0.$$

It is also clear that

$$|S_2| \leq \sum_{|\nu| > N} |r_\nu| = 0(N^{-1})$$

so that

$$\lim_{N \to \infty} \max_{\lambda} |S_2| = 0.$$

The third sum which contains the random part can be shown to be uniformly small with great probability. We have

$$E \max_{\lambda} |S_3| \leq \sum_{|\nu| \leq N} |w_\nu^{(N)}| \, E \, |r_\nu^* - r_\nu|.$$

But for a process of the type considered one can show that

$$\text{Var} \, (r_\nu^*) \leq \frac{A}{N},$$

where the constant A is independent of ν. Hence

$$E \, |r_\nu^* - r_\nu| \leq E \, \left| r_\nu^* - \frac{N - |\nu|}{N} \, r_\nu \right| + \left| r_\nu \frac{\nu}{N} \right| \leq \sqrt{\frac{A}{N}} + \left| r_\nu \frac{\nu}{N} \right|$$

so that

$$E \max_{\lambda} |S_3| \leq \sqrt{\frac{A}{N}} \sum_{|\nu| \leq N} |w_\nu^{(N)}| + \sum_{|\nu| \leq N} \frac{|w_\nu^{(N)}|}{(1 + |\nu|) \, N} = o \, (1).$$

Thus, given any $\varepsilon > 0$

$$P \, \{\max_{\lambda} |f_N^*(\lambda) - f(\lambda)| < \varepsilon\} \to 1$$

as $N \to \infty$ so that $f_N^*(\lambda)$ converges in probability to $f(\lambda)$ uniformly in λ as $N \to \infty$.

8.3. The Asymptotic Distribution of an Integral of a Spectrograph Estimate

Consider the statistic

$$\int_{-\pi}^{\pi} f_N^*(\lambda) \, dg \, (\lambda) = \iint_{-\pi}^{\pi} I_N(l) \, w_N(\lambda - l) \, dl \, dg \, (\lambda), \tag{1}$$

where $dg \, (\lambda) = dg \, (-\lambda)$ and $\int_{-\pi}^{\pi} |dg \, (\lambda)| < \infty$. Let the observed process x_t be normal. We also assume that

$$w_\nu^{(N)} = 0 \quad \text{when} \quad |\nu| > [N^\alpha] \tag{2}$$

for some α, $\frac{1}{2} < \alpha < 1$, and that given any $\varepsilon > 0$

$$|w_N(x - \lambda)| \to 0$$

uniformly as $N \to \infty$ when $|x - \lambda| > \varepsilon$. The asymptotic distribution of (1) as $N \to \infty$ will be obtained under these assumptions.

Consider
$$\int\int\limits_{-\pi}^{\pi} 2\,\pi\,f(l)\,I_{N,\xi}(l)\,w_N(\lambda-l)\,dl\,dg(\lambda) \tag{3}$$

as an approximation to (1). The difference between (1) and (3) is

$$\frac{1}{2\,\pi\,N}\sum_{r,s=-\infty}^{\infty} a_r\,a_s\,d_{rs},$$

where

$$d_{rs}=\sum_{n,m=1}^{N}\xi_{n-r}\,\xi_{m-s}\,w_{n-m}^{(N)}\,g_{n-m}-\sum_{\substack{n=1+r,\,N+r\\m=1+s,\,N+s}}\xi_{n-r}\,\xi_{m-s}\,w_{n-m}^{(N)}\,g_{n-m}$$

and $g_\nu=\int\limits_{-\pi}^{\pi} e^{i\nu\lambda}\,dg(\lambda)$. Now $E\,|d_{rs}|\le 2\,(|r|+|s|)\sum|w_p^{(N)}|\,|g_p|$ so that

$$E\left|\frac{1}{2\,\pi\,N}\sum_{r,s=-\infty}^{\infty} a_r\,a_s\,d_{rs}\right|\le\frac{1}{\pi\,N}\sum_{r,s}(|r|+|s|)\,|a_r|\,|a_s|\sum_p|w_p^{(N)}|\,|g_p|=o\left(\frac{1}{\sqrt{N}}\right).$$

Indeed, since $|f''(\lambda)|$ is bounded, the sequence $|g_p|$ is uniformly bounded and (8.2.1) holds. The difference between (1) and (3) is then $o\,(1/\sqrt{N})$ with probability close to one; this is negligible as we shall see. Let us now consider the approximation (3) which can be written

$$\frac{1}{2\,\pi}\sum_{\nu=-N}^{N}\left(\sum_{j=-N}^{N} r_{\nu-j}\right)w_\nu^{(N)}\,g_\nu=\frac{1}{2\,\pi}\sum_{j=-N}^{N}\frac{c_j}{N}\sum_{\nu=-N}^{N} r_{\nu-j}\,w_\nu^{(N)}\,g_\nu. \tag{4}$$

The variance of (4) is

$$\frac{1}{\pi^2}\frac{1}{N}\sum_{j=0}^{N}{}'\frac{N-j}{N}\left(\sum_{\nu=-N}^{N} r_{\nu-j}\,w_\nu^{(N)}\,g_\nu\right)^2,$$

where the primed summation indicates that the coefficient for $j=0$ is half that for $j\ne 0$. Because of (2) it follows that

$$\left|\sum_{\nu=-N}^{N} r_{\nu-j}\,w_\nu^{(N)}\,g_\nu\right|\le K\sum_{\nu=-[N^\alpha]}^{[N^\alpha]}|r_{\nu-j}|\le K'\frac{1}{|j|}$$

if $|j|>[N^\beta]$, $1>\beta>\alpha$, But then

$$\frac{1}{N}\sum_{j>[N^\beta]}^{N}\frac{N-j}{N}\left(\sum_{\nu=-N}^{N} r_{\nu-j}\,w_\nu^{(N)}\,g_\nu\right)^2\le\frac{K'}{N^{1+\beta}}$$

so that

$$\frac{1}{\pi} \sum_{j > [N^\beta]} \frac{c_j}{N} \left(\sum_{\nu = -N}^{N} r_{\nu - j} \, w_\nu^{(N)} \, g_\nu \right) = o\left(\frac{1}{\sqrt{N}} \right)$$

in probability as $N \to \infty$ which is negligible. It is therefore enough to consider

$$\frac{1}{\pi} \sum_{j=0}^{[N^\beta]} \frac{c_j}{N} h_j,$$

where

$$h_j = \sum_{\nu = -N}^{N} r_{\nu - j} \, w_\nu^{(N)} \, g_\nu.$$

Note that

$$\frac{1}{2\pi} h_0 = \int\limits_{-\pi}^{\pi} \int f(l) \, w_N(\lambda - l) \, dl \, dg(\lambda) \to \int\limits_{0}^{\pi} f(\lambda) \, dg(\lambda) \neq 0$$

as $N \to \infty$ so that

$$\sum_{|j| \le [N^\beta]} h_j^2 \sim \sum_{j = -N}^{N} h_j^2$$

as $N \to \infty$. Now

$$\frac{1}{\pi} \sum_{j=0}^{[N^\beta]} \frac{c_j}{N} h_j - \frac{1}{2\pi} h_0$$

$$= \frac{1}{2\pi} \sum_{\nu=1}^{N} \frac{\xi_\nu^2 - 1}{N} h_0 + \frac{1}{\pi} \sum_{j=1}^{[N^\beta]} \sum_{\nu=1}^{N-j} \frac{\xi_\nu \, \xi_{\nu+j}}{N} h_j$$

$$= \left\{ \frac{1}{2\pi} \sum_{\nu=1}^{N-[N^\beta]} \frac{\xi_\nu^2 - 1}{N} h_0 + \sum_{\nu=1}^{N-[N^\beta]} \sum_{j=1}^{[N^\beta]} \frac{\xi_\nu \, \xi_{\nu+j}}{N} h_j \right\} +$$

$$+ \left\{ \frac{1}{2\pi} \sum_{\nu = N-[N^\beta]+1}^{N} \frac{\xi_\nu^2 - 1}{N} h_0 + \frac{1}{\pi} \sum_{\nu = N-[N^\beta]+1}^{N} \sum_{j=1}^{N-\nu} \frac{\xi_\nu \, \xi_{\nu+j}}{N} h_j \right\}.$$

The variance of the second bracketed term is less than

$$\frac{N^\beta}{N^2} \sum_{-N}^{N} h_j^2 = o\left(\frac{1}{N} \sum_{-N}^{N} h_j^2 \right).$$

It will therefore be enough to consider the first bracketed term which will be shown to be asymptotically normal with mean zero and variance $\dfrac{1}{2\pi^2} \sum\limits_{j=-N}^{N} h_j^2$. In dealing with this term consider blocks in ν of length $[N^\gamma]$, $1 > \gamma > \beta$, separated by blocks of length $[N^\beta]$. There will

265

be roughly $N^{1-\gamma}$ blocks of each kind. The blocks of length N^γ are independent of each other since they are separated from each other by blocks of length N^β. The variance of a block of length N^γ is asymptotically the same as

$$\frac{1}{2\,\pi^2}\,N^{\gamma-1}\sum_{-N}^{N}h_j^2.$$

Adding over all blocks of length N^γ we have

$$\frac{1}{2\,\pi^2}\,\frac{1}{N}\sum_{-N}^{N}h_j^2.$$

Since the blocks are independent, it is clear that the sum of the blocks is asymptotically normal with mean zero and variance

$$\frac{1}{2\,\pi^2}\,\frac{1}{N}\sum_{-N}^{N}h_j^2.$$

The sum of the blocks of length N^β which have been left out has a variance asymptotically the same as

$$\frac{1}{2\,\pi^2}\,N^{\beta-\gamma-1}\sum_{-N}^{N}h_j^2=o\left(\frac{1}{N}\sum_{-N}^{N}h_j^2\right)$$

so that it can be neglected. All the approximations made can now be seen to have been justified. It is now clear that

$$\int_{-\pi}^{\pi}f_N^*(\lambda)\,dg(\lambda)$$

is asymptotically normally distributed with mean

$$\int\!\!\int_{-\pi}^{\pi.}f(l)\,w_N(\lambda-l)\,dl\,dg(\lambda)$$

and variance

$$\frac{1}{2\,\pi^2}\,\frac{1}{N}\sum_{-N}^{N}h_j^2=\frac{2\,\pi}{N}\int_{-\pi}^{\pi}f^2(l)\left(\int_{-\pi}^{\pi}w_N(l-\lambda)\,dg(\lambda)\right)^2dl.$$

A case of particular interest is that in which $g(\lambda)$ is a jump function with jump α_j at λ_j where $0<\lambda_1<\cdots<\lambda_k<\pi$. Then

$$\int_{-\pi}^{\pi}f_N^*(\lambda)\,dg(\lambda)=\sum_{j=1}^{k}\alpha_j f_N^*(\lambda_j).$$

Our result then implies that $f_N^*(\lambda_j)$, $j=1, \ldots, k$, are asymptotically normally distributed and independent with means

$$\int_{-\pi}^{\pi} w_N(\lambda_j - l) f(l) \, dl, \quad j=1, \ldots, k$$

and variances

$$\frac{2\pi}{N} f^2(\lambda_j) \int_{-\pi}^{\pi} w_N^2(x) \, dx, \quad j=1, \ldots, k.$$

This result still holds and can be proved in essentially the same way when x_t is a linear process such that

$$\sum r^2 a_r < \infty.$$

If x_t is normal it can be seen that any linear form in x_t, and $f_N^*(\lambda_1), \ldots,$ $f_N^*(\lambda_k)$ are asymptotically normal and independent. This is clearly useful in connection with statistical problems of well-known type. Thus $z(\lambda_j)$, $f_N^*(\lambda_j)$, $j=1, \ldots, k$, are asymptotically independent. It then seems plausible that the two processes $z(\lambda)$ and $f_N^*(\lambda)$ are asymptotically independent. This has not been proven but seems to be indicated by the reasoning above.

We shall discuss the mean square error of prediction when the spectrum is estimated in the next section. The computation will be carried out in a heuristic manner, as if there were independence between $z(\lambda)$ and $f_N^*(\lambda)$ for finite sample size.

8.4. The Mean Square Error of Prediction when the Spectrum is Estimated

The mean square error of prediction is computed heuristically when the observed process is normal and the spectrum is estimated. The weight function of the estimate is positive so that we have a positive estimate of the spectrum. The error of prediction is

$$E\,|x_1^* - x_1|^2 = E\left|\int_{-\pi}^{\pi} \frac{e^{i\lambda} c(0)}{c(e^{-i\lambda})} dz(\lambda)\right|^2.$$

The function $c(z)$ is a functional of $f_N^*(\lambda)$, the estimated spectral density. Moreover

$$E\,|dz(\lambda)|^2 = f(\lambda)d\lambda.$$

We have already noted that it seems plausible that $f_N^*(\lambda)$, $z(\lambda)$ are asymptotically independent as $N \to \infty$. We shall assume that the approximation is good if we carry out the computation as if $z(\lambda), f_N^*(\lambda)$ are independent for finite N and thus consider

267

$$\int_{-\pi}^{\pi} E \left| \frac{c\,(0)}{c\,(e^{-i\lambda})} \right|^2 f\,(\lambda)\, d\lambda.$$

Let us now mention that there is one situation where this assumption is automatically fulfilled, viz. when $f^*(\lambda)$ is obtained from a realization of the process x_t that is independent of the realization used for prediction. Of course, this case is of considerable practical interest.

Now

$$\left| \frac{c\,(0)}{c\,(e^{-i\lambda})} \right|^2 = \exp\left\{ \frac{1}{2\,\pi} \int_{-\pi}^{\pi} \log f_N^*\,(\lambda)\, d\lambda \right\} \Big/ f_N^*\,(\lambda).$$

We use the fact that

$$\max_{\lambda} \left| f_N^*\,(\lambda) - f\,(\lambda) \right| \to 0$$

as $N \to \infty$ in probability and make several approximations. We are interested in the expected value of

$$\exp\left\{ \frac{1}{2\,\pi} \int_{-\pi}^{\pi} \log f_N^*\,(\lambda)\, d\lambda \right\} \int_{-\pi}^{\pi} \frac{f\,(\lambda)}{f_N^*\,(\lambda)}\, d\lambda$$

$$= \sigma^2 \exp\left\{ \frac{1}{2\,\pi} \int_{-\pi}^{\pi} \log \frac{f_N^*\,(\lambda)}{f\,(\lambda)}\, d\lambda \right\} \frac{1}{2\,\pi} \int_{-\pi}^{\pi} \frac{f\,(\lambda)}{f_N^*\,(\lambda)}\, d\lambda. \tag{1}$$

This amounts to replacing $g\,(\lambda)$ by $f_N^*\,(\lambda)$ in (8.1.2) and taking the mean value of the resultant expression. Let

$$h\,(\lambda) = \frac{f\,(\lambda) - f_N^*\,(\lambda)}{f\,(\lambda)}.$$

The second factor of (1) can be written in terms of h as

$$\frac{1}{2\,\pi} \int_{-\pi}^{\pi} \frac{d\lambda}{1 - h\,(\lambda)} \exp\left\{ \frac{1}{2\,\pi} \int_{-\pi}^{\pi} \log\,(1 - h\,(\lambda))\, d\lambda \right\}$$

$$= \frac{1}{2\,\pi} \left[2\,\pi + \int_{-\pi}^{\pi} h\,(\lambda)\, d\lambda + \int_{-\pi}^{\pi} h^2\,(\lambda)\, d\lambda + 0\left(\int_{-\pi}^{\pi} |h\,(\lambda)|^3\, d\lambda \right) \right] \times$$

$$\times \left[\exp \frac{1}{2\,\pi} \left\{ -\int_{-\pi}^{\pi} h\,(\lambda)\, d\lambda - \tfrac{1}{2} \int_{-\pi}^{\pi} h^2\,(\lambda)\, d\lambda + 0\left(\int_{-\pi}^{\pi} |h\,(\lambda)|^3\, d\lambda \right) \right\} \right]$$

$$= \frac{1}{2\pi} \left[2\pi + \int_{-\pi}^{\pi} h(\lambda)\, d\lambda + \int_{-\pi}^{\pi} h^2(\lambda)\, d\lambda + 0\left(\int_{-\pi}^{\pi} |h(\lambda)|^3\, d\lambda \right) \right] \times$$

$$\times \left[1 - \frac{1}{2\pi} \int_{-\pi}^{\pi} h(\lambda)\, d\lambda - \int_{-\pi}^{\pi} h^2(\lambda)\, d\lambda + \frac{1}{8\pi^2}\left(\int_{-\pi}^{\pi} h(\lambda)\, d\lambda \right)^2 + R_1 \right]$$

$$= 1 + \frac{1}{4\pi} \int_{-\pi}^{\pi} h^2(\lambda)\, d\lambda - \frac{1}{8\pi^2}\left(\int_{-\pi}^{\pi} h(\lambda)\, d\lambda \right)^2 + R_2, \tag{2}$$

where $|R_2|$ is less than a finite number of terms of the form

$$\left| \int_{-\pi}^{\pi} h(\lambda)\, d\lambda \right| \int_{-\pi}^{\pi} h^2(\lambda)\, d\lambda, \quad \int_{-\pi}^{\pi} |h(\lambda)|^3\, d\lambda, \text{ etc.}$$

Since $f_N^*(\lambda)$ converges uniformly to $f(\lambda)$ in probability, it follows that $|R_2|$ is much smaller than the second term of (2) with great probability. We shall assume that $E|R_2|$ is much smaller than the expected value of the second term of (2) as $N \to \infty$.

Let

$$b_N(x) = E f_N^*(x) - f(x)$$

so that

$$h(x) = \frac{E f_N^*(x) - f_N^*(x) - b_N(x)}{f(x)}.$$

Then

$$E \int_{-\pi}^{\pi} h^2(x)\, dx = \int_{-\pi}^{\pi} \frac{b_N^2(x)}{f^2(x)}\, dx + \int_{-\pi}^{\pi} \frac{E\,(E f_N^*(x) - f_N^*(x))^2}{f^2(x)}\, dx$$

$$\sim \int_{-\pi}^{\pi} \frac{b_N^2(x)}{f^2(x)}\, dx + \frac{4\pi^2}{N} \int_{-\pi}^{\pi} w_N^2(x)\, dx$$

while

$$E\left(\int_{-\pi}^{\pi} h(x)\, dx \right)^2 = \left(\int_{-\pi}^{\pi} \frac{b_N(x)}{f(x)}\, dx \right)^2 + E\left(\int_{-\pi}^{\pi} \frac{E f_N^*(x) - f_N^*(x)}{f(x)}\, dx \right)^2$$

$$\sim \left(\int_{-\pi}^{\pi} \frac{b_N(x)}{f(x)}\, dx \right)^2 + \frac{2\pi}{N} \int_{-\pi}^{\pi} f^2(x)\left(\int_{-\pi}^{\pi} w_N(x-\lambda) \frac{1}{f(\lambda)}\, d\lambda \right)^2 dx$$

$$\sim \left(\int_{-\pi}^{\pi} \frac{b_N(x)}{f(x)}\, dx \right)^2 + \frac{4\pi^2}{N}.$$

Under the assumptions we have made the error of prediction is given by

$$\sigma^2 \left[1 + \frac{1}{4\pi} \int\limits_{-\pi}^{\pi} \left(\frac{b_N(x)}{f(x)} \right)^2 dx + \frac{\pi}{N} \int\limits_{-\pi}^{\pi} w_N^2(x) \, dx - \frac{1}{8\pi^2} \left(\int\limits_{-\pi}^{\pi} \frac{b_N(x)}{f(x)} dx \right)^2 \right]$$

up to terms of smaller order. If this argument could be made rigorous, the result would be useful for deciding which spectrograph estimate to use when constructing optimal predictors.

8.5. Other Types of Estimates of the Spectrum

The estimated spectral density $f_N^*(\lambda)$ is a trigonometric polynomial in λ. In computing the corresponding linear predictor we run into practical difficulties. Unless the order of the polynomial is very low this computation will become quite tedious.

Instead one might start out from another class of estimates

$$f_N^*(\lambda) = \left| \sum_{\nu=0}^{p} g_\nu^{(N)} e^{i\nu\lambda} \right|^{-2} = |g(e^{i\lambda})|^{-2},$$

where the coefficients $g_\nu^{(N)}$ of $g(e^{i\lambda})$ depend on the observations. $f_N^*(\lambda)$ can be considered as the spectral density of an autoregressive scheme. Such a process would satisfy the equation

$$\sum_{\nu=0}^{p} g_\nu^{(N)} x_{t-\nu} = \eta_t,$$

where η_t is an orthogonal process. The best predictor would be given by

$$x_1^* = -\frac{1}{g_0^{(N)}} \sum_{\nu=1}^{p} g_\nu^{(N)} x_{1-\nu}.$$

If $f_N^*(\lambda)$ is to be used mainly for prediction, this class of estimates would seem to be adequate.

At present almost nothing is known about the properties of such estimates. One could ask whether the estimate obtained by the application of least squares

$$\sum_{t=p-1}^{N} (x_t - g, \, x_{t-1} - \cdots - g_p \, x_{t-p})^2 = \text{minimum}$$

would be a good estimate and how p should be chosen in a given situation. At present we cannot consider such questions and still less the analogue of

$$= \frac{1}{2\pi} \left[2\pi + \int_{-\pi}^{\pi} h(\lambda)\, d\lambda + \int_{-\pi}^{\pi} h^2(\lambda)\, d\lambda + 0\left(\int_{-\pi}^{\pi} |h(\lambda)|^3\, d\lambda \right) \right] \times$$

$$\times \left[1 - \frac{1}{2\pi} \int_{-\pi}^{\pi} h(\lambda)\, d\lambda - \int_{-\pi}^{\pi} h^2(\lambda)\, d\lambda + \frac{1}{8\pi^2}\left(\int_{-\pi}^{\pi} h(\lambda)\, d\lambda \right)^2 + R_1 \right]$$

$$= 1 + \frac{1}{4\pi} \int_{-\pi}^{\pi} h^2(\lambda)\, d\lambda - \frac{1}{8\pi^2}\left(\int_{-\pi}^{\pi} h(\lambda)\, d\lambda \right)^2 + R_2, \tag{2}$$

where $|R_2|$ is less than a finite number of terms of the form

$$\left| \int_{-\pi}^{\pi} h(\lambda)\, d\lambda \right| \int_{-\pi}^{\pi} h^2(\lambda)\, d\lambda, \quad \int_{-\pi}^{\pi} |h(\lambda)|^3\, d\lambda, \text{ etc.}$$

Since $f_N^*(\lambda)$ converges uniformly to $f(\lambda)$ in probability, it follows that $|R_2|$ is much smaller than the second term of (2) with great probability. We shall assume that $E|R_2|$ is much smaller than the expected value of the second term of (2) as $N \to \infty$.

Let $$b_N(x) = E f_N^*(x) - f(x)$$

so that $$h(x) = \frac{E f_N^*(x) - f_N^*(x) - b_N(x)}{f(x)}.$$

Then

$$E \int_{-\pi}^{\pi} h^2(x)\, dx = \int_{-\pi}^{\pi} \frac{b_N^2(x)}{f^2(x)}\, dx + \int_{-\pi}^{\pi} \frac{E\,(E f_N^*(x) - f_N^*(x))^2}{f^2(x)}\, dx$$

$$\sim \int_{-\pi}^{\pi} \frac{b_N^2(x)}{f^2(x)}\, dx + \frac{4\pi^2}{N} \int_{-\pi}^{\pi} w_N^2(x)\, dx$$

while

$$E\left(\int_{-\pi}^{\pi} h(x)\, dx \right)^2 = \left(\int_{-\pi}^{\pi} \frac{b_N(x)}{f(x)}\, dx \right)^2 + E\left(\int_{-\pi}^{\pi} \frac{E f_N^*(x) - f_N^*(x)}{f(x)}\, dx \right)^2$$

$$\sim \left(\int_{-\pi}^{\pi} \frac{b_N(x)}{f(x)}\, dx \right)^2 + \frac{2\pi}{N} \int_{-\pi}^{\pi} f^2(x)\left(\int_{-\pi}^{\pi} w_N(x-\lambda)\frac{1}{f(\lambda)}\, d\lambda \right)^2 dx$$

$$\sim \left(\int_{-\pi}^{\pi} \frac{b_N(x)}{f(x)}\, dx \right)^2 + \frac{4\pi^2}{N}.$$

269

Under the assumptions we have made the error of prediction is given by

$$\sigma^2 \left[1 + \frac{1}{4\pi} \int\limits_{-\pi}^{\pi} \left(\frac{b_N(x)}{f(x)} \right)^2 dx + \frac{\pi}{N} \int\limits_{-\pi}^{\pi} w_N^2(x)\, dx - \frac{1}{8\pi^2} \left(\int\limits_{-\pi}^{\pi} \frac{b_N(x)}{f(x)}\, dx \right)^2 \right]$$

up to terms of smaller order. If this argument could be made rigorous, the result would be useful for deciding which spectrograph estimate to use when constructing optimal predictors.

8.5. Other Types of Estimates of the Spectrum

The estimated spectral density $f_N^*(\lambda)$ is a trigonometric polynomial in λ. In computing the corresponding linear predictor we run into practical difficulties. Unless the order of the polynomial is very low this computation will become quite tedious.

Instead one might start out from another class of estimates

$$f_N^*(\lambda) = \left| \sum_{\nu=0}^{p} g_\nu^{(N)} e^{i\nu\lambda} \right|^{-2} = | g(e^{i\lambda}) |^{-2},$$

where the coefficients $g_\nu^{(N)}$ of $g(e^{i\lambda})$ depend on the observations. $f_N^*(\lambda)$ can be considered as the spectral density of an autoregressive scheme. Such a process would satisfy the equation

$$\sum_{\nu=0}^{p} g_\nu^{(N)} x_{t-\nu} = \eta_t,$$

where η_t is an orthogonal process. The best predictor would be given by

$$x_1^* = -\frac{1}{g_0^{(N)}} \sum_{\nu=1}^{p} g_\nu^{(N)} x_{1-\nu}.$$

If $f_N^*(\lambda)$ is to be used mainly for prediction, this class of estimates would seem to be adequate.

At present almost nothing is known about the properties of such estimates. One could ask whether the estimate obtained by the application of least squares

$$\sum_{t=p-1}^{N} (x_t - g, x_{t-1} - \cdots - g_p\, x_{t-p})^2 = \text{minimum}$$

would be a good estimate and how p should be chosen in a given situation. At present we cannot consider such questions and still less the analogue of

where $\sigma_1^2 = \int d F(\lambda)$, $\sigma_2^2 = \int \lambda^2 d F(\lambda)$ are the variances of $x(t)$ and $x'(t)$ respectively. But then

$$E(N_n) = \frac{b-a}{\pi} \left(\frac{\int \lambda^2 d F(\lambda)}{\int d F(\lambda)} \right)^{\frac{1}{2}}. \tag{2}$$

The maxima of $x(t)$ are zeros of $x'(t)$ where $x''(t) < 0$. Using a completely analogous argument we see that the mean number of maxima M_n of $x(t)$ in (a,b) is

$$E(M_n) = \frac{b-a}{2\pi} \left(\frac{\int \lambda^4 d F(\lambda)}{\int \lambda^2 d F(\lambda)} \right)^{\frac{1}{2}}. \tag{3}$$

One can derive higher order moments of these statistics by an analogous procedure. The moments, however, are quite complicated and do not seem to be related simply to the structure of the process. See Rice [1] for a discussion of the second moment of the number of zeros of the process $x(t)$. One would expect expressions (2) and (3) still to be valid when $F(\lambda)$ is of a more general form as long as the moments of $F(\lambda)$ involved are finite.

8.7. Prefiltering of a Time Series

We have discussed estimation of the spectrum in Chapters 4 and 6. Many of the results obtained in these chapters are asymptotic. The sample size N at which such asymptotic results are reasonable approximations depends on the variation of the spectrum. This is especially true when estimating the spectral density. Suppose that the spectral density is estimated at the point λ. If the spectral density changes rapidly in relative magnitude in the neighborhood of λ, one must expect a certain amount of contamination of the estimate of $f(\lambda)$ from the spectrum in the neighborhood of λ. This is serious when $f(\lambda)$ has a relative minimum at λ. Interest in estimating the minimum would be great in the following situation. Suppose that f is the spectrum of vertical wind velocity and that some part of a plane has the resonant frequency λ. It would then be essential to get a decent estimate of $f(\lambda)$ even though f has a minimum at λ. We have already made a few remarks on such contamination of estimates of the spectrum in section 6.12, the section on computations.

Assume that one does have some a priori information about f in the neighborhood of λ and suspects that the situation described above holds. Tukey suggests that if one wishes to improve one's estimate of $f(\lambda)$, one should prefilter the time series so as to smooth out the spectrum in the neighborhood of λ and estimate the spectral density of the filtered process.

8.7

Let us see what effect such prefiltering has on estimation of the spectral density and how it should most advantageously be set up. For simplicity, let us say that the weight function $w_N(x)$ is the weight function proposed by Tukey (see section 4.6). The bias of the estimate is then asymptotically proportional to $f''(\lambda)$.

Let $\varphi(\lambda)$ be the frequency characteristic of the filter. The spectral density of the filtered process is then

$$g(\lambda) = |\varphi(\lambda)|^2 f(\lambda).$$

Let the estimate of the spectral density of the filtered process be $g^*(\lambda)$. Then

$$f^*(\lambda) = g^*(\lambda)/|\varphi(\lambda)|^2$$

is the natural estimate of $f(\lambda)$. The variance of $f^*(\lambda)$ is asymptotically

$$\frac{4\pi g^2(\lambda)}{N|\varphi(\lambda)|^2} \int_{-\pi}^{\pi} w_N^2(x)\,dx = \frac{4\pi f^2(\lambda)}{N} \int_{-\pi}^{\pi} w_N^2(x)\,dx.$$

Note that the asymptotic variance of the estimate of $f(\lambda)$ is the same whether there has been prefiltering or not.

Let us now see whether the bias of the estimate is affected by prefiltering. The estimate $f^*(\lambda)$ has a bias asymptotically proportional to

$$\frac{(|\varphi(\lambda)|^2 f(\lambda))''}{|\varphi(\lambda)|^2} = f''(\lambda) + \frac{2(|\varphi(\lambda)|^2)'}{|\varphi(\lambda)|^2} f'(\lambda) + \frac{(|\varphi(\lambda)|^2)'' f(\lambda)}{|\varphi(\lambda)|^2}.$$

If there is a minimum of f at λ

$$f''(\lambda) > 0, \qquad f'(\lambda) = 0$$

and $f(\lambda)$ is small. The bias is then proportional to

$$f''(\lambda) + \frac{|\varphi(\lambda)|^2}{|\varphi(\lambda)|^2}{}'' f(\lambda). \tag{1}$$

Clearly we ought to choose $|\varphi(\lambda)|^2$ as the reciprocal of the f conjectured on a priori grounds. Since we feel that $f(\lambda)$ has a minimum at λ, $|\varphi(\lambda)|^2$ will have a maximum at λ and

$$(|\varphi(\lambda)|^2)'' < 0.$$

But then (1) is decreased in absolute value. The prefiltering does not affect the variance asymptotically but it does decrease the bias. We might say that this method amounts to pulling yourself up by the bootstraps.

274

8.8. Comments on Tests of Normality

Many of the statistical techniques available for the analysis of stationary time series have been designed for normal processes. Today one urgently needs new methods of analysis valid under more general conditions. Although some work in this direction has already been carried out, a determined effort is necessary to obtain generally useful results.

When applying a method constructed under the very common assumption of normality, one has to verify that this condition is satisfied. In certain cases it is possible to show that this is true approximately by using physical arguments. Otherwise one has to investigate this question empirically by analyzing samples drawn from the process studied. One way of formulating this problem is to say that we want to test the hypothesis that the sample has been obtained from a normal process. It may be that this is not the best way to formulate the problem, and the following discussion should be considered more a preliminary discussion rather than a recommendation of specific methods.

Let x_t, $0 < t < T$, be the observed sample. It is clear that somewhere in the construction of the statistic formed for the purpose of testing normality a non-linear element has to be inserted. A. J. F. Siegert [1] has suggested the following test.

Suppose that the mean m and covariance function $R(t)$ have been specified. Then we introduce the statistic

$$s^2(a) = [\theta(a) - \phi(a)]^2,$$

where $\theta(a)$ is the fraction of the time T that x_t is greater than a and $\phi(a) = E\,\theta(a)$. To test the normality assumption we can choose as a critical region

$$W = \{s^2(a) > c\}$$

or

$$W = \left\{ \int_{-\infty}^{\infty} s^2(a)\, G(a)\, da > c \right\},$$

where $G(a)$ is a suitably chosen weight function. Unfortunately the significance level corresponding to a given value of c is difficult to evaluate. This will become still more difficult in the important situation when m and $R(t)$ are not known a priori but have to be estimated from the sample.

Another possible approach is given by the following test which is described in a discrete parameter context. If the process is completely nondeterministic we know (see section 2.2) that it can be represented as

$$x_t = \sum_{\nu=0}^{\infty} a_\nu \, \xi_{t-\nu}.$$

If we demand that $\xi_t \in \mathfrak{M}_t$, the stochastic variables ξ_ν are determined by the x_t's and there is a linear inversion formula

$$\xi_t = \mathcal{L}(x_t, x_{t-1}, \ldots)$$

using all or some of the past values of the process. In practice when we have observed only a finite sample $x_1, x_2, \ldots, x_n$ the operator $\mathcal{L}$ will have to be replaced by a linear form $\mathcal{L}^*$ in these variables. This introduces an end-effect, which one hopes will be negligible for large values of n. On estimating the form of $\mathcal{L}^*$ from the sample and applying the inversion formula we obtain a sequence of stochastic variables ξ_t^*. If it can be shown that for a suitable choice of $\mathcal{L}^*$ the ξ_t^* deviate only slightly from the "true" values ξ_t, we could apply one of the standard tests of normality of sequences of independent stochastic variables. One could, for example, consider the stochastic variables

$$\xi_t^* = \frac{1}{\sqrt{2\pi}} \sum c_\nu^* \, x_{t-\nu},$$

where

$$c_\nu^* = \frac{1}{2\pi} \int_{-\pi}^{\pi} e^{i\nu\lambda} \frac{d\lambda}{\sqrt{f^*(\lambda)}},$$

and $f^*(\lambda)$ is an estimate of the spectral density. This seems reasonable since

$$c_\nu = \frac{1}{2\pi} \int_{-\pi}^{\pi} e^{i\nu\lambda} \frac{d\lambda}{\sqrt{f(\lambda)}} \quad \text{and} \quad \xi_t = \frac{1}{\sqrt{2\pi}} \sum c_\nu \, x_{t-\nu}$$

implies that

$$E \, \xi_s \, \xi_t = \frac{1}{2\pi} \sum_{\nu,\,\mu} c_\nu \, \bar{c}_\mu \, r_{s-t-\nu+\mu}$$

$$= \frac{1}{2\pi} \int_{-\pi}^{\pi} | \sum c_\nu \, e^{i\nu\lambda} |^2 \, e^{i(s-t)\lambda} f(\lambda) \, d\lambda$$

$$= \frac{1}{2\pi} \int_{-\pi}^{\pi} e^{i(s-t)\lambda} \, d\lambda = \delta_{st}.$$

The ξ_t are orthonormal stochastic variables, and hence independent and identically distributed under the normality assumption.

276

This has been a heuristic discussion of possible tests of normality. It would be interesting to investigate the conjectures made above in a rigorous manner. It would also be desirable to discuss in some detail the alternative hypotheses one has in mind when constructing these tests. A reasonable alternative hypothesis might be $e = E\xi_t - 3 \neq 0$.

PROBLEMS

Chapter 1

1. Let x_t, $Ex_t \equiv 0, t = \cdots, -1, 0, 1, \ldots$, be a weakly stationary process with spectral distribution function $F(\lambda)$. One often finds a statement saying that x_t has the representation

$$x_t = \int_{-\pi}^{\pi} e^{it\lambda} \, dZ(\lambda),$$

where $E\, dZ(\lambda)\overline{dZ(\mu)} = \delta_{\lambda\mu} d F(\lambda)$. Here $\delta_{\lambda\mu}$ is the Kronecker δ. How should one interpret the differential notation so as to make this a meaningful statement?

2. A real-valued weakly stationary process x_t, $t = \cdots, -1, 0, 1, \ldots$, $Ex_t \equiv 0$, has the complex representation given in the preceding example and the real representation

$$x_t = \int_0^{\pi} \cos t\lambda \, dZ_1(\lambda) + \int_0^{\pi} \sin t\lambda \, dZ_2(\lambda),$$

where $\qquad E\, dZ_i(\lambda) dZ_j(\mu) = \delta_{ij}\delta_{\lambda\mu} 2 d F(\lambda), \quad i,j = 1,2.$

Show that $dZ_1(\lambda) = 2 \operatorname{Re} d Z(\lambda)$, $dZ_2(\lambda) = -2 \operatorname{Im} d Z(\lambda)$.

3. Let x_t, $Ex_t \equiv 0$, $t \in [0, 2\pi]$ be weakly stationary on the unit circle. We understand by this that $t = 0$ is identified with $t = 2\pi$ and that

$$Ex_t \bar{x}_s = r_u \qquad u = t - s \bmod (2\pi).$$

Show that $\qquad r_t = \sum_{n=-\infty}^{\infty} a_n e^{itn},$

where the coefficients a_n are the Fourier coefficients of r_t and that

$$x_t = \sum_{n=-\infty}^{\infty} Z_n e^{itn},$$

where $EZ_n \bar{Z}_m = \delta_{nm} a_n$.

4. Let x_t, $Ex_t \equiv 0, t = \cdots, -1, 0, 1, \ldots$ be a strictly stationary normal process. Show that the process is ergodic if and only if the spectral distribution

278

function $F(\lambda)$ of x_t is continuous, that is, if and only if $F(\lambda)$ has no jumps (see Grenander [1] and Maruyama [1]).

5. Let x_t be a strictly stationary normal process just as in the previous example. A strictly stationary process is said to be mixing if for every two measurable sets A, B $P(A \cap T^n B) \to P(A)P(B)$ as $n \to \infty$. Here T is the one-step translation operator. Show that the normal process x_t is mixing if and only if $r_t \to 0$ as $|t| \to \infty$ (see Maruyama [1]).

6. Give an example of a normal strictly stationary process with a singular distribution function that is mixing.

7. Show that a strictly stationary process that is mixing is ergodic (see Hopf [1]).

8. Let $x_t = (x_t^{(1)}, x_t^{(2)})$, $E x_t \equiv 0, t = \cdots, -1, 0, 1, \ldots$ be a weakly stationary process with real-valued components. Since x_t has real-valued components, it follows that

$$d F_{ij}(\lambda) = \overline{d F_{ij}(-\lambda)}, \quad i, j = 1, 2.$$

Show that the process x_t has the real representation

$$x_t^{(1)} = \int_0^\pi \cos t\lambda \, d Z_1^{(1)}(\lambda) + \int_0^\pi \sin t\lambda \, d Z_2^{(1)}(\lambda)$$

$$x_t^{(2)} = \int_0^\pi \cos t\lambda \, d Z_1^{(2)}(\lambda) + \int_0^\pi \sin t\lambda \, d Z_2^{(2)}(\lambda),$$

where

$$E d Z_i^{(1)}(\lambda) d Z_j^{(1)}(\mu) = E d Z_i^{(2)}(\lambda) d Z_j^{(2)}(\mu) = 2\delta_{ij}\delta_{\lambda\mu} d F_{ij}(\lambda)$$
$$E d Z_i^{(1)}(\lambda) d Z_i^{(2)}(\mu) = 2\delta_{\lambda\mu} \operatorname{Re} d F_{12}(\lambda), \quad i, j = 1, 2,$$
$$E d Z_1^{(1)}(\lambda) d Z_2^{(2)}(\mu) = - E d Z_2^{(1)}(\lambda) d Z_1^{(2)}(\mu) = 2\delta_{\lambda\mu} \operatorname{Im} d F_{12}(\lambda).$$

If the process has an absolutely continuous spectral distribution function, the real and imaginary parts of the cross-spectral density $\operatorname{Re} f_{12}(\lambda)$, $\operatorname{Im} f_{12}(\lambda)$ are sometimes referred to as the cospectrum and quadrature spectrum of $x_t^{(1)}$ and $x_t^{(2)}$.

9. Show that a harmonizable process x_t with

$$F(\lambda, \mu) = \int_{-\pi}^\lambda \int_{-\pi}^\mu f(u, v) \, d u \, d v$$

279

absolutely continuous has covariances

$$r_{s,\,t} \to 0$$

as $|s| \to \infty$ or $|t| \to \infty$. What kind of a harmonizable process has $f(u,v) \equiv f$?

10. Let $x_n, n = \cdots, -1, 0, 1, \ldots$, be a family of independent and identically distributed stochastic variables with probability distribution $P\{x_n = \pm 1\} = \frac{1}{2}$. Let $y_n = f(x_n, x_{n+1})$, where $a = f(-1, -1)$, $b = f(-1, 1)$, $c = f(1, -1)$, $d = f(1, 1)$. Thus $y_n = a, b, c, d$ each with probability $1/4$. Find $\mathrm{cov}(y_j, y_k)$. For what values of a, b, c, d is the process y_n an example of "white noise" but not an example of "pure white noise"?

11. Let $x_t, E x_t \equiv 0, -\infty < t < \infty$, be a weakly stationary process. Let the spectrum of the process be band-limited to the band from $-\pi w$ to πw so that x_t has the representation

$$x_t = \int\limits_{-\pi w}^{\pi w} e^{it\lambda}\, dZ(\lambda).$$

Show that

$$x_t = \sum_{n=-\infty}^{\infty} x_{n/w} \frac{\sin \pi (wt - n)}{\pi (wt - n)}.$$

Chapter 2

1. Let $x_t, E x_t \equiv 0, t = \ldots, -1, 0, 1, \cdots$, be an autoregressive process with spectral density

$$f(\lambda) = \frac{1}{2\pi} |a(e^{-i\lambda})|^{-2},$$

where $a(z) = \sum_{k=0}^{p} a_k z^k$ has all its zeros $z_1, \ldots, z_p$ outside the unit circle $|z| \leq 1$. Assume that the roots z_i are simple. Find an explicit expression for the best linear predictor ν steps ahead in the sense of least squares in terms of the random variables x_t.

2. Assume that

$$x_t = \sum_{k=1}^{p} z^k e^{it\lambda_k},$$

$t = \cdots, -1, 0, 1, \ldots$, where $E z_i = 0$, $E z_i^2 < \infty$ and $0 \leq \lambda_i \leq \pi$. The λ_i are assumed to be known. Such a process is completely deterministic. If $x_1, \ldots,$

x_p have been observed, show that x_{p+1} is determined. Give an explicit expression for x_{p+1} in terms of $x_1, \ldots, x_p$.

3. Let x_t, $E x_t \equiv 0$, $-\infty < t < \infty$, be a weakly stationary process. Show that x_t is infinitely differentiable if

$$\int_{-\infty}^{\infty} e^{|\lambda t|}\, d F(\lambda) < \infty$$

for some $t \neq 0$, where $F(\lambda)$ is the spectral distribution function of x_t.

4 (*Continuation*). Show that the whole history of x_t can be predicted without any error if

$$\int_{-\infty}^{\infty} e^{|t\lambda|}\, d F(\lambda) < \infty$$

for some $t \neq 0$.

5 (*Continuation*). Give an explicit representation of the predictor that would verify the preceding statement.

6. In both the continuous and discrete parameter case, a weakly stationary process is completely deterministic if its spectrum is band limited. With a finite part of the past one can predict perfectly in the continuous parameter case. Verify that this is not generally true in the case of a discrete parameter process.

7. Let $y_t = x_t + m$, $t = \cdots, -1, 0, 1, \ldots$, $E y_t \equiv m$, where x_t is a weakly stationary process. The mean value m is assumed to be unknown. Find the one-step prediction error for the best linear unbiased (the mean value of the predictor is m) predictor.

8. Let x_t, $E x_t \equiv 0$, $t = \cdots, -1, 0, 1, \ldots$, be a strictly stationary Markov process with a finite number of states and transition probability matrix M. Assume that M has only simple eigenvalues. Find the spectrum of x_t in terms of the eigenvalues of M.

Chapter 3

1. Select a sequence of random numbers from a table of random numbers. Illustrate Slutzky's theorem by repeatedly applying a fixed smoothing operation to the sequence.

2. Consider the ratio $x' A x / x' x$ where $x = (x_1, x_2, \ldots, x_n)$ and the x_i's are normal, independent stochastic variables with mean zero and variance σ^2. Let

$$A = \begin{pmatrix} B & 0 & 0 \\ 0 & \lambda I & 0 \\ 0 & 0 & B \end{pmatrix},$$

where B is a real symmetric $k \times k$ matrix with distinct eigenvalues $\lambda_1 > \lambda_2 > \cdots > \lambda_k$ and $\lambda \leq \lambda_k$ or $\lambda \geq \lambda_1$. Here I is an identity matrix of order p. Find the probability distribution of the ratio $x' A x / x' x$ (see Durbin and Watson [1]).

3 (*Continuation*). What is the distribution of the ratio $x' A x / x' x$ if $p = 0$?

4 (*Continuation*). Find the exact probability distribution of

$$\sum_{\substack{j=1 \\ j \neq m}}^{n-1} x_j x_{j+1} \bigg/ \sum_{j=1}^{n} x_j^2, \quad n = 2\,m,$$

and

$$\sum_{\substack{j=1 \\ j \neq m,\, m+1}}^{n-1} x_j x_{j+1} \bigg/ \sum_{\substack{j=1 \\ j \neq m+1}}^{n} x_j^2, \quad n = 2\,m+1.$$

5. (*Continuation*). Find the exact distribution of

$$\sum_{\substack{j=1 \\ j \neq m}}^{n-1} (x_j - x_{j+1})^2 \bigg/ \sum_{j=1}^{n} (x_j - \bar{x})^2, \quad n = 2\,m,$$

and

$$\sum_{\substack{j=1 \\ j \neq m,\, m+1}}^{n-1} (x_j - x_{j+1})^2 \bigg/ \sum_{j=1}^{n} (x_j - \bar{x})^2, \quad n = 2\,m+1,$$

where

$$\bar{x} = \frac{1}{n} \sum_{j=1}^{n} x_j.$$

Chapter 4

1. Let (x_t, y_t), $E\,x_t = E\,y_t \equiv 0$, $t = \cdots, -1, 0, 1, \ldots,$ be a normally distributed stationary process with an absolutely continuous spectral distribution function. The spectral density, which is matrix-valued (2×2), is assumed to be nonsingular for all λ. The observations $(x_1, y_1), \ldots, (x_N, y_N)$ are made. Let

$$12r_\nu^* = \begin{cases} \dfrac{1}{N} \sum_{t=1}^{N-\nu} x_t\, y_{t+\nu} & \text{if } \nu \geq 0 \\[2mm] \dfrac{1}{N} \sum_{t=1+\nu}^{N} x_t\, y_{t+\nu} & \text{if } \nu < 0. \end{cases}$$

Show that

$$\operatorname{Re} {}_{12}f_N^*(\lambda) = \frac{1}{2\pi}\, {}_{12}r_0^*\, w_0^{(N)} + \frac{1}{\pi} \sum_{\nu=1}^{N} {}_{12}r_\nu^*\, w_\nu^{(N)} \cos \nu\lambda$$

and

$$\operatorname{Im} {}_{12}f_N^*(\lambda) = \frac{1}{\pi} \sum_{\nu=1}^{N} {}_{12}r_\nu^*\, w_\nu^{(N)} \sin \nu\lambda$$

are consistent estimates of the cospectrum $\operatorname{Re} f_{12}(\lambda)$ and the quadrature spectrum $\operatorname{Im} f_{12}(\lambda)$ respectively as $N \to \infty$ if

$$w_\nu^{(N)} \to 1$$

as $N \to \infty$ for every fixed ν and

$$\sum_{\nu=0}^{N} \frac{\nu}{N}\, w_\nu^{(N)^2} \Big/ \sum_{\nu=0}^{N} w_\nu^{(N)^2} \to 0$$

as $N \to \infty$ (see Grenander and Rosenblatt [6]).

2 (*Continuation*). Obtain an asymptotic expression for the variance of the estimate $\operatorname{Re} {}_{12}f^*_N(\lambda)$ of the cospectrum as $N \to \infty$.

3 (*Continuation*). Obtain an asymptotic expression for the variance of the estimate $\operatorname{Im} {}_{12}f^*_N(\lambda)$ of the quadrature spectrum as $N \to \infty$.

4 (*Continuation*). Obtain asymptotic expressions for the bias of the estimates of the cospectrum and quadrature spectrum as $N \to \infty$.

5. Let $x_{t,\tau}$, $E x_{t,\tau} \equiv 0$, $t, \tau = \cdots, -1, 0, 1, \ldots$, be a normally distributed stationary process. The process $x_{t,\tau}$ is assumed to have an absolutely continuous spectral distribution function and a continuous spectral density. The process is observed for $t, \tau = 1, \ldots, N$. The function

$$I_N(\lambda, \mu) = \frac{1}{4\pi^2 N^2} \left| \sum_{t,\tau=1}^{N} x_{t,\tau}\, e^{it\lambda + i\tau\mu} \right|^2$$

is a two-dimensional analogue of the periodogram. Obtain an asymptotic expression for the variance of $I_N(\lambda,\mu)$ as $N \to \infty$. Is $I_N(\lambda,\mu)$ asymptotically unbiased? See Grenander and Rosenblatt [6].

6 (*Continuation*) Let

$$r^*_{t,\tau} = \frac{1}{N^2} \sum_{\alpha,\beta} x_{\alpha,\beta}\, x_{\alpha+t,\,\beta+\tau}$$

and
$$f^*_N(\lambda,\mu) = \sum_{t,\tau=-N}^{N} r^*_{t,\tau}\, w^{(n)}_{t,\tau}\, e^{-it\lambda - i\tau\mu}.$$

Show that $f^*_N(\lambda,\mu)$ is a consistent estimate of the spectral density $f(\lambda,\mu)$ at $N\to\infty$ if

$$w^N_{t,\tau} \to 1$$

as $N\to\infty$ for every fixed t,τ and

$$\sum_{t,\tau=-N}^{N} \frac{|t\,\tau|}{N^2}\, w^{(N)^2}_{t,\tau} \Bigg/ \sum_{t,\tau=-N}^{N} w^{(N)^2}_{t,\tau} \to 0$$

as $N\to\infty$.

7 (*Continuation*). Obtain an asymptotic expression for the variance of $f^*_N(\lambda,\mu)$ as $N\to\infty$.

8. Let x_t, $E x_t \equiv 0$, $t = \cdots, -1,0,1,\ldots$ be a normal stationary process. Let $f^*_N(\lambda)$ be a spectrograph estimate of the spectral density $f(\lambda)$. Under the assumptions made in Chapter 4 on the spectrum and the weights $w^{(N)}_\nu$, obtain an asymptotic expression for

$$\int_{-\pi}^{\pi} E\,|f^*_N(\lambda) - f(\lambda)|^2\, d\lambda$$

9. Let x_t, $E x_t \equiv 0$, $-\infty < t < \infty$, be a weakly stationary process with an absolutely continuous spectral distribution function and a continuous spectral density. Assume that one wishes to estimate the spectral density function and that one has to discretize the data in order to carry out the computations. One can discretize the data by considering $y_k = x_{kn}$, $k = \cdots, -1, 0, 1, \ldots$, or else by looking at

$$y_k = \frac{1}{h} \int_{(k-\frac{1}{2})h}^{(k+\frac{1}{2})h} x_t\, dt, \quad k = \cdots, -1, 0, 1, \ldots.$$

Discuss the advantages and disadvantages of these two ways of discretizing the data.

10. Explain the discontinuity in the asymptotic expressions for the variance of spectrograph estimates of the spectral density at $\lambda = 0$.

11. What is the effect of observing a finite sample $x_1, \ldots, x_N$ on the resolving power of a spectrograph estimate of the spectral density?

Chapter 6

1. Let $x_t = \sum_{k=-\infty}^{\infty} a_{t-k}\,\xi_k$ where the ξ_k are independent and identically distributed and

$$E\xi_k = 0, \; E\xi_k^2 < \infty, \quad \Sigma a_k^2 < \infty.$$

The values $x_1, x_2, \ldots, x_N$ are observed. Consider the correlation coefficients r_ν^*/r_0^*, $\nu \neq 0$. Obtain asymptotic expressions for the covariances of the correlation coefficients (see Bartlett [3]).

2 (*Continuation*). Bartlett has suggested using $G_N^*(\lambda) = F_N^*(\lambda)/r_0^*$ as a statistic in estimating $G(\lambda) = F(\lambda)/r_0$, the normalized spectral distribution function. Find the asymptotic distribution of

$$\max_{0 \leq \lambda \leq \pi} \left| G_N^*(\lambda) - G(\lambda) \right|,$$

when x_t is pure white noise, as $N \to \infty$ (see Bartlett [3]).

3 (*Continuation*). Find an asymptotic expression for the covariance function of the process $G_N(\lambda)$, when x_t is a general linear scheme, as $N \to \infty$.

4. Let x_t, $E x_t \equiv 0$, $-\infty < t < \infty$, be an ergodic strictly stationary process. Assume that x_t has an absolutely continuous spectral distribution function with spectral density $f(\lambda)$, and that

$$\int_{-\infty}^{\infty} e^{|t\lambda|} f(\lambda)\, d\lambda < \infty$$

for some $t \neq 0$. Show that knowledge of any finite part of the record of the process x_t, $a < t < b$, is enough to determine the spectrum exactly.

Chapter 7

1. Let $y_t = x_t + m$, $E x_t \equiv 0$, $t = \cdots, -1, 0, 1, \ldots$, where x_t is a first order stationary autoregressive scheme. Assume that $y_1, \ldots, y_n$ are observed. Get exact expressions for the least squares and Markov estimates of m for finite sample size n.

2 (*Continuation*). Get exact expressions for the variances of the least squares and Markov estimates of m for finite sample size n. What is the magnitude of these variances for $n = 10, 15, 25$?

3. Let

$$y_t = \begin{pmatrix} {}_1y_t \\ {}_2y_t \end{pmatrix} = x_t + m_t = \begin{pmatrix} {}_1x_t \\ {}_2x_t \end{pmatrix} + \begin{pmatrix} {}_1m_t \\ {}_2m_t \end{pmatrix},$$

$E\,x_t \equiv 0$, $t = \cdots, -1, 0, 1, \ldots$, where x_t is a weakly stationary process with an absolutely continuous spectral distribution function and a continuous and nonsingular spectral density function. The components of x_t are real-valued. Assume that $y_1, \ldots, y_n$ are observed. Let ${}_1m_t \equiv m$, ${}_2m_t \equiv m$. Get asymptotic expressions for the variances of the least squares and Markov estimates of m as $n \to \infty$ and compare them (see Rosenblatt [1], [2]).

4 (*Continuation*). Let ${}_1m_t = m_1 \cos t\lambda$, ${}_2m_t = m_2 \cos t\lambda$. Get asymptotic expressions for the covariance matrices of the least squares and Markov estimates of (m_1, m_2) respectively as $n \to \infty$ and compare them.

5 (*Continuation*). Let ${}_1m_t = \alpha_1 \cos t\lambda + \beta_1 \sin t\lambda$, ${}_2m_t = \alpha_2 \cos t\lambda + \beta_2 \sin t\lambda$. Get asymptotic expressions for the covariance matrices of the least squares and Markov estimates of $(\alpha_1, \beta_1, \alpha_2, \beta_2)$ respectively as $n \to \infty$ and compare them.

6. Let $y_{t,\tau} = x_{t,\tau} + m$, $E\,y_{t,\tau} \equiv m$, $t, \tau = \cdots, -1, 0, 1, \ldots$, where $x_{t,\tau}$ is a weakly stationary process with an absolutely continuous spectral distribution function and a continuous spectral density. Assume that $y_{t,\tau}$, $t, \tau = 1, \ldots, n$, is observed. Get asymptotic expressions for the least squares and Markov estimates of m as $n \to \infty$ and compare them.

7. Let (x_t, y_t), $E\,x_t \equiv E\,y_t \equiv 0$, $t = \cdots, -1, 0, 1, \ldots$, be a normal process with an absolutely continuous spectral distribution function and a continuous nonsingular spectral density. Find the conditional spectral density of the process x_t, $t = \cdots, -1, 0, 1, \ldots$, under the condition that $y_t \equiv y$.

Chapter 8

1. Consider the asymptotic expression derived in Chapter 8 for the one-step prediction error when the spectral density has been estimated by a spectrograph estimate. Use this expression to evaluate the prediction error when the weight function of the spectrograph estimate is

$$w_n (\lambda) = \begin{cases} 1/2\, h_N & |\lambda| < h_N \\ 0 & \text{otherwise.} \end{cases}$$

How should one let h_N behave as a function of N so as to have the prediction error approach the limiting prediction error as $N \to \infty$ as fast as possible?

2. Let x_t, $E\,x_t \equiv 0$, $-\infty < t < \infty$, be a normal stationary process with continuously differentiable sample functions. Evaluate the probability of x_t passing through zero in the interval $(t, t + dt)$ with negative slope on condition that x_t passes through zero at $t = 0$ with positive slope. This probability can be used to get an approximation to the probability distribution of the distance t between zeros when t is small (see Rice [1]).

3. Let x_t, $E\,x_t \equiv 0$, $t = \cdots, -1, 0, 1, \ldots$ be a real-valued strictly stationary process. Consider the third order moments (which are assumed to exist)

$$r_{t_1 - t_2,\ t_1 - t_3} = r_{t_1, t_2, t_3} = E\,x_{t_1} x_{t_2} x_{t_3}.$$

Define a third order spectral distribution function in terms of these moments. What symmetry conditions on the moments and the third order spectrum are implied by the fact that x_t is real-valued? What happens to the third order spectrum when x_t is passed through a linear filter?

4 (*Continuation*). Consider the corresponding questions for the fourth order moments

$$r_{t_1 - t_2,\ t_1 - t_3,\ t_1 - t_4} = r_{t_1, t_2, t_3, t_4} = E\,x_{t_1} x_{t_2} x_{t_3} x_{t_4}.$$

5 (*Continuation*). What is the character of the third and fourth order spectra if x_t is a normal process?

APPENDIX ON COMPLEX VARIABLE THEORY

Let $f(z)$ be a function analytic in the unit circle $|z| < 1$. The mean value

$$\mu_\alpha (f;\, r) = \frac{1}{2\pi} \int\limits_0^{2\pi} |f(r\,e^{i\theta})|^\alpha d\theta, \quad \alpha > 0, \quad (r < 1)$$

according to a theorem of Hardy (see Hardy [1]) is a nondecreasing function of r. *The function $f(z)$ is said to belong to the class H_α if $\mu_\alpha(f;r)$ is bounded as $r \to 1 -$ and tends to a limit $\mu_\alpha(f)$.* The classes H_2 and especially H_1 will be of particular interest to us.

If $f(z) \in H_2$ then as $r \to 1 -$, $f(re^{i\theta})$ converges in the mean square to a limit function $f(e^{i\theta})$ of the class L^2. Since $f(z) \in H_2$

$$\lim_{r \to 1-} \mu_2 (f;\, r) = \lim_{r \to 1-} \sum_{n=0}^\infty |a_n|^2 r^{2n} = \sum_{n=0}^\infty |a_n|^2 < \infty,$$

where $f(z) = \sum\limits_{n=0}^\infty a_n z^n$. But then

$$\lim_{r',r \to 1-} \int_0^{2\pi} |f(r\,e^{i\theta}) - f(r'\, e^{i\theta})|^2 d\theta = \lim_{r',r \to 1-} \sum_{n=0}^\infty |a_n|^2 |r^n - r'^{\,n}|^2 \to 0$$

so that there is a limit in the mean square and it is easily seen that this limit is

$$f(e^{i\theta}) = \sum_{n=0}^\infty a_n e^{in\theta} \in L_2.$$

From the proof it can be seen that *$\mu_2(f;r)$ is a nondecreasing function of r.*

Write $f(z) = u(z) + iv(z)$, $f(e^{i\theta}) = u(e^{i\theta}) + iv(e^{i\theta})$, where u and v are real. Let $a_n = \alpha_n + i\beta_n$, where α_n, β_n are real. Then

$$u(r\,e^{i\theta}) = \sum_{n=0}^\infty r^n (\alpha_n \cos n\,\theta - \beta_n \sin n\,\theta)$$

so that

$$\alpha_n = \frac{1}{\pi} \int\limits_0^{2\pi} u(e^{i\theta}) \cos n\,\theta\, d\theta, \quad \beta_n = -\frac{1}{\pi} \int\limits_0^{2\pi} u(e^{i\theta}) \sin n\,\theta\, d\theta.$$

Thus

$$u(re^{i\theta}) = -\frac{1}{2\pi} \int_0^{2\pi} u(e^{i\phi})\,d\phi + \sum_{n=1}^{\infty} r^n \frac{1}{\pi} \int_0^{2\pi} u(e^{i\phi}) \cos n(\theta-\phi)\,d\phi$$

$$= \frac{1}{2\pi} \int_0^{2\pi} \frac{1-r^2}{1-2r\cos(\theta-\phi)+r^2} u(e^{i\phi})\,d\phi$$

holds for $r<1$. Similarly

$$v(re^{i\theta}) = \sum_{n=0}^{\infty} r^n \frac{1}{\pi} \int_0^{2\pi} u(e^{i\phi}) \sin n(\theta-\phi)\,d\phi$$

$$= \frac{1}{2\pi} \int_0^{2\pi} \frac{r\sin(\theta-\phi)}{1-2r\cos(\theta-\phi)+r^2} u(e^{i\phi})\,d\phi$$

holds for $r<1$. But then

$$f(re^{i\theta}) = u(re^{i\theta}) + iv(re^{i\theta})$$

$$= \frac{1}{2\pi} \int_0^{2\pi} \frac{e^{i\phi}+re^{i\theta}}{e^{i\phi}-re^{i\theta}} u(e^{i\phi})\,d\phi, \quad r<1.$$

Let $u(e^{i\phi}) \in L$. If

$$u(re^{i\theta}) = \frac{1}{2\pi} \int_0^{2\pi} \frac{1-r^2}{1-2r\cos(\theta-\phi)+r^2} u(e^{i\phi})\,d\phi$$

then $u(re^{i\theta}) \to u(e^{i\theta})$ as $r \to 1-$ almost everywhere.

Now

$$|u(re^{i\theta}) - u(e^{i\theta})| \leq \frac{1}{2\pi} \int_0^{2\pi} \frac{1-r^2}{1-2r\cos(\theta-\phi)+r^2} |u(e^{i\phi}) - u(e^{i\theta})|\,d\phi.$$

Clearly

$$\frac{1}{2\pi} \int_{|\phi-\theta|>\varepsilon} \{\ \}\,d\phi \to 0$$

as $r \to 1-$. But

$$\Phi(t) = \int_{|\phi-\theta|\leq t} |u(e^{i\phi}) - u(e^{i\theta})|\,d\phi = o(t)$$

289

as $t \to 0$ for almost all θ. Thus

$$\frac{1}{2\pi} \int_{|\phi-\theta|<1-r} \frac{1-r^2}{1-2r\cos(\theta-\phi)+r^2} |u(e^{i\phi})-u(e^{i\theta})| \, d\phi$$

$$\leq \frac{1}{2\pi} \frac{1+r}{1-r} \Phi(1-r) = o(1)$$

for almost all θ. Moreover

$$\frac{1}{2\pi} \int_{1-r\leq|\phi-\theta|\leq\varepsilon} \frac{1-r^2}{1-2r\cos(\theta-\phi)+r^2} |u(e^{i\phi})-u(e^{i\theta})| \, d\phi$$

$$= \frac{1}{2\pi} \frac{1-r^2}{1-2r\cos\varepsilon+r^2} \Phi(\varepsilon) - \frac{1}{2\pi} \frac{1-r^2}{1-2r\cos(1-r)+r^2} \Phi(1-r) +$$

$$+ \frac{1}{2\pi} \int_{(1-r)\leq|\phi-\theta|\leq\varepsilon} \frac{(1-r^2)2r\sin(\theta-\phi)}{(1-2r\cos(\theta-\phi)+r^2)^2} \Phi(|\theta-\phi|) \, d\phi$$

$$\leq \frac{1}{2\pi} \frac{1-r^2}{1-2r\cos\varepsilon+r^2} \Phi(\varepsilon) + (1-r)\cdot o\left(\int_{1-r\leq|\phi-\theta|\leq\varepsilon} \frac{d\phi}{(\theta-\phi)^2}\right)$$

$$= o(1)$$

for almost all θ.

If $f(z) \in H_2$ then $-if(re^{i\theta})$ is analytic in $|z|<1$ and belongs to H_2. But $v(re^{i\theta})$ is the real part of $-if(re^{i\theta})$ and thus converges to $v(e^{i\theta})$ in the mean square as $r \to 1-$. The Poisson formula then holds for $v(re^{i\theta})$ in terms of $v(e^{i\theta})$ and so $v(re^{i\theta}) \to v(e^{i\theta})$ as $r \to 1-$ almost everywhere. Thus, *if* $f(z) \in H_2$ *then* $f(re^{i\theta}) \to f(e^{i\theta})$ *as* $r \to 1-$ *for almost all* θ.

We now show that $\mu_1(f,r)$ *is a nondecreasing function of* r. Let $0 < r_1 < r_2 < 1$ and let $k(\theta)$ and $F(z)$ be defined by

$$k(\theta) f(r_1 e^{i\theta}) = |f(r_1 e^{i\theta})|, \quad 0 \leq \theta \leq 2\pi,$$

$$F(z) = \frac{1}{2\pi} \int_0^{2\pi} f(ze^{i\theta}) k(\theta) \, d\theta.$$

$F(z)$ is regular for $|z| \leq r_2$ and hence $|F(z)|$ attains its maximum in this circle on the boundary, say at $r_2 e^{i\lambda}$. Then

$$\mu_1(f;r_1) = F(r_1) \leq |F(r_2 e^{i\lambda})| \leq \mu_1(f;r_2).$$

We show that *every function* $f(z) \in H_1$ *has a decomposition into two factors* $f(z) = g(z)h(z)$, *where* $h(z)$ *is regular and bounded in* $|z|<1$, $|h(e^{i\theta})| \equiv 1$,

290

while $g(z) \in H_1$ *and never vanishes in* $|z| < 1$. This theorem holds for H_α in general and is due to F. Riesz, "Über die Randwerte einer analytischen Funktion", *Math. Zeit.*, vol. 18, pp. 87–95. If $f(z)$ does not vanish for $|z| < 1$, the representation is given by $g(z) = f(z)$, $h(z) = 1$. Let $\alpha_1, \alpha_2, \ldots$ be the zeros of $f(z)$ in $|z| < 1$ arranged in order of increasing absolute value. First assume $f(0) \neq 0$. Set

$$h_n(z) = \prod_{k=1}^{n} |\alpha_k| \frac{1 - \dfrac{z}{\alpha_k}}{1 - \bar{\alpha}_k z}, \quad g_n(z) = \frac{f(z)}{h_n(z)}.$$

$h_n(z)$ and $g_n(z)$ are regular in $|z| < 1$. On the circle $z = e^{i\theta}$, $|h(z)| = 1$ and for every n and for every positive ε

$$|h_n(r e^{i\theta})| > 1 - \varepsilon$$

as soon as r lies close enough to 1. Then

$$\mu_1(g_n; r) \le \frac{1}{(1-\varepsilon)} \mu_1(f; r) \le \frac{1}{(1-\varepsilon)} \mu_1^*(f)$$

if r lies sufficiently close to 1. But since $\mu_1(g_n; r)$ is a nondecreasing function of r

$$\mu_1(g_n; r) \le \frac{1}{(1-\varepsilon)} \mu_1^*(f)$$

and on letting $\varepsilon \to 0$, $\mu_1(g_n; r) \le \mu_1^*(f)$. If there are only a finite number of zeros $\alpha_1, \alpha_2, \ldots, \alpha_n$ we already have the desired decomposition

$$F(z) = g_n(z) h_n(z).$$

If there are infinitely many zeros, then

$$|g_n(0)| = \mu_1(g_n; 0) \le \mu_1^*(f)$$

while

$$g_n(0) = \frac{f(0)}{h_n(0)} = \frac{f(0)}{|\alpha_1 \cdots \alpha_1|}$$

so that

$$|\alpha_1 \cdots \alpha_k| \ge |f(0)| \{\mu_1^*(f)\}^{-1}$$

for every n and hence the infinite product $\prod |\alpha_k|$ converges. But then the infinite product

$$h(z) = \lim_{n \to \infty} h_n(z) = \prod_{k=1}^{\infty} |\alpha_k| \frac{1 - \dfrac{z}{\alpha_k}}{1 - \bar{\alpha}_k z}$$

converges uniformly in every circle $|z| \leq r < 1$. The function $h(z)$ is regular in $|z| < 1$ and there $|h(z)| \leq 1$. Note that $|h(e^{i\theta})| \equiv 1$. $h(z)$ has the same zeros as $f(z)$ so that for $|z| < 1$ the function

$$g(z) = \frac{f(z)}{h(z)}$$

is regular and not zero. Further $g_n(z)$ converges to $g(z)$ uniformly on every circle $|z| \leq r < 1$ so that $\mu_1(g; r) \leq \mu_1^*(f)$. Now if $f(0) = 0$, set $f(z) = z^m f_1(z)$, where $f_1(z)$ is regular at $z = 0$ and $f_1(0) \neq 0$. Then

$$\mu_1(f_1; r) = r^{-m} \mu_1(f; r) \to \mu_1^*(f)$$

so that $\mu_1^*(f_1) = \mu_1^*(f)$ and in particular $f_1(z) \in H_1$. The decomposition $f_1(z) = g(z)h(z)$ yields the decomposition of $f(z)$ into $g(z)$ and $z^m h(z)$.

Given any function $f \in H_1$, consider its decomposition into $g(z)$ and $h(z)$. Since $g(z)$ vanishes nowhere in the unit circle there is a unique determination $\gamma(z)$ of $\{g(z)\}^{\frac{1}{2}}$. Now $\gamma(z) \in H_2$. The function $h(z)$ is bounded and thus also belongs to H_2. It then follows from what has been proved earlier that $\gamma(re^{i\theta})$, $h(re^{i\theta})$ approach $\gamma(e^{i\theta})$, $h(e^{i\theta})$ respectively almost everywhere as $r \to 1 -$. It is clear that $f(re^{i\theta})$ *approaches* $f(e^{i\theta}) = \{\gamma(e^{i\theta})\}^2 h(e^{i\theta})$ *almost everywhere as $r \to 1 -$.*

We shall now show that *if $f(z) \in H_1$, then* $\int_0^{2\pi} |f(e^{i\theta}) - f(re^{i\theta})| d\theta \to 0$ as $r \to 1 -$. First we show that for any measurable set M

$$\int_M |f(r_n e^{i\theta})| d\theta \to \int_M |f(e^{i\theta})| d\theta$$

where $r_n \to 1 -$. Now

$$D = \int_M \{|f(e^{i\theta})| - |f(r_n e^{i\theta})|\} d\theta$$

$$= \int_M \{|h| |\gamma|^2 - |h_n| |\gamma_n|^2\} d\theta$$

$$= \int_M \{|h| - |h_n|\} |\gamma|^2 d\theta - \int_M |h| \{|\gamma|^2 - |\gamma_n|^2\} d\theta.$$

Since $|h(re^{i\theta})| \leq 1$ it follows that the integrand of the first integral is less than $|\gamma|^2$ in absolute value and since $h_n \to h$ almost everywhere the first expression tends to zero.

The integrand of the second integral is less than $||\gamma|^2 - |\gamma_n|^2| \leq |\gamma^2 - \gamma_n^2| = |\gamma - \gamma_n| |\gamma + \gamma_n|$ and so the second integral is less than the square root of

$$\int\limits_M |\gamma - \gamma_n|^2 \, d\theta \int\limits_M |\gamma + \gamma_n|^2 \, d\theta \leq 4\, \mu_1^*\,(f) \int\limits_M |\gamma - \gamma_n|^2 \, d\theta \to 0$$

by the Schwarz inequality. Since $f(r\,e^{i\theta}) \to f(e^{i\theta})$ almost everywhere, by Egoroff's theorem there are sets of arbitrarily small measure M such that $f(r\,e^{i\theta}) \to f(e^{i\theta})$ uniformly in the complementary set. Let M be of sufficiently small measure so that

$$\int\limits_M |f|\, d\theta < \varepsilon.$$

Then for n large enough

$$\int\limits_M |f_n|\, d\theta < \varepsilon$$

so that $\int\limits_M |f - f_n|\, d\theta < 2\,\varepsilon.$ However

$$\int\limits_{CM} |f - f_n|\, d\theta \to 0$$

because of uniform convergence. Here CM is the complement of M. Since ε is arbitrarily small the theorem is proven.

BIBLIOGRAPHY

AITKEN, A. C. [1]: *Determinants and Matrices*. Edinburgh, 1944.

ANDERSON, R. L. [1]: Distribution of the serial correlation coefficient. *Ann. Math. Statistics*, **13** (1942), 1–13.

ANDERSON, R. L. and ANDERSON, T. W. [1]: Distribution of the circular serial correlation coefficient for residuals from a fitted Fourier series. *Ann. Math. Statistics*, **21** (1950), 59–81.

ANDERSON, T. W. [1]: On the theory of testing serial correlation. *Skand. Aktuarietidskr.*, **31** (1948), 88–116.

—— [2]: The integral of a symmetric unimodal function over a symmetric convex set and some probability inequalities. *Proc. Amer. Math. Soc.*, **6** (1955), 170–176.

BARTLETT, M. S. [1]: On the theoretical specification and sampling properties of autocorrelated time series. *Suppl. J. Roy. Statist. Soc.*, **8** (1946), 27–41.

—— [2]: Periodogram analysis and continuous spectra. *Biometrika*, **37** (1950), 1–16.

—— [3]: *An Introduction to Stochastic Processes*. Cambridge, 1955.

—— [4]: Problèmes de l'analyse spectrale des séries temporelles stationnaires. *Publ. Inst. Stat. Univ. de Paris*, Vol. 3, Fasc. 3, pp. 119–134.

BATCHELOR, G. K. [1]: *The Theory of Homogeneous Turbulence*. Cambridge Monographs on Mech. and Appl. Math., Cambridge, 1953.

BIRKHOFF, G. and KOTIK, J. [1]: Fourier analysis of wave trains. *Gravity Waves*, Nat. Bureau of Standards Circular 521, Washington, D.C., 1952, pp. 221–234.

BLANC-LAPIERRE, A. and FORTET, R. [1]: *Theorie des fonctions aléatoires*. Paris, 1953.

BOCHNER, S. [1]: *Vorlesungen über Fouriersche Integrale*. Leipzig, 1932.

BUSSBANG, J. [1]: *Crosscorrelation Functions of Amplitude Distorted Gaussian Signals*. Tech. Rep. No. 216, 1952, Research Lab. Electronics, M.I.T.

CHAMPERNOWNE, D. G. [1]: Sampling theory applied to autoregressive schemes. *J. R. Statist. Soc.*, 1948, Vol. 10.

COBINE, J. D. and CURRY, J. R. [1]: Range extender for general radio 760A sound analyzer. *Rev. Sci. Instruments*, **17** (1946), 190–194.

CRAMÉR, H. [1]: On the theory of stationary random processes. *Ann. of Math.*, **41** (1940), 215–230.

—— [2]: On harmonic analysis in certain functional spaces. *Ark. Mat. Astr. Fys.*, **28 B** (1942), 7 pp.

—— [3]: *Mathematical Methods of Statistics*. Princeton, 1946.

—— [4]: A contribution to the theory of stochastic processes. *Proc. Second Berkeley Symposium on Math. Stat. and Probability*, Berkeley, 1951, pp. 329–339.

DAVENPORT, W. B., Jr., JOHNSON, R. A., and MIDDLETON, D. [1]: Statistical errors in measurements on random time functions. *J. Appl. Phys.*, **23** (1952), 377–388.

294

Davis, R. C. [1]: On the detection of sure signals in noise. *J. Appl. Phys.*, **25** (1954),76–82.

de Finetti, B. [1]: La prévision: ses lois logiques, ses sources subjectifs. *Ann. Inst. H. Poincaré*, **7** (1937), 1–68.

Diananda, P. H. [1]: Some probability limit theorems with statistical applications. *Trans. Cambr. Phil. Soc.*, **49** (1953), 239–246.

Dixon, W. J. [1]: Further contributions to the problem of serial correlation.*Ann. Math. Statistics*, **15** (1944), 119–144.

Doob, J. L. [1]: Heuristic approach to the Kolmogoroff-Smirnov theorems. *Ann. Math. Statistics*, **20** (1949), 393–403.

—— [2]: *Stochastic Processes*. New York, 1952.

Durbin, J. and Watson, G. S. [1]: Exact tests of serial correlation using noncircular statistics. *Ann. Math. Statistics*, **22** (1951), 466–451.

Eklind, J. R. and Jung, J. [1]: Estimation of the spectral density. To be published.

Fejér, L. [1]: Lebesguesche Konstanten und divergente Fourierreihen. *J. reine angew. Math.*, **138** (1910), 22–53.

Fisher, R. A. [1]: Tests of significance in harmonic analysis. *Proc. Roy. Soc. London, Ser. A*, **125** (1929), 54–59.

Goldman, S. [1]: *Frequency Analysis, Modulation and Noise*. New York, 1948.

Goldstein, H. [1]: *Classical Mechanics*. Cambridge, Mass., 1950.

Grenander, U. [1]: Stochastic processes and statistical inferencè. *Ark. Mat.*, **1** (1950), 195–277.

—— [2]: On empirical spectral analysis of stochastic processes. *Ark. Mat.*, **1** (1951), 503–531.

—— [3]: On Toeplitz forms and stationary processes. *Ark. Mat.*, **1** (9151), 555–571.

—— [4]: On the estimation of regression coefficients in the case of an autocorrelated disturbance. *Ann. Math. Statistics*, **25** (1954), 252–272.

—— [5]: Recent trends in time series analysis, to appear in the Sankhyā.

Grenander, U. and Rosenblatt, M. [1]: On spectral analysis of stationary time series. *Proc. Nat. Acad. Sci. U.S.A.*, **38** (1952), 519–521.

—— [2]: Statistical spectral analysis of time series arising from stationary stochastic processes. *Ann. Math. Statistics*, **24** (1953), 537–558.

—— [3]: An extension of a theorem of G. Szegö and its.application to the study of stochastic processes. *Trans Am. Math. Soc.*, **76** (1954), 112–126.

—— [4]: Comments on statistical spectral analysis. *Skand. Aktuarietidskr.*, **36** (1953), 182–202.

—— [5]: Regression analysis of time series with stationary residuals. *Proc. Nat. Acad. Sci. U.S.A.*, **40** (1954), 812–816.

—— [6]: Some problems in estimating the spectrum of a time series. To be published in *Proc. Third Berkeley Symposium on Math. Stat. and Probability*.

Grützmacher, M. [1]: Eine neue Methode der Klanganalyse. *Z. Technische Physik*, **8** (1927), 506–509.

Halmos, P. R. [1]: *Measure Theory*. New York, 1950.

—— [2]: *Finite Dimensional Vector Spaces*. Princeton, 1942.

HANNAN, E. J. [1]: Exact tests for serial correlation. *Biometrika* 1955, Vol. 42.

HARDY, G. H. [1]: On the mean value of the modulus of an analytic function. *Proc. London Math. Soc.*, Ser. 2, **14** (1915), 269–277.

HARDY, G. H., LITTLEWOOD, J. E., and POLYÀ, G. [1]: *Inequalities*. Cambridge, 1952.

HERGLOTZ, G. [1]: Über Potenzreihen mit positivem reellen Teil im Einheitskreis. *Ber. Verh. Kgl. Sächs. Ges. Wiss., Leipzig, Math.-Phys. Kl.*, **63** (1911), 501.

HODGES, J. L., Jr., and LEHMANN, E. L. [1]: Some applications of the Cramér-Rao inequality. *Proc. Second Berkeley Symposium on Math. Stat. and Probability*, 1951, pp. 13–22.

HOEFFDING, W. and ROBBINS, H. [1]: The central limit theorem for dependent random variables. *Duke Math. J.*, **15** (1948), 773–780.

HOPF, E. [1]: *Ergodentheorie*. Ergebnisse der Math. und ihrer Grenzgebiete, Vol. 5, 1937.

HSU, P. L. [1]: On the asymptotic distributions of certain statistics used in testing the independence between successive observations from a normal population. *Ann. Math. Statistics*, **17** (1946), 350–354.

JAMES, H. M., NICHOLS, N. B., and PHILLIPS, R. S. [1]: *Theory of Servomechanisms*. New York, 1947.

KAC, M. [1]: Probability methods in analysis and number theory. *Bull. Amer. Math. Soc.*, **55** (1949), 641–665.

—— [2]: On the average number of real roots of a random algebraic equation. *Bull. Amer. Math. Soc.*, **49** (1943), 314–320.

KARHUNEN, K. [1]: Über lineare Methoden in der Wahrscheinlichkeitsrechnung. *Ann. Acad. Sci. Fennicae, I. Math.-Physica*, **37** (1947), 79 pp.

—— [2]: Über die Struktur stationärer zufälliger Funktionen. *Ark. Mat.*, **1** (1949), 141–160.

KENDALL, M. G. [1]: *The Advanced Theory of Statistics*. London, Vol. I (1943) and Vol. II (1946).

KOLMOGOROFF, A. [1]: *Grundbegriffe der Wahrscheinlichkeitsrechnung*. Ergebnisse der Math., Vol. 2, 1933.

—— [2]: Stationary sequences in Hilbert space. (In Russian.) *Bull. Math. Univ. Moscow*, Vol. 2, No. 6 (1941), 40 pp.

KOOPMANS, T. [1]: Serial correlation and quadratic forms in normal variables. *Ann. Math. Statistics*, **13** (1942), 14–33.

—— [2], ed.: *Statistical Inference in Dynamic Economic Models*. Cowles Commission for Research in Economics, Monograph No. 10, New York, 1950.

LAMB, H. [1]: *Hydrodynamics*. Cambridge, 1924.

LAWSON, J. L. and UHLENBECK, G. E. [1]: *Threshold Signals*. M.I.T. Radiation Lab. Series, Vol. 24, New York, 1950.

LEHMANN, E. L. and SCHEFFE, H. [1]: Completeness, similar regions, and unbiased estimation I. *Sankhya*, **10** (1950), 305–340.

LEIPNIK, R. B. [1]: Distributions of the serial correlation coefficient in a circularly correlated universe. *Ann. Math. Statistics*, **18** (1947), 80–87.

LIEPMAN, H. W. [1]: Aspects of the turbulence problem. Survey report. *Z. angew. Math. Physik*, **3** (1952), 321–342.

LOEVE, M. [1]: Fonctions aléatoires du second ordre. Supplement to P. LEVY: *Processus stochastiques et mouvement Brownien*, Paris, 1948.

MADOW, W. G. [1]: Note on the distribution of the serial correlation coefficient. *Ann. Math. Statistics*, **16** (1945), 308–310.

MANN, H. B. and WALD, A. [1]: On the statistical treatment of linear stochastic difference equations. *Econometrica*, **11** (1943), 173–220.

MARUYAMA, G. [1]: The harmonic analysis of stationary stochastic processes. *Mem. Fac. Sci. Kyusyu Univ. Ser. A*, **4** (1949), 45–106.

McCOMBIE, C. W. [1]: Fluctuation theory in physical measurements. *Reports on Progress in Physics*, **16** (1953), 266–320.

MORAN, P. A. P. [1]: The oscillatory behaviour of moving averages. *Proc. Cambridge Phil. Soc.*, **46** (1950), 272–280.

—— [2]: Some theorems on time series I. *Biometrika*, **34** (1947), 281–291.

PALEY, R. E. A. and WIENER, N. [1]: *Fourier Transforms in the Complex Domain*. New York, 1934.

PARZEN, E. [1]: On consistent estimates of the spectrum of a stationary time series. To be published.

PIERSON, W. J., Jr. [1]: *Wind Generated Gravity Waves*. Advances in Geophysics, Vol. 2, Academic Press, New York, 1955.

PIERSON, W. J., Jr., NEUMANN, G., and JAMES R. W. [1]: *Practical Methods for Observing and Forecasting Ocean Waves by Means of Wave Spectra and Statistics*. Hydrographic Office Publication No. 603 (1956).

QUENOUILLE, M. H. [1]: Approximate tests of correlation in time series. *J. Roy. Statist. Soc., Ser. B*, **11** (1949), 68–84.

RICE, S. O. [1]: Mathematical analysis of random noise. *Bell System Tech. J.* **23** (1944), 282–332; **24** (1945), 46–156.

ROSENBLATT, M. [1]: On estimation of regression coefficients of a vector-valued time series with a stationary disturbance. Ann. Math. Stat., 27 (1956), 99–121.

—— [2]: On some regression problems in time series analysis. To be published in *Proc. Third Berkeley Symposium on Math. Stat. and Probability*.

—— [3]: A central limit theorem and a strong mixing condition. *Proc. Nat. Acad. Sci. U.S.A.*, **42** (1956), 43–47.

RUBIN, H. [1]: On the distribution of the serial correlation coefficient. *Ann. Math. Statist.*, **16** (1945), 211–215.

RUDNICK, P. [1]: The detection of weak signals by correlation methods. *J. Appl. Phys.*, **24** (1953), 128–131.

SCHEFFE, H. [1]: Statistical inference in the nonparametric case. *Ann. Math. Statist.*, **15** (1943), 305–332.

SIEGERT, A. J. F. [1]: On the evaluation of noise samples. *J. Appl. Phys.*, **23** (1952), 737–742.

SLUTZKY, E. [1]: The summation of random causes as the source of cyclic processes. *Econometrica*, **5** (1937).

SOMMERFELD, A. J. W. [1]: *Partial Differential Equations in Physics*. New York, 1949.

SPETNER, L. M. [1]: Errors in power spectra due to finite sample. *J. Appl. Phys.*, **25** (1954), 653–659.

STONE, W. M. [1]: On the statistical theory of detection of a randomly modulated carrier. *J. Appl. Phys.*, **24** (1953), 935–939.

STONER, I. and BATES, M. [1]: *The Analysis of a Narrow Bandpass Filter for Measuring Power Spectra, DSM-58-AM.* Bell Aircraft Corporation, Buffalo N.Y., 1953.

SZEGÖ, G. [1]: Beiträge zur Theorie der Toeplitzschen Formen. *Math. Z.*, **6** (1920), 167–202; **9** (1921), 167–190.

THIEDE, H. [1]: Schallvorgänge mit kontinuierlichem Frequenzspectrum. *Elektr. Nachr. Techn.*, **13** (1936).

TINTNER, G. [1]: *The Variate-Difference Method.* Bloomington, Indiana, 1940.

TITCHMARSCH, E. C. [1]: *The Theory of Functions.* Oxford, 1932.

TOLMAN, R. C. [1]: *The Principles of Statistical Mechanics.* Oxford, 1946.

TUKEY, J. W. [1]: Measuring noise color. Unpublished manuscript.

UBEROI, M. S. and KOVASZNAY, L. G. [1]: On mapping and measurement of random fields. *Quart. Appl. Math.*, **10** (1953), 375–393.

WHITTAKER, E. T. and WATSON, G. N. [1]: *A Course of Modern Analysis.* Cambridge, 1935.

WHITTLE, P. [1]: *Hypotheses Testing in Time Series Analysis.* Uppsala, 1951.

WIENER, N. [1]: *The Extrapolation, Interpolation and Smoothing of Stationary Time Series.* New York, 1949.

WINTNER, A. [1]: *Spektraltheorie der unendlichen Matrizen.* Leipzig, 1929.

WISE, J. [1]: The autocorrelation function and the spectral density function. *Biometrika* 1955, Vol. 42.

WOLD, H. [1]: *A Study in the Analysis of Stationary Time Series.* Uppsala, 1938.

—— [2]: A large-sample test for moving averages. *J. Roy. Statist. Soc., Ser. B,* **11** (1949), 297–305.

—— [3]: in association with JURÉEN, L.: *Demand Analysis. A Study in Econometrics.* Uppsala, 1952.

WOODWARD, P. M. [1]: *Probability and Information Theory, with Applications to Radar.* New York, 1953.

INDEX

GRENANDER + ROSENBLATT: Statistical analysis